Captain Cousteau's Underwater Treasury

BOOKS BY THE EDITORS:

By Jacques-Yves Cousteau
THE SILENT WORLD *with Frédéric Dumas*

By James Dugan
THE GREAT IRON SHIP
MAN UNDER THE SEA
UNDERSEA EXPLORER

Captain Cousteau's Underwater Treasury

EDITED BY *Jacques-Yves Cousteau*
AND *James Dugan*

"SEA-DISCOVERERS TO NEW WORLDS HAVE GONE."—*John Donne*

 HARPER & BROTHERS, PUBLISHERS, NEW YORK

CAPTAIN COUSTEAU'S UNDERWATER TREASURY

Copyright © 1959 by Harper & Brothers

Printed in the United States of America

D-K

Library of Congress catalog card number: 59-12820

910.4

ACKNOWLEDGMENTS

"Beyond the Gray-Green Barrier," from *The Open Sea*, by Sir Alister C. Hardy, published by William Collins Sons & Co., London, 1956, and Houghton Mifflin Co., Boston.

"The Compleat Goggler," from *The Compleat Goggler*, by Guy Gilpatric. Copyright 1934, 1935, 1937, 1938 by Guy Gilpatric, © 1957 by Dodd, Mead & Co., Inc., New York.

"The Bishop's Cross," from *Dig for Pirate Treasure*, by Robert I. Nesmith. Copyright © 1958 by Robert I. Nesmith; published by Devin-Adair Co., New York.

"A Man in the Atlantic," from *The Sea Wolves*, by Wolfgang Frank. Copyright © 1955 by Rinehart & Co., Inc., New York. Reprinted by permission of the publishers.

"Life at High Pressure," by Professor J. B. S. Haldane, F. R. S., published in *Science News IV*, 1947, by Penguin Books.

"The Fountain of Vaucluse," from *To Hidden Depths*, by Captain Philippe Tailliez. Copyright 1954 by E. P. Dutton, Inc., New York. Reprinted by permission of the publishers.

"The Story of Michels," from *I Like Diving*, by Tom Eadie, published in 1929 by Houghton Mifflin Co., Boston.

"From a Novelist's Diving Log," from *Underwater Hunting for Inexperienced Englishmen*, by James Aldridge. Copyright 1955 by George Allen & Unwin Ltd., London.

"Submarine Disaster," from *Undersea Patrol*, by Edward Young. Copyright 1952 by Edward Young. Reprinted by permission of McGraw-Hill Book Company, Inc., New York.

"I Found Undersea Insects," from *Greenland to the Great Barrier Reef*, by Noel Monkman; reprinted by permission of Doubleday & Co., Inc., New York.

"Up from the Well of Time," by Luis Marden, *National Geographic Magazine*, January, 1959. Copyright © 1959 by the National Geographic Society, Washington, D.C.

"California Gold Divers," by Richard Anderson, from *The Skin Diver*. Copyright © 1958 by *The Skin Diver*, Lynwood, Calif.

"The Oldest Statues in the World," from *Ten Years under the Earth*, by Norbert Casteret. Translated from *Dix Ans Sous Terre*, published by Librairie Académique Perrin, Paris.

"Laurentic Gold," from *Man under the Sea*, by James Dugan. Copyright © 1956 by James Dugan; published by Harper & Brothers, New York.

"Beyond the Reefs," from *Beyond the Reefs*, by William Travis. Copyright © 1959 by George Allen & Unwin, Ltd. First published in the United States 1959 by E. P. Dutton & Co., Inc. Reprinted by permission of the publishers.

"Supplying Guadalcanal," from *Sunk*, by Mochitsura Hashimoto. Copyright 1954 by Henry Holt & Co., Inc. Reprinted by permission of the publishers.

"Cadavers," from *Treasure Divers of Vigo Bay*, by John S. Potter, Jr. Copyright © 1958 by John S. Potter, Jr. Reprinted by permission of Doubleday & Co., Inc., New York.

"Sharks of Raraka," by Wilmon Menard, from *Water World*, Sept.–Oct. 1957. Reprinted by permission of the Peterson Publishing Co., Los Angeles, Calif.

"Submarine Through the North Pole," by Lt. William G. Lalor, Jr., *National Geographic Magazine*, January, 1959. Copyright © 1959 by the National Geographic Society, Washington, D.C.

"Listening for Fish," from *Malay Fishermen*, by Prof. Raymond Firth. Reprinted by permission of Routledge & Kegan Paul Ltd., London.

"The Coral Coast," from *The Edge of the Sea*, by Rachel Carson. Copyright © 1955 by Rachel L. Carson. Reprinted by permission of Houghton Mifflin Co., Boston.

"Art Salvaged from the Sea," by Professor George Karo, from *Archeology*, Winter 1948. Reprinted by permission of *Archeology* and the author.

"Trapped!," from *Discharged Dead*, by Sydney Hart. First published 1956 by Odhams Press Ltd., London. Reprinted by permission of the publisher.

"An Octopus in Borneo," from *Danger Is My Life*, by Victor Berge. Reprinted by permission of Hutchinson & Co. (Publishers) Ltd., London, and A/S Bookman, Copenhagen.

"Coral Reefs," by Charles Darwin, published in 1910 by Ward Lock & Co., Ltd., London.

"Jewels of the Deep," from *Welcome to Bahrein*, by James H. D. Belgrave. Reprinted by permission of the author.

"Wahoo," from *Submarine!*, by Captain Edward L. Beach. Copyright 1952 by Edward L. Beach. Reprinted by permission of Henry Holt & Co., Inc., New York.

"Surrounded by Piranhas," from "An Underwater Picture Opportunity," by E. R. Fenimore Johnson, published in *Waterbug* magazine, Feb. 1955. Reprinted by permission of the author.

"Coral Magic," from *Manta*, by Hans Hass. Copyright 1952 by Hans Hass. Reprinted by permission of Rand McNally & Co., publishers.

"Top Secret Dive," from *Ordeal by Water*, by Peter Keeble and William Kerr. Copyright © 1957 by Peter Keeble. Reprinted by permission of Doubleday & Co., Inc., New York.

"Animal Life of the Deep Sea Bottom," from *The Galathea Deep Sea Expedition*, edited by Anton Bruun. Reprinted by permission of George Allen & Unwin Ltd., London, and The Macmillan Co., New York.

"Raising the *Leonardo da Vinci*," from *Wonders of Salvage*, by David Masters. Reprinted by permission of Eyre & Spottiswoode (Publishers) Ltd., London.

"The Consular Agent," from *Sea Devils*, by J. Valerio Borghese, published by Henry Regnery Co., New York, and The Hutchinson Group, London. Reprinted by permission of the publishers.

"Shark," from *Alexandre Dumas' Dictionary of Cuisine*, by Louis Colman, published by Simon & Schuster, New York.

"Exploration of the Sunken Liner *Andrea Doria*," by Ramsey Parks, from *The Skin Diver*, June 1957, copyright © 1957 by *The Skin Diver*, Lynwood, Calif.

"Beneath a Jungle Stream," from *The Reefs of Taprobane*, by Arthur C. Clarke. Copyright © 1956, 1957 by Arthur C. Clarke. Reprinted by permission of Harper & Brothers, New York.

"Midget Attack on a Japanese Cruiser," from *Frogman V.C.*, by Ian Fraser. Copyright © 1957 by Ian Fraser. Reprinted by permission of Angus & Robertson, London.

"A Descent into Perpetual Night," from *Half Mile Down*, by William Beebe. Reprinted by permission of Duell, Sloan & Pearce, New York.

"The Bufferini Treasure," from "Autobiography of a Skin Diver," by Guido Garibaldi, in *The Skin Diver*, June 1954. Copyright 1954 by *The Skin Diver*, Lynwood, Calif.

"The Best Spearfisherman in the World," from *Lady with a Spear*, by Eugenie Clark. Copyright 1951, 1952, 1953 by Eugenie Clark Konstantinu. Reprinted by permission of Harper & Brothers, New York.

"The Cycle of Water," from *Realms of Water*, by P. H. Kuenen. Reprinted by permission of John Wiley & Sons, Inc., New York, and Cleaver-Hume Press Ltd., London.

"Underwater Duck Hunt," by Jon M. Lindbergh, from *Water World*. Reprinted by permission of the author.

"The Wakulla Cave," by S. J. Olsen, from *Natural History*, Aug.–Sept. 1958. Reprinted by permission of the author and *Natural History*, New York.

"The Accra Pipe-Line," from *Down to the Ships in the Sea*, by Harry Grossett. Reprinted by permission of Hutchinson & Co. (Publishers) Ltd., London.

"Shark Close-ups," from *The Silent World*, by Jacques-Yves Cousteau with Frédéric Dumas. Copyright 1953 by Harper & Brothers, New York.

"Diving in Polar Seas," by Cmdr. Francis D. Fane, from *Naval Institute Proceedings*, Feb. 1959. Reprinted by permission of the author and publisher.

"The Phantoms of the Gubbet," from *The Blue Continent*, by Folco Quilici. Reprinted by permission of the publishers, Weidenfeld & Nicholson, London.

"Two and a Half Miles Down," by Cdt. Georges S. Houot, *National Geographic Magazine*, July 1954, copyright 1954 by the National Geographic Society, Washington, D.C.

FOR HAROLD EDGERTON,
magician of a thousand and one nights beneath the sea.

Contents

*W*ith the exception of verse, vision, and Verne, the accounts in this book are true. In a few cases we omitted brilliant achievements which were obscurely reported due to the pall of naval style—the passive mode. This requires the author to pretend he wasn't there. For instance, he writes, "After some difficulty due to nitrogen narcosis, a depth of 197 feet was attained," when he means, "I had a hard time fighting off nitrogen narcosis to reach 197 feet." The impersonal is also rife among oceanographers and is infecting the young. For example, the speleological group of the French Undersea Research Center in Marseille has carried out extensive cave-diving expeditions whose thorough preparation and elegant execution overcame serious dangers. The only report by the group is a geological paper which does not mention diving. Underwater explorers must, of course, recount their results objectively in scholarly journals, but they too often fail to tell the interested layman what it is like and how it feels to penetrate the virgin depths.

In contrast, a popular literature on space travel has arisen, before a single space man has arisen. Recently I saw an accomplished free diver, who enjoys the three-dimensional liberty of inner space, queuing up for an autograph from a chairborne novelist who writes outer space copy. In "The Enchafèd Flood," W. H. Auden remarks, "What comes from the sky is a spiritual or supernatural visitation. What lies hidden in the water is the unknown powers of nature." The writers in this collection address themselves to, or have their adventures in this decisive element. The mantling waters are man's real concern.

To build this random coralline structure the editors had many assisting polyps, who nominated favorite pieces or performed services above and beyond the call of booty. Among them, we wish to especially thank Jim Auxier, editor of *The Skin Diver*, Lynwood, California; Theda S. Bassett of the Submarine Library, Groton,

Connecticut; Ruth Dugan; Paul Koston; Violet Nyitray; Frederick B. Opper, Radio Free Europe, Stockholm; Fred Fisher; Jean Pozzi and Peter Throckmorton.

A fathom is six feet and a meter is about 3.3 feet.

James Dugan

The Conquest of Inner Space

*W*e are living in the opening of the age of underwater exploration. These are the founding years of submarine industry and agriculture. We are mounting increasing scientific campaigns in the waters "that compass us about," the last frontier on our planet. They present a challenge larger and more mysterious than the terrestrial wilderness, the deserts, the peaks and the white wastes of the Poles.

Underwater exploration is a reunion of man's past and future. Long before the Greek sea gods and Aristotle's scientific studies of marine life, there were legends and evidence of diving. The Sumerian civilization about 5000 B.C. left the story of Gilgamesh, a diver who sought the weed of eternal life beneath the waves. The theme lived on in Glaucus, the diving god of Greek mythology, and is a reality today in Samoa, where a certain seaweed in the intertidal zone has the properties of a depressant, a sedative, an anesthetic, or a fatal poison, according to the amount consumed. The easy availability of this extraordinary plant contributes to a high suicide rate in the islands.

It can be argued that fishing was man's first industry. If industry is a collective technical effort to produce goods, the early men who waded in estuaries to gather oysters and clams, and who formed cordons to herd fish into shallows where they could be seized, constituted an industry. From this fish-hunger developed spears and boats, and, it seems probable, diving techniques when the waders, putting their heads under, got beyond their depth and dived for oysters.

Certainly diving was a craft by the time men came to live in villages and it was commonplace in the day of Homer. Underwater products of the type that could best be gathered by divers were widespread in classic civilization. Aegean sponge picking must have occupied thou-

sands of Greek sphoungarades, whose yield was used for many purposes other than bathing. Mothers gave small honey-soaked sponges
to babies as pacifiers and the Roman legions marched with canteens
consisting of water-filled sponges. Imperial purple dye was made
from grinding the iodine-rich conch shell, Murex. Red coral, a
magical substance believed to insure fertility in women, was one of
the main articles carried in the caravan trade to China in pre-Chris-
tian times. The followers of Christ carried over pagan sea symbols
such as the baptismal font of a giant scallop shell. Among His early
believers the symbolic initials for Jesus Christ, Son of God, Saviour,
formed the Greek word for fish. Early records of sea battles mention
"frogman" actions, and submarine boats recur often in the annals
of warfare.

Why, then, with this ubiquity of diving, are there so few credible
accounts and pictures of the technique from ancient times? Aristotle's
shrewd observations of fish have the air of authentic underwater
observation, but he never mentions diving. I believe underwater work
was taken for granted, as was ancient merchant shipping. The few
vase pictures of early Mediterranean trading vessels are unbelievable
caricatures compared with the real ships, of which we are now
privileged to inspect a few through the labors of marine archaeology.
The ten-thousand-amphora ship of the third century B.C. which my
group has been excavating off Marseille was a gigantic freighter.
Unless it was a freak—which is not likely—the Greeks sailed on
argosies that would win attention for size even today. Perhaps they
were so commonplace the artists did not bother drawing them. So
it may have been with divers. No glamour whatsoever attaches to
contemporary Greek sponge divers in their own country.

Modern undersea exploration is only a hundred years old and may
be dated from Matthew Fontaine Maury's 1859 hydrography of the
North Atlantic, the appearance of a practical helmet diving suit in
England in 1837 and the bold assay of Prof. Henri Milne-Edwards,
who went down in a helmet in 1844 to see the life forms he had been
speculating about in the laboratory. In recent decades improved tools
for underwater exploration have appeared, notably William Beebe's
bathysphere, Auguste Piccard's concept of the free-diving bathyscaph, the recording echo sounder, the automatic compressed-air
diving lung, and Harold Edgerton's electronic-flash depth cameras.
The addition of man himself—the free diver—to the instruments of
oceanography is an interesting feature of our period. Yesterday's
"small sect" of helmet divers, as they were called by that great hard-

hat man Captain G. C. C. Damant, has given way to a popular invasion of the sea. Among the free divers, I am happy to note, is a growing number of marine scientists.

We have no apology for including several reports by scholars in this collection: science is the course that underwater activity is taking. If young Charles Darwin was able to decipher the riddle of coral reefs with no equipment other than a vaulting pole and a sounding lead, the opportunities in oceanography for free divers would seem spectacular. There is really no alternative for the human race but to pursue this return to the sea, to fulfill Eugene Noël's hundred-year-old admonition, "The ocean can be turned into an immense food factory. It can be made into a more fruitful laboratory than the earth. Fertilize it! Seas, rivers and ponds! Only the earth is cultivated. Where is the art of cultivating the waters? Hear, ye nations!"

We are beginning to search under the ocean for food, natural resources and energy—but only just beginning. The undersea movement today is the larval stage of what will come when it matures. Men have penetrated only to the average depth of the oceans in one dive of the bathyscaph *FNRS 3*. As striking as the offshore oil and sulphur wells may be, they are timid waders compared with the deep marine mines of tomorrow; as ingenious as are the twelve-fathom oyster ranches of Brittany tended by Aqua-Lung peasants, they are only the pilot farms of submarine agriculture to come; as impressive as the Pluto English Channel pipeline was in 1944, or Sammy Collins' twenty-mile underwater tubes may be, they will be eclipsed by the Trans-Mediterranean pipeline. Hydro-engineers are confident they can drive the Channel Tunnel and a Trans-Atlantic pipeline!

A few years ago in Washington an informal symposium on earth science called the Miscellaneous Society was formed to pool exploration ideas and shock administrators by the alarming disparity between geophysical appropriations and the experiments possible today. Among the gay deliberations of the Miscellaneous Society was a scheme called "Mohole," which called for drilling eight miles into the earth to reach the Mohorovicic Discontinuity, the supposed inner crust of the planet. The Schlumberger drill rig, already used in oil exploration, was capable of making a true diametrical hole four miles into the earth. (Former oil drills could go four miles, but one never knew in what direction, and it was possible for them to meander up and protrude back through the surface.) How do you drill eight miles with a four-mile bit? Through four miles of water and into the ocean floor four miles. Mohole is now under serious consideration.

Today at Toulon the French Navy is building a big bathyscaph, designed to carry three men to the greatest depth of the oceans, seven miles down in the Marianas Trench. She is the successor to the middle-range *FNRS 3*, whose record dive to 13,287 feet is described by her skipper, Georges Houot, in this book. If the abyssal boat succeeds in carrying Houot, his engineer and a scientist to the basement, it will be the nearest man shall ever come to the core of his planet. To me, the comparatively inexpensive super-bathyscaph is vastly more important to mankind than ten billion dollars' worth of outer-space engineering. This is where we live and shall continue to live, here on earth.

All levels of the oceans remain to be explored, not only the chill abyss. Between the pit and the compressed-air diving range in the top thirty fathoms lies an enormity of inner space to be voyaged and described. Observation vehicles suited to the various depth zones are now in plan and some in construction. The first urgency is for machines to survey the continental shelf, the shallow boom lands rich in fish and mineral resources. The continental shelf was legally defined in 1945 as the offshore escarpment out to a depth of 100 fathoms; the boundary seemed then to encompass all future oil-well possibilities. Eight years later the limit was thoroughly out of date. The United States, which was the first nation to claim sovereignty of its continental shelf, then extended the boundaries as far out as the bottom could be used. This means 200 miles out to sea in some places and dropoff line at around 1,500 feet. The Mohole project may render even this concept obsolete. The continental shelf is therefore not an *ultima Thule*, as the Northwest Passage was in the age of the great surface navigators: it is next on the agenda for scientific submarines.

In Marseille, my colleagues of the OFRS undersea engineering laboratory have constructed a shelf submarine, capable of cruising by jet propulsion in the 1,000-foot stratum, with a pressure safety factor of three to one. This "diving saucer" carries two prone explorers with viewing ports, external still and movie cameras plus lighting systems, and hydraulic grabs for taking specimens. The *DS 1* is the best attempt at a continental shelf prototype that we can produce within our slender means, but she may suggest how the problem is to be tackled. Also we need agile undersea craft that can operate in the continental slope range, down to about a mile, below which the medium-range boats on the Piccard principle have already proved their effectiveness. A German civil engineer, Heinz Sellner, is building a slope submarine, the *Nitroscaph*, at our OFRS yard, and an

American project for an "Aluminaut" holds interesting prospects for exploring this zone.

To the oceanographer the nuclear submarine is a wonderful tool. From its motionless platform in the quiet depths, during prolonged submersions we can make precision soundings of the bottom, even under the Polar icecap. These space ships are now correcting and increasing previous soundings and, in many years of work, may compile an atlas of the world beneath the sea with its high ranges, volcanoes, plains, canyons and trenches deeper than the Himalayas are high.

One question stands before all others: how can mankind increase its marine food harvest? There are now about three billion people alive. In twenty years, at the present rate of reproduction, there will be four billion. The problem of feeding the increment has been approached by political "foreign relief" programs, depending on land agriculture, which is already insufficient. Food is raised on less than 5 per cent of the total surface area of the earth, while all these new people are crowding forward, demanding it. The globe's inundated surface comprises 71 per cent of the expanse, and beneath the waters there is a volume of life a thousand times as great as that which sustains all animals that live on earth and in the air. Four hundred years ago, Edmund Spenser said in the *Faerie Queene:*

> *Oh, what an endless work have I in hand,*
> *To count the sea's abundant progeny!*
> *Whose fruitful seeds far passeth those on land*
> *And also those which wonne in th'azure sky!*

What will feed the explosive human race, except the fishes and those who teach us how to find them?

A small but significant approach to the marine food problem has come from amateur diving clubs which have volunteered for conservation studies and dive to plot shellfish distribution, observe predatory starfish, make charts of seaweed pastures, and assist extermination of such pests as the sea lamprey, which has been marauding among fresh-water fish in the American Great Lakes since ship channels were opened to the Atlantic. Another echelon must be brought into this crisis of the fishery—submarine boats. What better use for submarines than to find fish? We will need undersea trawlers, echo-ranging for big schools and netting them deep down before submarine freighters, tankers and mail packets are required.

Undersea agriculture is in the tentative stage. It should be called stock farming, since seaweed has long been reaped for cattle cake, medicines, wall boards, iodine, and gummy algins which hold ice cream together. Wet ranching is being studied in the Mediterranean, the Japan Sea, and the U.S. Pacific Coast, by placing concrete labyrinths or retired trolley cars on the floor to form piscatorial housing projects. Every salt-water angler knows the most fish are found around wrecks, which play host to nutritive algae and shellfish and offer refuge to those citizens of the sea which care to move in, rent-free. We have staked out a three-square-mile experimental submarine piggery under the Oceanographic Museum at Monaco to see if we can domesticate rockfish, fatten them from a submarine breadline which jets nitrates and phosphates into the water, and butcher them in season without reducing the stock. Commercial fishermen and underwater hunters are barred from the farm, and the herdsmen are one with old diving Proteus, who guarded Amphitrite's fold of seals.

As we gaze below the waves into the future of the race, we see the ultimate hero of Homo sapiens, a naked man mingling long and deep among the fishes, breathing water as they do. (He calls himself Gilgamesh, after the Sumerian diver.) He wears no tanks of air or bladders of oxygen, nor a shell around him. He has reversed the divine moment of evolution—when his kind crawled ashore, stopped breathing water, and survived in air. The guarantee that human beings can reconvert from inspiring air to water in order to draw oxygen is the universal prenatal adventure. In the womb we live for months drowned in the salt sea and come into the air with a shock and a cry while the doctor or midwife applies crude artificial respiration to assist the transformation.

To backbreed man and restore his gills may not be as terrible as the supreme crisis of his life struggle, the moment he is born. Perhaps in the remote future surgical manipulation of healthy adolescents could produce menfish. It is a dream, but all human dreams come true in the long run. However, the daring surgeon who attempts the operation must not remove the patients' ability to breathe air. We must have both worlds!

Jacques-Yves Cousteau

Captain Cousteau's Underwater Treasury

Alister Hardy, the Linacre Professor of Zoology at Oxford University, has been campaigning at sea for thirty years, beginning in the Mediterranean and with the British Discovery *Expedition to Antarctica. He has worked on fishery research and makes his own fine sketches and water colors for his reports. Some years ago Professor Hardy set out to convey his knowledge and enthusiasm to the public in a book,* The Open Sea. *As he marshaled material, the book split into two rewarding volumes:* The World of Plankton *and* Fish and Fisheries. *He was surprised with a knighthood in 1958. Sir Alister, born in 1899, is a seaman and philosopher, two assets of an oceanographer.*

Beyond the Gray - Green Barrier

BY ALISTER C. HARDY

*T*here is a very simple fact about the sea which makes its inhabitants seem even more remote from us than can entirely be accounted for by their being largely out of sight. To make my point allow me to imagine a world just a little different from our own.

Suppose for a moment that we live in a country which is bounded on one side by a permanent bank of fog. It is a gray-green vapor, denser even than that often known as a London particular, and it has a boundary as definite as the surface of a cloud, so that it is like a curtain hanging from the sky to meet the ground; we cannot enter it without special aids except for a momentary plunge and as quickly out again for breath. We can see into it for only a very little way, but what we do see is all the more tantalizing because we know it must be just a glimpse—a tiny fraction of all that lies beyond. We find it has life in it as abundant as that of our own countryside, but so different that it might be life from another world. No insects dwell beyond the barrier, but other jointed-legged creatures take their place. Unfamiliar floating forms, like living parachutes with trailing tentacles, show their beauty and all too quickly fade from view; then sometimes at night the darkness may be spangled with moving points of light—living sparks that dart and dance before our eyes. Occasion-

1

ally gigantic monsters, equal in size to several elephants rolled into one, blunder through the curtain and lie dying on our land.

To make a reality of this little flight of fancy all we have to do is to swing this barrier through a right angle so that it becomes the surface of the sea. How much more curious about its unfamiliar creatures many of us might be if the sea were in fact separated from us by a vertical screen—over the garden wall as it were—instead of lying beneath us under a watery floor. Who as a child has not envied the Israelites as they passed through the Red Sea as if marching through a continuous aquarium: "and the waters were a wall unto them on their right hand, and on their left"? What might they not have seen? Because normally our line of vision stretches out across the sea to the skyline and carries our thoughts to other lands beyond, many of us tend to overlook this perhaps more wonderful realm beneath us, or we seem to think it must be too difficult of access ever to become a field for our exploration or delight.

The seashore can be studied by direct observation as the tide recedes and has long been a happy hunting ground for the naturalist; he can lift up the fronds of seaweed, turn over stones, probe into rock-pools and dig into the sand and mud. Our methods of studying the life of the open sea must be very different; it is far from "open" to the investigator, being in fact a hidden world, but this makes its exploration all the more exciting. Deep-sea photographic and television cameras are important new developments which promise much for the future; they, however, as also submarine observation chambers like the bathyscaph, must for some time to come be regarded as very costly and specialist equipment giving us here and there direct confirmation of what we usually have to find out by other means. The diving helmet and the Aqua-Lung may help us to see something of this enchanting world in shallow water, but for the discovery of what is happening over wide stretches of the underwaters of the open sea we must devise more indirect methods.

The fact that we can see only a very little way below the surface indicates a property of water, and particularly of the sea, which is of fundamental importance to the life it contains. Held up in a glass, water appears so very transparent that we are at first surprised to find how quickly light is absorbed in the sea itself and what a little distance its rays will penetrate. Measurements made in the English Channel off Plymouth show that at a depth of five meters (just over sixteen feet) the intensity of light is less than half that just below the surface, while at twenty-five meters it is only an insignificant fraction, varying between 1.5 and 3 per cent. This at once tells us that the green plants, which must have sunlight in order to live, will only be found in the upper layers of the water.

The one real difference, of course, between animals and plants is a matter of their mode of feeding. We know that an animal of any kind, whether mammal, fish, shrimp, or worm, must have what we call organic food: proteins, carbohydrates (sugars, starches and the like) and fats, which have been built up in the bodies of other animals or plants. One animal may feed upon another kind of animal which in turn may have lived upon other kinds, and perhaps these upon yet others, but always these food-chains, long or short, must begin with animals feeding upon plants. Only the green plants, with that remarkable substance chlorophyll acting as an agent, can build themselves up from the simple inorganic substances by their power of using the energy of sunlight (photosynthesis); they split up the molecules of carbon dioxide, liberate the oxygen, and combine the carbon with the oxygen and hydrogen of water to form simple carbohydrates, which are then elaborated into more complex compounds by being combined with various minerals in solution. On the land we are all familiar with this elementary fact of natural history; my reason for recalling it is to emphasize that it is of universal application. The plants are the producers and the animals the consumers as much in the sea as on the land. Indeed, "*all* flesh is grass."

Where then in the sea, we may ask ourselves, are all the plants upon which the hordes of animals must depend? They cannot grow in the darkness of dim light of the sea floor, and the seaweeds, forming but a shallow fringe along the coasts, are of no real importance in the economy of the open sea. From the deck of a ship, or even from a rowing boat, we can see no plant life floating near the surface; yet we know it must be there. Another little flight of imagination will, I think, help us to get some idea of the extent of this elusive vegetation.

Let us suppose for a moment that the herring is not a fish, but a land animal. We know that some three thousand million herring are landed every year at ports in the British Isles; these, together with all those landed in other countries, must be only a small fraction of their total number, for we also know that herring are the food of so many other abundant animals of the sea. For simplicity let us consider them to be feeding directly upon plants—and let us imagine them in their unnumbered millions sweeping across the continent. If we do this it needs no imagination to see that the countryside would be stripped of vegetation as if by locusts. Now let us think of the other fish in the sea besides the herring: the cod, haddock, plaice, skate and such that fill our trawlers to the extent of more than a million tons a year; then also think of the crowded invertebrate life of the sea bottom. If all these animals were on the land as well, what an immense crop of plants it would take to keep them supplied with food! There are indeed such luxuriant pastures in the sea but they are not obvious because the individual plants composing them are so small as to be invisible to the unaided eye; we can only see them through a microscope. Their vast numbers make up for their small size.

Let us consider the natural economy of the sea in its simplest terms. We have the sun shining down, its rays penetrating the upper layers of the water; we have the grass, oxygen and carbon dioxide, dissolving in it from the atmosphere; we have also the various mineral salts —notably phosphates and nitrates and iron compounds—continually being brought in by the erosion of the land, and there are minute traces of some essential vitamin-like substances. These are ideal conditions for plant growth. Just as these are spread through the water, so is the plant life itself scattered as a fine aquatic "dust" of living microscopic specks in untold billions. In a shaft of sunlight slanting into a shaded room we have all watched the usually invisible motes floating in the air, floating because they are so small and light; these tiny plants remain suspended in the water in just the same way. Many of them are provided with fine projections like those of thistle-down to assist in their suspension.

Feeding upon these tiny floating plants, and also like them scattered through the sea in teeming millions, are little animals. Crustacea, little shrimplike creatures of many different kinds, predominate; mostly they range in size from a pin's head to a grain of rice, but some are larger. There are hosts of other animals as well: small wormlike forms, miniature snails with flapping fins to keep them up, little jelly-fish and many other kinds which surprise us with their unexpected shapes and delicate beauty when first we see them through the microscope.

All these creatures, both animals and plants, which float and drift with the flow of tides and ocean currents are called by the general name of *plankton*. It is one of the most expressive technical terms used in science and is taken directly from the Greek. It is often translated as if it meant just "wandering," but really the Greek is more subtle than this and tells us in one word what we in English have to say in several; it has a distinctly passive sense meaning *"that which is made to wander or drift,"* i.e. drifting beyond its own control—unable to stop if it wanted to. It is most useful to have one word to distinguish all this *passively* drifting life from the creatures such as fish and whales which are strong enough to swim and migrate at will through the moving waters: these in contrast are spoken of as the *nekton* (Greek: *nektos*, swimming). Actually when they are very young, the baby fish are strictly speaking part of the plankton too, for they are also carried along at the mercy of the currents until they are strong enough to swim against them.

A number of fish, including the herring, pilchard, sprat, mackerel and the huge basking shark, feed directly upon the little plankton animals; and so also, curiously enough, do the great whalebone whales, the largest animals that ever lived. From this world of planktonic life, dead and dying remains are continually sinking toward the bottom and on the way may feed other plankton animals living in the deeper layers. For this reason the zooplankton (animal plankton—Greek: *zoon*, an animal) is not confined to the upper sunlit layers as is the phytoplankton (plant plankton—Greek: *phyton*, a plant). On the sea bed we find a profusion of animals equipped with all manner of devices for collecting this falling rain of food. Some, rooted to the bottom, spread out their branchlike arms in umbrella fashion and so look like plants; others, such as many shellfish, have remarkable sieving devices for trapping their finely scattered diet. Feeding upon these are hosts of voracious, crawling animals. These and their prey together—worms, starfish, sea urchins, crustaceans, mollusks and many other less familiar creatures—in turn form the food of the fish such as cod, haddock and plaice which roam the sea floor in search of them. Finally comes man: catching the herring and mackerel with his fleets of drift nets near the surface, hunting the great whales with explosive harpoons, and sweeping the sea bed with his trawls for the bottom-living fish.

We see how all-important the plankton is. All the life of the open sea depends for its basic supply of food upon the sunlit "pastures" of floating microscopic plants.

The American writer Guy Gilpatric was one of the first "skindivers," those who go down without breathing apparatus, and wrote the first book about it, The Compleat Goggler, *1938, from which we give a part. The original Aqua-Lung team—Dumas, Tailliez and Cousteau —were inspired by his lively book. Gilpatric (1896–1950) was born in New York City, and set an airplane altitude record of 4,665 feet when he was sixteen years old. He flew for the American Expeditionary Forces in France in World War I, and after the war began writing fiction. He became famous for his* Inchcliffe Castle *stories of the merchant marine, which were written on the French Riviera. He began goggling around 1929, and his pioneering reports on the sport in the* Saturday Evening Post *initiated it in the United States. During World War II, Gilpatric was an intelligence officer. When he learned that his beloved wife had an incurable cancer, the Gilpatrics took their own lives. Although free-diving technique has changed greatly since the descents described here, Gilpatric's adventure still appeals: it is a true and gay book about an astonishing concept of marine exploration. Incidentally, Gilpatric went back the third year after his* merou *(grouper) and found that someone had dynamited the reef— no doubt killing the famous Bonehead that Gilpatric had been telling everyone about.*

The Compleat Goggler

BY GUY GILPATRIC

> *A*s inward love breeds outward talk,
> The hound some praise, and some the hawk;
> Some, better pleased with private sport,
> Use tennis; some a mistress court:
> But these delights I neither wish,
> Nor envy, while I freely fish.
>
> *The Compleat Angler*

*F*or nearly three hundred years after Izaak Walton wrote his masterly treatise on angling, the world was content to accept him as final authority on the art, science and mystery of catching fish.

6

From time to time false prophets arose with patent hooks and chemical and electrical contrivances for knocking fish cold in wholesale quantities, while during the war the French infantry perfected an ingenious technique of chucking hand grenades into the Moselle River, thereby blasting many a gasping and disillusioned mud-gubbin out into the adjacent vineyards, and at the same time altering the course of the historic stream considerably. But all such devices of science, though effective, were flagrantly unsportsmanlike and therefore anathema to true amateurs of the rod and reel.

Then, suddenly, there came strange rumors. Somebody, somewhere, had evolved a radical and super-sportsmanlike manner of fishing— or, at least, so he claimed. His name (it was whispered by Seminole guides, Canuck gaffers, Highland gillies and Negro boatmen) was olde Guyzaak Gilpatric. His method, they said, was called goggle fishing. Here is the dope on it.

First, because so many fish go through life handicapped by names like scrod, chub, guppy and squid, I must explain that goggle fishing doesn't mean fishing for goggles, because goggles aren't fish. Goggle fishing is fishing with watertight eyeglasses and a spear—going down like McGinty to the bottom of the sea and scragging the wary denizens of the deep on their own home grounds. It is a sport so full of special tricks and dodges that I was minded to entitle this volume The Sport of Kinks until better judgment prevailed.

The first thing you need, to be a successful goggle fisher, is a body of good clear water. Personally I use the Mediterranean Sea and there is still plenty of room in it, but parts of the Atlantic, the Pacific, the Mexican Gulf and the Caribbean will do just as well, and I know of many lakes and streams which would provide grand goggling. Next you need a pair of watertight goggles. I made my first pair myself from an old pair of flying goggles, plugging up the ventilating holes with putty and painting over it. The ones I now use were built for sponge and pearl diving.

In goggle fishing, the spear is thrust like a sword and is never thrown, for you cannot throw a spear much farther under water than you can throw a motorbus on land. The spear being of necessity fairly short, you will be wondering how it is possible to approach within striking range of a fish. The answer is partly skill but mostly the fact that a fish is less suspicious of a man swimming under water, right in its own element, than of men or boats floating on the surface. I discovered this characteristic quite by accident, shortly after I began swimming with goggles and before I had any thought of spearing fish.

My idea, originally, was merely to study the submarine scenery which in the clear warm water of this Riviera region I believed would be worth seeing. Accordingly, one day, I shoved off from shore on an innocent sight-seeing trip. I had ridden in the glass-bottomed boats of Catalina and Bermuda and used waterscope boxes in the Gulf of Mexico, but I was unprepared for the breath-taking sensation of free flight which swimming with goggles gave me. It wasn't at all like flying in a plane, where you are conscious of being borne by something tangible; there was a nightmare quality to this sensation as in a dream of falling, and in that instant I knew how Icarus felt when his wings melted off. I jerked my head out of water and looked around to reassure myself. The bottom was fifteen feet below me, now, but every pebble and blade of grass was distinct as though there were only air between. The light was a soft bluish-green—even restful, and somehow wholly appropriate to the aching silence which lay upon those gently waving meadows and fields of flowers. On the pinnacle of a rock like a little mountain I saw a dwarf palm tree. I swam down to study it. I touched its trunk and—zip!—the feathery foliage vanished as quickly as the flame of a blown candle. I came up for air, a portion of which I used in vowing to get the explanation of this flummery. I swam along on the surface until I found another palm tree. This one I sneaked up on (or rather, down to) stealthily. I reached forward, touched the leaves and—they weren't! But this time it hadn't fooled me. The trunk had simply sucked the leaves inside itself. If my finger had been an anchovy or other small fish, it might have been sucked in with them, there to be consumed for the nourishment of the confounded plant. I have since learned that this was the *Spirographis Spallanzanii*, not a plant at all, but an animal; but I decided right then and there that it is as foolhardy to go picking flowers on the sea bottom as it is in front of the cop in a public park.

Soaring on my way above hills and valleys upon which grew blossoms snowy white and flaming red, I came to a great submerged rock from one side of which projected a wide shelf. I could see small fish flashing in and out along its edges, and went down to have a look at them. The underside of the shelf, though only ten or twelve feet below the surface, was fifty feet above the bottom. It was heavily grown with weeds. Anchovies and sardines—thousands of them—were swimming around eating this foliage. But—I rubbed my goggles—they were swimming on their backs! Had I discovered a new species? At first I couldn't believe what I saw; then a larger fish happened along and he, too, was swimming on his back. I dove right under the ledge, where it was dark and cold, and shooed the whole crowd out. As soon as they left the shadow and saw the sunlight above them, they turned right side up and went their ways like any self-respecting fish. Now those fish did not have to turn on their backs in order to eat weeds on the ceiling, for fish can eat in any reasonable position as well as in several which I might call scandalous. No, those fish were not aware that they were on their backs. They thought that the ceiling was the floor; they didn't know up from down being in practically the same fix as the old-time aviators who, lacking instruments for flying in clouds and fog, used to lose all sense of direction and turn upside down without realizing it until loose objects, such as bottles, commenced falling upwards out of the cockpit.

Feeling pretty pleased with myself, I swam around to the other side of the rock. This face of it went down sheer until its base was lost in deep blue gloom. I had the sensation of flying in the chasm of a New York street. Below me I saw vague forms moving—fish they were, and whoppers. I watched them for a long time as they lazed about in stately grace or poised in rumination, fearing that my slightest move would startle them. But presently a couple came up to within fifteen feet of me and seemed to be giving me the once-over. I thought I'd return the compliment. Swimming down as close to them as I dared, I hovered in suspense which they didn't seem to share. They were big fat dorads; I was so close that I could see the gold bands on their blue foreheads but I didn't hope that they'd let me come closer. I needed air and started upward. Suddenly, I found myself staring into the eyes of what looked like a German U-Boat— a three-foot *loup* in a fine state of indignation, his dorsal fin jutting up like the bristles of a bulldog. Without stopping to think, I cut loose my right and pasted him square on the jaw. I heard a whirring sound like that of wings as Mr. Loup departed under forced draft.

I came to the surface, gulped some air, and pondered on the sorry state to which I had fallen in being unable to knock out a three-foot fish. No use kidding myself, that blow wouldn't have bruised a stewed oyster. My knuckles were bleeding but this merely meant I'd scratched them on the little needles along the edges of his gill. I filled my lungs, swam down a way and indulged in some experimental shadowboxing. I soon found the trouble. Being lighter than water, my punches simply pushed me backward, and the harder I walloped, the faster I shoved myself away from what I was aiming to hit. Also, I was using a lot of energy in resisting my tendency to float to the surface. I blew out my air, sank down further, and uncorked a couple of rights and lefts. Now, I felt that my blows really had a little steam behind them. My body being heavier than water, my punches had something to react against.

I was feeling pretty tired, and I noticed that the skin on my fingers was shriveled from being in the water too long. As I swam toward the beach, I thought of what I'd learned—namely, that some fish are not afraid of swimmers, and that to exert power under water you have to empty your lungs. It occurred to me that in these discoveries might lie the basis of a new sport. Still, I didn't feel that socking fish in the jaw was quite the way to do things, so I determined to buy a spear. When I reached the beach, I found that I had been swimming for two hours and a half. It had seemed like twenty minutes.

My first spear was a trident with piano-wire teeth forged into barbs. The handle—it was the handle of a hayrake—was six feet six inches long.

I thought that my best bet would be to work in fairly shallow water, so I scouted along parallel to the beach in a depth of eight to ten feet. Pretty soon I spotted a school of slim, streamlined mullets —fish rather like trout and running from a foot to two feet in length. They were milling around on the bottom, eating, their sides flashing silver through the cloud of sand which their fins fanned up. Before I could get down to them, they spotted me and darted away. I followed on the surface, waiting for them to commence feeding again. They circled around at a good safe distance, watching me. Apparently they didn't care for the view, for with a skitter of tails, they beat it. A second school of them acted the same way. Now this was discouraging. The *loup* and the dorads of the day before had not behaved thus, so I concluded that fish are more wary in the shallows than in the depths. Diving is their instinctive means of escape, and when this avenue is closed to them, they won't take chances.

I headed for the submerged rock and deep water. The anchovies were swimming on their backs, as usual, and around on the far side were the dorads. Blowing out my air I sank down a way and then swam toward them: one lazed away from the group and came to meet me, his big-lipped mouth opening and closing as though saying, "Howdy, buddy, howdy!" When I thought the distance was right I lunged—and missed him by a yard!

I went up to breathe, to cuss and to ponder. Well, the lunge had been short, because I hadn't bided my time and come close enough to the fish. The direction had been cockeyed, because my spear was too light. I put my face under water and peered down. The dorads were still there. One of them—he looked as big as a guitar—was tearing mussels from the side of the rock and chawing them horsily. I sank toward him. This time, I vowed, I wouldn't fire till I saw the whites of his eyes. The nearer I approached the more greedily he ate, as though fearing that I intended to horn in on his meal. Ten feet. Eight feet. Six. There were the whites of his eyes. Now— zippo—I let him have it!

The spear was yanked out of my grasp. I saw the white wooden handle streak past my face. I grabbed it with both hands and tried to kick my way up to the surface. I had to have air, but the spear felt as though the Loch Ness Monster's big brother was on the other end of it. Suddenly it tore loose, and as I shot upward I saw the dorad heading in the other direction. The heavy piano-wire teeth of my trident were bent and twisted like hairpins. Back on the beach I told my friends that I had jabbed a rock. "Well," they said, "anybody could do that!"

Next day I put to sea with a spear which would have held a walrus. I had learned that when a fish is eating he could be scragged, and I planned to wait around until mealtime. But suddenly, perhaps ten feet under and a little ahead of me, I saw a gray fish with dark tiger stripes. He was coming in a straight line, evidently intending to pass under me. This, I thought, would be like wing shooting. I sank to meet him. Our paths crossed just as he came within range. I lunged and caught him fair and square. This fellow, a *mourme*, was only a little over a foot long, but he raised a great ruction. Fearing that he would pull himself off the barbs, I took him clear to the bottom and jammed him good and hard against the sand.

Well, my return to the beach with that *mourme* saw my stock rise considerably in Juan-les-Pins. People had been kidding me in five or six languages about my expeditions with goggles and spear, but now they allowed as how maybe, *peut-être*, *quiza* and *vielleicht*, the thing was a pretty good sport. Next day, when I brought in a two-foot sargus and a dorad measuring twenty-six inches and weighing between six and seven pounds, a considerable portion of the summer population sprouted spears and goggles and started after the game in a big way.

Goggle fishing is like hunting on land in that you frequently stalk an individual fish for half an hour or longer, watching him from the surface, and then either get him or miss him when you submerge, according to your luck and water skill. We have found it better sport to single out a big fish and then go after him than to swim around taking pot-shots at whatever we happen to meet. Unless you are a howling genius, you'll miss five fish for every one you get. That's the sport of goggle fishing.

I was swimming home late one afternoon, face in the water and spear couched, when I saw a batlike shadow moving along below me. It was dark brown and a yard across. It swam with an undulating slither close to the bottom. Occasionally a portion of it would fold together, and then the folded part became a long tapering tentacle which licked around the rocks like a whiplash in slow action. Even if I hadn't guessed what it was I'd have recognized an octopus soon enough, for suddenly it folded itself into eight distinct tentacles radiating from a central tumorous lump like a derby hat and looked up at me with a pair of protruding gold-rimmed eyes. Not knowing what else to do, I looked back at him through a pair of nickel-rimmed goggles. He didn't make a hostile move, and neither did I. I could see his head, which was also his body, pulsating in an oozy, intestinal sort of way, and as his tentacles writhed gently I caught glimpses of the rows of bony white suction cups along the undersides of them. Floating there watching him and wishing I was ashore, I formed a true conception of the meaning of the word "obscene."

Italian fishermen had told me that if an octopus gets you when you are unarmed, the thing to do is bite him between the eyes, thus paralyzing the master nerve which controls his tentacles. Not caring to make the headlines by improving upon the old newspaper formula "MAN BITES DOG," I swam down and jabbed him with the spear. I was nervous and my lunge went wild; I missed his eyes, but got him through the bulbous, palpitating body. Instantly the submarine day turned into darkest night, and I found myself being towed through a cloud of ink which he shot from his breathing apparatus as he pumped himself along. Once clear of the cloud, I saw that he was swimming with his tentacles streaming out behind him like the tail of a comet. He groped down, grabbed a rock and started climbing. If the five-pronged spear was hurting he didn't show it; all he registered was annoyance.

Well, I had to have air, but though I dragged with all my force, he dragged harder. I let go the spear, struggled up and breathed in so much air that the barometers for miles around marked a record low-pressure area for the Alpes-Maritimes. I went under again. The octopus was out of sight now, but the spear handle was jutting from the cave. I grabbed it with both hands. I tried using it as a lever against the top of the cavern, but slowly it was dragged inward. Then suddenly, a tentacle lashed out and wrapped itself around the wood, then another, and another. In his rage he was letting go of the rock and trying to strangle the spear. A fourth tentacle snaked out, caught the spear handle and licked across the back of my left hand. The part that touched me was only the tapering tip, but I didn't care for the nasty sucking feel of it. With a final tug I broke his hold on the rock, brought him to the surface and then ashore.

It was along toward the end of October and the days were pulling in pretty short. Sometimes the storm clouds would stack up on the mountains to the west of us and swallow the sun by four in the afternoon. Our front yard, the Mediterranean Sea, was as full of fish as ever and so clear that you could see bottom in sixty feet, but with the diminishing sunlight, its greens and blues and purples had taken on a grayish tinge and it was turning colder every day. All summer long we'd had priceless sport. For month after month, with water temperatures of between 70° F. and 80° F., we goggled for six hours a day; and more than once, in August, we had worked the beach and harbor of Sainte Maxime for eight hours straight. We had learned things about fish and their habits which certainly no fisherman and perhaps no scientist had ever known; we had observed submarine phenomena which we couldn't explain ourselves and which were so strange that we hesitated to mention them to outsiders lest they stroke their chins and murmur, "Oh, yair?"

Around the ends of the rocky capes of Antibes, Ferrat and Roux, on the reefs beyond the Lérins Islands and at the foot of the red rock cliffs where the Estérel Mountains go into the sea, we had looked down upon scenes of grandeur beyond the dry land's grandest and had seen no billboards. But now, if we goggled for only half an hour, diving down fifteen or twenty feet or following the fish into the rock grottoes which the sun never penetrates, the cold knotted us up until we couldn't have speared a crate of dried codfish with a mile of picket fence. All along the Riviera, from Le Lavandou to Menton, people were complaining about the unmuffled speedboat motors when what they really heard was the chattering of goggle fishers' teeth.

November 1 dawned a rotten day, with a high layer of clouds moving eastward and another scudding oppositely just above the sea. Ducks, geese and herons were going over in bunches headed for Egypt, proving that ducks, geese and herons do not believe all they read about the Riviera's winter climate. But at ten o'clock, faithful to our daily tryst, the Antibes Local of the Gogglers' Guild convened with spears on the wave-pounded beach, and a solemn lot we were. Our number included a Russian, two Frenchmen, an Irishman and myself. Any of us could see with half a goggle that our sport was finished for the season.

There was a long silence while we viewed the desolate scene.

"Well, what shall we do?" asked somebody.

"What is there left to do?" snarled somebody else.

"I know!" I said, brightly. "Let's go fishing!"

"Fishing?" inquired an incredulous voice. "Fishing? You mean—fishing?"

"Yes, fishing. With hooks and lines and bait and boat. Regular old-fashioned fishing."

Well, the sheer novelty of the stunt swept them off their feet, and so an hour later we were bobbing at anchor just west of the tip of Cap d'Antibes. We dropped our lines over the side and waited for something to happen. For a long time nothing did happen. It was a frightful bore. Even when we started pulling in a few fair-sized ones our tackle kept getting tangled in our yawns. Once a man has goggled —once he has hunted his fish, stalked it, pursued it in its own element and finally speared it or lost it as he or the fish was the smarter— the conventional flummery of hooks and lines and rods and reels is merely so much near beer.

By noon I'd had enough—and at noon, precisely, the sun came out. "Madam Chairman and beloved lodge sisters," I said, "I'm going overboard for a final hack at it." I peeled off, put on goggles and knife belt, took my five-pronged spear and slid over the gunwale into the (br-r-rh!) water. I swam toward the cape, which at that point goes down from the surface in sheer walls like the façades of Florentine palaces. At some places the depth was thirty or forty feet; at others I could not see bottom at all and everything below was the dark velvety blue of February evening sky. A school of black mullets like a flock of crows passed under me. I saw a rock as big as a church swinging back and forth, back and forth; I lifted my face out of water to keep from feeling dizzy and to remind myself that I and not the rock was seesawing in the swell. And when I put my face under again I saw Merou the Bonehead.

I didn't recognize him, at first. I only knew that the biggest fish I'd encountered to date was lying on a rock ledge twenty feet below me. I blew out my air and sank toward him. Before I was halfway down I realized that even if I speared him I'd have a tough time bringing him up. I stayed where I was, watching him. He returned the scrutiny with an eye the size of a horse's. His pectoral fins barely stirring, he moved majestically along the ledge and as a beam of sunlight struck him I saw that he was a merou. I swam up to the surface and back to the boat with the news.

All we knew about the merou was that he was a very athletic and very nasty fish and that, having speared him, you should not grab him by the throat lest he crush your fingers in his edged and armored gills—or maybe hers. At length we decided to row to within fifty yards of the rocks, put a rope around me and my spear and try our luck. When I yanked on the line the people in the boat would yank me and (we hoped) the merou up to the surface; meanwhile I would be giving him appropriate treatment with my knife.

I went over the side again—and have you ever noticed how much colder cold water is the second time? It was awkward, swimming with the line around me; my feet kept getting tangled in it. The merou was still on his ledge but he had moved a little way along it to a spot where he could watch the proceedings better. He wasn't in the least afraid of me as I started down but as soon as he spotted the rope curling and snaking in the water, he ducked back into a crevice out of sight. Evidently, sometime in his career, he'd had an unfortunate experience with a line with a hook at the end of it and he wasn't intending to fall for that gag again.

No, the rope wouldn't do. I went up for air, cast it off and called to the boat to stand by. I now planned to dive, plant the spear in him and then let go of it, hoping that once wounded he wouldn't be able to swim far. When he had tired himself by thrashing around I could go down again, do a little knifework on him and eventually bring him to the surface. Soon I saw the great brown snout come out of the crack—cautiously. I was about to dive when it bobbed in again. I lay on the surface and watched and shivered and cursed and shivered and watched for fifteen minutes. Yes, and shivered. Suddenly, further along the crack, I saw his whole head. I beckoned the boat to come closer; then, blowing out all my air to enable me to sink fast, deep and with minimum effort and water disturbance, I went for him. Just as I came within range—say four feet—he started back into the crevice. I couldn't see his body, only his head, and I knew I would have to hit him quickly and hard. "All right, Sir or Madam, as the case may be!" I said. "How's—THIS?"

I let him have it smack on the dome. There was a frightful ruction, a brown flash and—Merou was gone!

All five spear teeth had struck him at once. The shock of the blow through the spear handle made my elbow tingle as though I'd hit a rock. Each of those teeth was needle-pointed and razor-edged. But as far as I had seen or felt, not a single one of them had gone more than skin deep into Merou. Merou the Bonehead!

I felt that something was wrong. My spear should have gone into that merou—and it hadn't. Why not? The answer come from India. A Britisher just back from Benares was telling us how simple the fakirs' tricks are when you stop to figure them out. The famous couch of nails, for instance, is simply so chuckful of nails that the holy man's weight, distributed over the points of all of them, does not bear down hard enough on any one point to puncture the skin. "But," said our friend, "I offered any number of them seventy-five rupees to sit on a single nail and there wasn't a sportsman in the lot." Right then and there we saw the trouble with our five-toothed spears. The force of the blow was divided among all the teeth and distributed over too great an area of the fish. What we needed was a spear with a single point in which the full force could concentrate.

For weeks, then, as the word went forth and good gogglers got together, the marble tops of café tables throughout the Alpes-Maritimes were covered with penciled designs for single-toothed harpoons. We whittled wooden models of harpoon heads and jabbed oranges and loaves of bread with them to study the nature of the wounds. We figured out a design which looked good to all. This was a steel shaft three-eighths of an inch square with a forged triangular head and a hinged barb. The barb would close tight against the shaft while entering the fish but would swing out at right angles at the slightest opposite pull, thus preventing the fish's escape. My own harpoon was six feet long and weighed about two pounds. It was a mean weapon. The only trouble was, we didn't know whether we could hit anything with it. Our five-toothed spears had given us a margin of error of almost six inches, but with our new harpoons every shot had to be a bull's-eye.

It wasn't until the first week in May that the water warmed up enough for a tryout. I was still gasping a little, cursing each and every cigarette I'd smoked during the winter and gazing down with joy at the underwater world which I hadn't seen for months, when out of the sand where it had been buried came something which looked like a carelessly made mud pie. It was a fish of a kind I'd never seen before and he rather suggested the result of a morganatic alliance of a stingray with a horseshoe crab. My shadow crossed him;

he put on speed and tried to get out from under. Right then I gave the harpoon its first taste of fish. It went into him as neatly as two goes into four. He didn't like it. He thrashed and bucked and even bit, but the hinged barb had opened up and he was caught.

I brought him ashore and flopped him on the beach. We gathered around trying to decide what sort of a beast he was when—zippo!—I got a jolt of electricity through the harpoon shaft which very nearly knocked me over backward. He had introduced himself in characteristic fashion as that curious living power station, the *torpille*, or electric ray.

The electric ray is one of those things which everybody has heard about but in which nobody believes. Well, we converted a lot of unbelievers that day, inviting them to touch our *torpille* and watching them jerk back and cuss as though they'd blown out a fuse. As far as we could observe, it was only when he bent up his tail and arched his back that he could give you a shock. When he had delivered eight or ten jolts his batteries ran down, but he recharged them rapidly and was ready for business again. And batteries they really were—honeycomb-like structures of squashy white cells within both sides of his forward section. Even when he was dead and partially dissected we received weak shocks if we happened to short-circuit his wiring system.

Well, from then on it was a glorious summer. We landed more and bigger fish than we'd ever caught before. Of course some succeeded in tearing loose, but then the fault was ours in having speared them too far back, too near the edge or through the soft part of the belly. By the middle of summer we began to realize that certain individual fish spend their time in fixed neighborhoods and that others, like some migratory birds, come back to the same spot at the same time year after year. We had known all along that many rock fish, such as the *sargue* and the *serre*, are confirmed stay-at-homes and we had come to know a number of them by their first names, but it surprised us to meet a giant *linte* for the third successive August in a little cove where no other *linte* is ever seen. At least three of us saw and recognized him and believed that he recognized us. Thinking of this and talking it over with the others made me wonder if Merou the Bonehead, the only merou any of us had seen thus far, was not one of these confirmed homebodies. Certainly he'd known all the ins and outs of that crevice as though he'd lived there a long time. Four of us went out to look for him. Because I remembered the bottom from the year before (somehow a goggle fisher acquires the knack of finding his way by the bottom, unerringly, and rarely uses landmarks) I had no difficulty in leading the caravan to the proper territory. And there on his ledge, looking up at us with his horsy eye, lay Merou the Bonehead, exactly as I'd first seen him eleven months before!

I could see his whole body and I believe I could have scragged him then and there. But a merou is not to be taken lightly, and at least two of our number had legitimate scientific reasons for wanting to see such a grand specimen at large. The grand specimen, however, had legitimate scientific reasons for getting the hell out of there, and he did so with a single caudal flip which took him into the crevice and out of sight. It was apparent that he didn't care for crowds. Now by all rules of goggling, this merou was my own personal fish; and so, with the gesture of a matador ordering his *peons* from the ring and hoping to God that they won't take it seriously, I waved my companions away and prepared myself to settle the thing, man to Merou. They swam away twenty yards or so and lay with their faces under water to witness the drama of life and death which all of us felt would shortly unfold.

I floated with spear couched and knife loosened in its sheath, ready to sink down and deal the lethal blow. He didn't come out. I lay there for a long, long time—so long that I studied his old homestead in detail, even noting that the seaweed on his ledge—a species of white flower very like the gardenia of dry land—had a foot-wide path worn through it by the friction of his belly. He stuck his head out exactly where I knew he would. I went down, just as I had planned and hoped and dreamed and known I'd go down. I drew back my arm, sighted along the spear, uncorked my soul and—SMACK!

There was a frightful ruction, a brown flash and—Merou the Bonehead was gone! When I came to the surface I found that the steel shaft of my harpoon was bent two inches out of line. Excalibur had failed us!

Thus ended the goggling for another season.

The learned numismatist Robert Nesmith is an incurable treasure hound. Hallucinated amateur treasure hunters and promoters, as well as serious marine archaeologists, make pilgrimages to the open door of his Foul Anchor Archives in Rye, New York, to find out just what it is they are looking for. One-Dive Bob, as he calls himself, is a fountainhead of data on coins, wrecks and marine archives. It was he who authenticated the famous "McKee Galleon" wreck in the Florida Keys as a sixty-gun Spanish ship sunk July 15, 1733 in a hurricane that destroyed half of the annual treasure convoy from the Mexico City mint to Old Spain. Nesmith's motto is "Treasure or pleasure" and he is as happy to see one of the strivers as one of the finders like Edward Tucker or Arthur McKee, the legendary underwaterman who is now excavating the 1733 ship.

The Bishop's Cross

BY ROBERT I. NESMITH

One of the most successful undersea treasure hunters of recent years lives in Bermuda. His discovery was remarkable for its historical and monetary value. Edward B. (Teddy) Tucker of Gwelly Hole, Somerset, is a native-born Bermudian. The first Tucker settled in Bermuda in 1620 and Tuckers have been there ever since. Teddy is short, husky, and soft-spoken. He has the weatherbeaten hide of one who has spent his life on, in, and under the sea. He was raised so close to the ocean that had he fallen from his window when a baby, he says he would have landed in the surf. And he has never left the sea. His youth from twelve on was spent with fishermen. He quit school early to fish and dive for conch shells to sell the tourists. He came to know intimately the ragged reefs that surround Bermuda in a hundred-mile circle, and has looked down on dozens of wrecks where the fish hide in rusted hulls. Teddy has found cannon bare of coral on the reefs, where the coral growth has hardly increased since the last ice age, and he has found cannon completely cemented over with coral where it grows rapidly and tall and breaks off in storms.

From his boyhood days, Teddy has been interested in wrecks and it seems fitting that he should be the one to bring up a famous treasure. He used the first Japanese face mask in Bermuda waters while diving for conch shells. Joining the British Navy early in World War II, he spent five years diving from light mine sweepers. He gained experience in Singapore, the Bay of Bengal, and the Gulf of Aden. Sometimes wallowing up to his armpits in the mud in strong tides and unable to see an inch in front of his face mask, he was happy to get home to the clear waters of Bermuda in 1947.

Tucker and his brother-in-law, Robert Canton, had ideas. They formed a partnership, bought a boat, rebuilt and rerigged her with air compressors and hoisting equipment, and went into business. They made surveys for insurance companies, and salvaged copper, lead, brass, and other salable material. One of the largest vessels lost in the area, the French sixty-gun ship *Hermione,* was wrecked off the west end of the islands in December, 1838. The muzzle-loading cannon in her main battery weigh about seven thousand pounds each, and fired shot six inches in diameter and weighing sixty-four pounds. The name of a famous cannon maker "Ruelle" and the date "AN 1828" can still be read on the breeches of the eleven cannon that remain on the wreck. Tucker and Canton have explored her thoroughly and have recovered some fifty swords and cutlasses, flintlock muskets, brass and copper fittings, and nautical instruments. The *Hermione* when she sailed to her end was the last word in armed sailing ships. She now rests in a sea so clear that Peter Stackpole, famous underwater photographer of *Life* magazine, filmed a color movie of Tucker and Canton at work on the wreck.

In the Spanish galleon era, Bermuda was called "Isle of Devils" by superstitious mariners. A pinpoint on their crude charts, uninhabited, unlit, low on the horizon, the "Barmudas" were a death trap for many a treasure ship in foggy or stormy weather and on dark nights. The islands lay astride the homeward path of the plate fleets, the last landfall between Havana and Old Spain. There in 1955 Tucker and Canton made one of the most important discoveries of wealth ever raised from the sea in modern times. The treasures in gold and jewels had lain on the ocean bottom for over 350 years lightly covered with sand.

On a calm, clear winter's day in 1950, Tucker was out in a small boat looking around the reefs when he spied three cannon sticking up out of the sand. The following summer he went back to the location and recovered six cannon, a bucketful of lead musket balls, and a very old anchor, with a large eye—the kind used with rope before the days of chain cable. The cannon were purchased by the local Historical Society and they now repose on the lawn of the Bermuda aquarium. In 1955 Tucker and Canton thought of returning to the wreck site on a pleasant Sunday to prospect the area. On the bottom, in a depth of thirty feet or less, they dug around in the sand with their hands. The first object they recovered was a bronze apothecary's mortar, marked "Petrus Van Den Ghein" with the date 1561. Mendel L. Peterson of the Smithsonian Institition has identified the maker as a famous Flemish caster of bronze bells and objects who died in 1561. The mortar must have been one of his last works. Spurred on by this find, Tucker and Canton gathered a bucketful of blackened silver coins, some stuck together in clumps of coral. Clinging to one lump was the remains of the pigskin pouch in which the coins were originally enclosed. Then a small square of bright gold shone in the sand—a cube cut from a larger bar.

"This was the first gold I had ever seen on the ocean bottom," said Tucker. "It was as clean and bright as jewelry in a Fifth Avenue store. One corner had been sliced off either to assay or for small change. We hated to stop work but it was nine miles back to port so we quit for the day. We were really excited," Tucker continued, "and returned to comb the small pocket among the rocks where the relics had been uncovered. We tried a suction pipe operated by eighty pounds' air pressure but it was unsatisfactory. We tried a water jet, using a small hose and less pressure. Finally, we just dug with our hands and used a small paddle like a ping-pong bat, to fan away the sand. This paid off well—I later hung the paddle on the wall at home. I guess we are the only treasure divers to fan ourselves into a small fortune from a sunken galleon. Over a period of days we found three gold buttons studded with pearls; a gold bar ten and a half inches long weighing thirty-six ounces; two rounded lumps of gold weighing twenty-three and nineteen ounces; something over two thousand Spanish and French silver coins, and a second small square of gold. We uncovered some breech loading culverins or swivel guns; hand grenades; a steel breastplate; sounding leads, in which the British Museum was most interested; a terra-cotta inkwell in the form of a lion's head; brass hourglasses and a pair of navigator's brass dividers; a set of nested brass weights; and the finest prize of all—a bishop's gold pectoral cross studded with seven emeralds, an almost priceless relic. It is of native Indian workmanship and from the ends of the cross bar hang two small golden nails. Whether a bishop was wearing it on his homeward trip to

Spain or whether some wealthy patron of the Church was carrying it as a gift may never be known.

"We also recovered some interesting pottery of native Carib make. One cruet for vinegar or oil is red clay with green glaze. A small six-inch pitcher with a spout is set on a ten-degree angle so that its center of gravity makes it less likely to tip over when used on shipboard. It was made by a left-handed potter who held it in his right hand while he molded the clay handle with his left; this can be detected by his fingerprints. Nothing like it in style has been seen before.

"A collection of Carib Indian weapons was being carried by some passenger to show the folks in Spain. One ceremonial spear five feet long is carved in an intricate design for about two feet along the handle. We also found bows and arrows. These weapons were fire-treated to harden them, and the water and worms that attack ordinary wood have had no effect on them.

"One of our strangest finds was human bones—scattered ribs, finger, forearm, and foot bones—now undergoing tests in England. Bones generally dissolve after five years under the sea and it is unheard of to recover them after some 350 years. One British bone specialist has suggested that they are possibly the bones of some dignitary whose mummified body was being returned to Old Spain for burial. Could they have been the remains of the bishop who wore the emerald cross? The latest dated coin found on the site is a Spanish piece of eight of 1592, so the wreck must have happened at some later time, probably in the late 1590's. If church records list some bishop lost at sea on his return trip during the period, we may be able to date and name the wreck.

"We uncovered a pair of woman's leather shoes in the sand which fell apart when disturbed, but not before Pete Stackpole made photographs of them. I believe the ship hit the rocks, lay there for a short time, and then split apart, letting the material fall through her broken hull. There was no sign of timbers or the major parts of a ship. Apparently the wooden parts drifted away. We found only rock ballast, with the relics scattered around in the sand, the cannon and anchor on top. We moved everything and cleaned out the pothole, so I doubt whether anything more of value remains. It was an easy place to work, as there was no large coral; the water is not over thirty feet deep and in some places is so shallow that we could stand with our heads above water. The ship could not have been a large one, as her armament consisted of six large cannon, four breech-loading swivel guns, and some matchlock muskets."

The gold bars and cakes are as bright and clean as the day they were cast. They are marked with the circular stamp of the Royal Spanish Tax Collector, a circular design showing castles, lions and a pomegranate denoting Castile, Leon, and Granada in a shield surrounded with the legend "PHILLIPVS.II.D.G.REX." This stamp denotes that the king's *quinto* or royal fifth had been deducted. The long bar is stamped "Pinto," the name of the mining locality in Colombia (then Nuevo Reino de Granada) from which the gold came. One of the rounded ingots is stamped "ESPANA" and the other is stamped with the name "DºHERNANDZ" (Diego, or Domingo, Hernandez), the assayer. One of the small squares of gold, cut from a larger bar, is stamped with the monogram "PHVS" for "PHILLIPVS" above a large pomegranate, denoting Nuevo Reino de Granada. The various bars are also individually stamped with the Roman numerals XX, XXI, XXII and XXIII, which are probably the lot numbers.

*

Naval Doctrine

Napoleon:	Monsieur le Ministre, you are proposing to me a naval academy on land. It is like starting a cavalry school on shipboard.
Admiral Decres	(Minister of the Navy): O, no, sire!
Napoleon:	On the contrary, that's just it. Do you know how to bring up youngsters underwater?
Decres:	No, sire.
Napoleon:	When you have found the way, we will train them down there.

A Man in the Atlantic

BY WOLFGANG FRANK

While operating against a convoy in fog near the Azores, a U-boat was surprised on the surface by a destroyer and rammed. The position seemed hopeless; as the enemy ship swept down upon them, the U-boat captain ordered, "Lifebelts on—stand by to abandon ship!" The order was promptly executed by a petty officer and a rating on the bridge, who, when the destroyer's sharp stem cut into the U-boat's stern, jumped overboard without waiting for further orders, believing the U-boat to be doomed. As the men came to the surface and looked about them, they saw their boat diving steeply with a gaping hole in her stern. At the same time the destroyer was crawling painfully away with a heavy list and badly damaged bows, her half-exposed screws splashing the water wildly beneath her stern; within a few seconds she had disappeared in the fog.

The two survivors started to swim in the rough sea, which plucked them hither and thither. Crazy things happened sometimes; perhaps the corvette would turn back. But the fog was thickening and there was nothing to be seen but waves and more waves.

The rating lost his nerve, shouting and yelling for help. The petty officer, who was made of sterner stuff, managed to calm his comrade and for a time they trod water in silence. "It's hopeless," said the rating. "We'll drown sooner or later, anyway—why not now?" "It's not cold," said the petty officer. "I can stand it and I'm not going to drown before I have to." They swam a little further; the wind was rising, dissolving the fog into tiny raindrops that splashed softly around them. Suddenly a gap in the fog revealed a dark object drifting in their direction—a raft. With difficulty they swam toward it and clambered over the barnacle-covered side. It had evidently belonged to some sunken ship and must have been drifting for a long time, half-submerged; but it bore their weight. As dusk fell, the seas

24

rose higher and higher, tossing them to and fro, while the sharp-edged barnacles tore at their clothes, their hands and knees. They were weak with hunger and desperately weary; twice the raft overturned and each time the petty officer managed to drag his apathetic companion back to it. The third time, however, the attempt failed and the petty officer was alone.

With the first hint of dawn the wind freshened again. The solitary survivor could see nothing but huge waves with foaming crests. Before he was properly aware of it, the raft was torn from under him; when next he rose on a wave crest he could see that it had drifted thirty yards away. He knew he could never reach it again and so he waited patiently for the end.

But what in Heaven's name was this? Barely a stone's throw away the seas parted—and a U-boat came to the surface! The unique, the utterly improbable thing had happened. In all the vast spaces of the Atlantic, a U-boat had chosen to surface precisely where one man was about to drown. The captain came on to the bridge and took his first careful look round the horizon; he was on the point of ordering the diesels to start when he heard a faint cry and saw a man bobbing about on the waves. Within a minute he had turned the boat and picked him up.

The captain made a routine signal to Admiral U-Boats, and there the story seemed to end. But that same evening the rescued man's U-boat was heard reporting by wireless that it had lost two men after being rammed, but had crash-dived and managed to escape. Headquarters then ordered a meeting point for the two boats, and the survivor, restored to his own boat, soon recovered from his ordeal and sailed happily home with his comrades.

This strange tale of chance evoked much speculation at the U-boat base. It was suggested, with all respect, that God Almighty must have had a special reason for intervening, having gone to the trouble of picking this man out of the vast Atlantic, only to set him back on his little U-boat.

Among the experimental scientists who have taught man to acclimate himself to the world under the sea, few have made more useful contributions than Prof. J. B. S. Haldane, F.R.S. As a boy he participated in his father's historic Admiralty Deep Diving Committee which established the basic diving tables in 1906. Haldane is a distinguished geneticist. He holds two Darwin Medals for the discovery by his research team of the first linkage between vertebrates and polyploid plants and the first estimate of a human mutation rate. His "more or less persistent attempts to live maximally have brought [him] into conflict with a variety of authorities," Haldane says. In 1957 he settled in India, whose biological research opportunities he finds "considerably better than in England." One of his junior colleagues at the Indian Statistical Institute in Calcutta has "made a discovery in the improvement of agricultural yields which may alter the course of world history," he reports. This narrative of Haldane's wartime experiments in underwater safety is the clearest and most readable essay on diving physiology we have seen. Recently he has been diving in the Bay of Bengal.

Life at High Pressure

BY J. B. S. HALDANE

*M*y main job during the war was to tackle the physiological dangers to which divers and men trying to escape from submarines were exposed, apart from any enemy action.

A lot of our work was done "in the dry" in compressed air, for many of a diver's troubles are simply due to the pressure, and you can give good imitations of them and find out how to prevent them, without going under water. Most of our "dry" work was done in Siebe Gorman's Chamber No. 3. This is a steel cylinder like a boiler. It lies on its side and is eight feet long and four feet in diameter. So three people can sit in it, but one can't begin to stand up. At one end is a steel door. This opens inward and has a rubber flange, so once there is a good air pressure inside, it is extremely tight. There are some glass plugs in the side and the door, which act as windows, and of course inlets and outlets for air, but no lamps or telephone inside.

One communicates by a code of taps, by shouting, or by holding messages to the window. This factory has no water more than twenty feet deep, so to simulate a deep dive we used a steel tank about six feet across and ten feet high. It had about seven feet of water in it in which the diver could stand, sit, crawl or lie. There was a pulley with a weight so that the diver could do measured amounts of work, and a slate to write on. Above this was an air space where the attendant sat on a shelf with his feet in the water. He kept an eye on the diver, and could haul him or her up with a rope if he or she lost consciousness.

By letting compressed air into the air space, one could put any desired pressure on the water, and we were able to reproduce all the symptoms reported in genuine dives. There was one extra symptom. Divers are tough men, but some of them got a genuine claustrophobia in this tank. They longed for the wide open spaces of the sea bottom. Certainly it was a queer experience to wait under water in this rather dark tank, knowing that one might lose consciousness at any moment, and perhaps wake up with a broken back, conceivably to not wake up at all, and to look out through the very small window at butterflies, bicycles and other familiar things. My father called this tank the Chamber of Horrors. The Navy called it the Pot.

Such was our setup. Now for the dangers which we had to investigate. The first, and least important, group arises from very rapid changes of pressure. One feels pressure changes in one's ears, because if the pressure on the two sides of the drum is unequal, it is strained. The drum is a thin membrane across a bony passage which goes from the outside to one's throat, and incidentally was a gill-slit when our ancestors were fish. The air gets freely enough to the drum from the outside, unless, indeed, one has a lot of wax in the ear. But the passage to the throat, called the Eustachian tube, is normally shut. Most people can open it by holding the nose and blowing vigorously. When the air pressure is raised, there is some pain in the ears, which one relieves by blowing in this way, so as to equalize the pressure. Of course a helmet diver cannot do this, as he has a window between his nose and finger. So he has to learn to open his Eustachian tube. One method is to swallow. When you do so you may hear a clicking as the tubes open and shut. Another place where pain is often felt is in the frontal sinuses. There are air spaces in the bone of the forehead which ought to open freely into the nose. But the passage may be blocked, and commonly is when one has a cold. Some people cannot even open their Eustachian tubes when they have a cold. I can, but if my sinuses are blocked I bleed in a spectacular manner from the nose. One of the methods for getting into Norwegian fiords under water was to ride in a self-contained diving dress on a torpedo-like vessel called a chariot. Occasionally an inexpert charioteer put his chariot's nose down too fast. If so he was liable to hurt his ear, and one or two may have burst their drums. This makes one deaf for a month or so, but the drum generally heals up; and if a hole remains in it, although one is somewhat deaf, one can blow tobacco smoke out of the ear in question, which is a social accomplishment.

Airmen suffer from the same ear trouble. To a diver, this is almost unintelligible. For the pressure changes which airmen experience are relatively very slow. The quickest "dive" I have done was in the dry from one to seven atmospheres' pressure (the equivalent of surface to two hundred feet) in ninety seconds. Some divers have descended quicker than this, but not much quicker. The rate at which pressure increases is the same as a pilot would experience if his plane were diving vertically at 1,500 m.p.h., or twice the speed of sound. At this very fast rate of compression or decompression one gets pain in teeth which have been filled. During compression the air does not get in quick enough to cavities under the filling, so the tooth may cave in. During the ascent the air cannot get out and the tooth may explode. One of mine perished in this manner.

The serious danger in rapid decompression occurs to very few people. But these few are born with weak patches in their lungs in which a bubble of air apparently gets nipped off, and these pockets may burst. The lung then collapses like the inner tube of a punctured tire. Provided the other lung holds there is no great danger, though the patient must go to bed. If both collapse he dies. One of my colleagues, Dr. Rendel, had a lung collapse in this way after a dry "dive" and unfortunately it has repeatedly done so since. The technical name for this condition, by the way, is pneumothorax, so called because there is air in the chest between the lung and the ribs.

In 1940 the view was current in the Navy that it took a long time to learn to stand rapid compression, and I rather think the qualified divers encouraged this superstition. When I told certain officers that I did not share it they said that no doubt trained biologists could learn quickly, but ordinary people could not. So I applied to the Communist Party for four tough guys of genuine working-class origin with no experience of diving or compressed air work. We got every one of them up to a pressure of ten atmospheres (three hundred feet) in five minutes at the first attempt, though of course they were allowed to hold their noses. For one can hold one's nose when wearing the Davis oxygen apparatus, and at that time I was being asked for advice on submarine escape. I think one of them lost consciousness during the compression, but none of them asked for it to be stopped. I should say that however physiologically tough one's subjects may be, about one in four would have difficulty in opening his or her Eustachian tubes, and would burst one or both eardrums if compressed at this rate. And it usually takes several dozen dives before one can open them without holding the nose or even thinking about it. I suspect the Navy's trouble was partly due to the fact that a man can usually learn to make a physiological adjustment quicker if you talk to him gently than if you shout at him. Fortunately Warrant Officer Brown, who instructed personnel for the Admiralty Experimental Diving Unit, realized this fact fully, and is in fact one of the kindliest people I know.

Before we get on to discuss the reasons why divers get killed, it is worth while describing some of the simple physical phenomena which one notices. Our chamber was filled from bottles containing air at 100 or 120 atmospheres pressure. It cooled down a great deal as it left the bottles, but warmed up a bit on its way through the pipes. However the air in the chamber was rapidly compressed by the incoming air, and became intensely hot. In fact the temperature rose from about 60° F. to 110° F. or more during a quick compression. We had a flexible metal tube attached to the inlet so that we could blow the cool incoming air onto our faces. The reason for this heating is of course the same as the reason why your bicycle pump gets hot. Effectively we were inside a bicycle pump in which the air was being compressed with a piston of air. Similarly when some of the air was let out, what was left cooled down rapidly, and a fog formed, which cleared up in a few minutes, but left everything damp. This had a serious effect on our watches. Either a watch is more or less airtight, in which case the pressure strains it very severely, or it is not, in which case fog forms in it during compression, moisture condenses, the spring rusts through, and the watchmaker says you should not drop your watch into the water.

At ten atmospheres there is ten times as much air in a cubic inch as at normal pressure. You feel hot, and try to fan yourself with a newspaper. But the resistance is so great that the newspaper tears to pieces. If you get hold of a large bit of cardboard for a fan, it is

quite an effort to force it through the air. But if you then flap
it toward a colleague four feet or so away, nothing happens for some
seconds. Then you see his or her hair being violently disturbed.
Your flapping has started a vortex ring which travels slowly, but
owing to the density of the air, has a considerable mechanical
effect. Rather to my surprise I found that a canary could fly at
ten atmospheres, though it did not do so very well. Small flies
refused to do so though they could walk. I suppose they found the
resistance of the air too great for their fine wings.

The human voice is greatly affected. Englishmen sound as if they
were trying, not very successfully, to imitate an American accent.
So are some musical instruments. At eleven atmospheres my colleague
Dr. E. M. Case found that a flageolet or "tin whistle" needed a greater
effort to blow, but gave a fuller and rounder note than normal,
rather like that of a recorder. A tuning fork gave its normal note,
but the pitch of an oboe's reed was much reduced. We did not try
any wooden instruments, as the compressed air soaks into the wood,
and when it expands in the pores during decompression, quantities
of resin are forced out.

Finally the air becomes effectively stickier in certain circumstances.
In order to remove carbon dioxide one often has to breathe through
a canister, rather like that of a gas mask, full of a coarse powder
made of lime and soda. At atmospheric pressure this is easy, but at
high pressures it may be very difficult. The volume of air per breath
and the number of breaths per minute are unchanged. So at ten
atmospheres one breathes ten times as much air per minute as at
one, that is to say ten times the weight or ten times the number of
molecules. At low pressure the flow is smooth, but at high pressures it
becomes turbulent, that is to say eddies develop. So the resistance to
breathing goes up, and one may inhale a very unpleasant dust.

After these preliminaries we come to the real dangers. They arise
from the fact that all gases dissolve in liquids, and the amount dissolved is proportional to the pressure. Our body consists mainly of
liquids, so at ten atmospheres there is, after a sufficiently long stay,
about ten times as much nitrogen in solution in our bodies as normally. Our tissues use oxygen and make carbon dioxide, so these gases
do not obey the rule so accurately.

All gases are poisonous. This has not yet been proved, but I
believe it to be true, and hope to make it plausible to my readers.
All solids and liquids are not poisonous, because they do not dissolve
in our blood and tissues. Thus a lead shrapnel bullet under the skin

is not deadly, though lead acetate is so; and we can swallow kerosene with safety or even advantage, though the same amount injected into a vein would be fatal. In particular, nitrogen is a poison.

If one is compressed to ten atmospheres one feels very abnormal. The feelings are rather like those of alcoholic intoxication, but perhaps more like those of mild intoxication with gasoline vapor or nitrous oxide. I have little control over my thoughts, and my consciousness is invaded by childhood memories, and nonsensical words which seem to me very important. Another subject was first ashamed at finding a little nasal secretion on her hand, then ashamed at her shame, and finally convinced of the necessity either of divine grace or the extinction of her personal identity. At atmospheric pressure she is a materialist. Others merely "felt awful" or thought they were dying. A few were elated. I had no abnormal sensations, except occasionally a curious velvety sensation on the lips, first noted by Dr. Juan Negrin, the former Spanish Prime Minister, who was compressed with me on one occasion. Others said that everything felt like ivory or that their fingers felt like bananas. A few saw things as if through a white mist.

For practical purposes what matter are disturbances of behavior. We used two tests. One consisted of putting steel balls into holes, lifting them with the fingers and with special instruments. The test was originally designed to weed out the clumsier candidates for the profession of dentistry. One compared the scores at one and ten atmospheres. The deterioration was quite slight. A good scorer was still good under pressure. But a number of the subjects were detected cheating, for example by using both hands. The other test was doing multiplications such as 7486 x 5137 as quickly as possible. Here the deterioration was enormous. Instead of getting about nine sums out of ten right, I usually got about three. One distinguished Fellow of the Royal Society put down two figures in five minutes, one of which was wrong, and said he thought it was a bloody silly test. The main difficulty with such tests was that the tester was usually as intoxicated as the testee, and often forgot to press the spindle of his stop watch, or to take proper notes.

Captain A. R. Behncke, of the U.S. Naval Medical Corps, first showed that these symptoms disappear if a mixture of four volumes of helium and one of oxygen is breathed, that is to say the nitrogen in air is replaced by helium. Case and I showed that hydrogen is equally effective. We made up a mixture of one volume of air with nine of hydrogen. This contains only 2 per cent of oxygen. But at ten atmospheres it contains as much oxygen per cubic inch as air at atmospheric pressure, and as much oxygen is taken up by the blood going through the lungs. So it supplied all the oxygen we needed. On the other hand there was not enough oxygen in it to render it explosive. So it was safe to store it in a cylinder, whereas with a possibly explosive mixture there is a chance that the friction as it leaves the cylinder may set it off. The moment we switched over from air to helium-oxygen or hydrogen-air we felt more normal within a few seconds, and were capable of doing arithmetic within one or two minutes.

A Swedish engineer called Arne Zetterstrom independently, though slightly later, discovered that hydrogen was as good as helium. He used a mixture of 4 per cent of oxygen with the gas, consisting of three volumes of hydrogen to one of nitrogen, which is made by "cracking" ammonia. He also used a nitrogen-air mixture for switching over from air to the mixture used at great depths, so that at no time was the mixture in his suit explosive. With these mixtures he descended to a depth of 450 feet, and answered the telephone rationally. Unfortunately he was pulled up by means of a platform; and owing to some mistake, which has not been very adequately explained, this was done too rapidly, and he died of bubbles in the blood, in the way which I explain later. Since helium is almost a monopoly of one of the great American oil trusts, it will doubtless continue to be boosted. But hydrogen is probably as safe as helium, and certainly vastly cheaper. Zetterstrom's death was due to an error committed at the surface.

Oxygen is a poison of quite a different sort. There are two kinds of symptoms. At high pressures the symptoms are nervous. One ends up with loss of consciousness and a convulsion quite like an ordinary epileptic fit, except that occasionally the muscular contractions are violent enough to break a bone. Before the fit there are almost always vague feelings of discomfort. Usually, though certainly not always, the muscles of the face stiffen and begin to twitch. Some people get uncontrollable hiccups. There is never any confusion like that produced by nitrogen. Unfortunately certain people often get no warning signs, though I generally do so myself.

At pressures below three atmospheres one may last long enough without a fit to develop lung irritation. This begins as mild coughing, followed by pain, and develops into a pneumonia which may be fatal. However it is of very little practical importance. At two and one-half atmospheres (fifty feet) I did not even start coughing for three and one-half hours, and when I knocked off after four and one-half, I had nothing worse than a chest pain which lasted for a day or two. Dr. Case had a very similar experience. Most people would get a fit long before this.

The most curious fact about oxygen poisoning is that the effects on the central nervous system are extremely variable in their time of onset, both between different people, and in the same person from day to day. Even after I had had two severe fits and crushed some vertebrae, I remained more resistant than the average. But after about a hundred experiments in half of which I had had some nervous symptoms, I became so sensitive that I began to twitch after breathing oxygen for five minutes at atmospheric pressure. Of course this may be attributed to hysteria, a conditioned reflex, or some such cause. But as I started breathing air through a mouthpiece, and nobody told me when the oxygen was turned on, neither explanation seems very likely. Other people varied irregularly. My wife breathed oxygen at ninety feet pressure on seventeen occasions. On one she lasted for eighty-eight minutes and knocked off with warning symptoms. On another she had a fit after thirteen minutes. Her other times were intermediate.

Besides this great variation in the same person, there are differences between different people. Some people always seem to be sensitive, and are clearly no good for underwater work involving oxygen breathing. It is very important to weed such people out. There is no way of predicting beforehand how anyone will behave. Men who had been on several commando raids or got a George Cross for dealing with underwater mines, crumpled up, when a woman who screams on rather slight provocation, or an elderly and rather flabby professor, were quite happy. Worse still, one could not predict very accurately from experiments in air to what would happen underwater. I had one of my fits for this reason.

One of the naval ratings who was being trained in the use of oxygen underwater was a boxer. While coming round from a fit he asked, "Who did that?" As he was lying down and someone was wiping him with a towel he probably thought he had been knocked out. The attendant answered, "Oxygen Pete." Oxygen Pete caught on. Would-be oxygen divers were first tested in No. 3 chamber. In one corner of it someone wrote "Oxygen Pete sits here." If several people had fits on the same morning people said "Oxygen Pete's in form today," and if one lasted unusually long one boasted of having got the better of him. I suppose a number of gods and devils started their mythological lives in some such way in the past. Fortunately Oxygen Pete arrived on the scene too late to be incorporated into a religion.

The oddest thing we found out was that oxygen has a taste. The textbooks say it is a colorless, inodorous, tasteless gas. At six atmospheres I described its state a "like dilute ink with a little sugar in it." My colleague Dr. Kalmus described it as "like flat ginger beer." Anyway it is both sweet and sour. Of course this is an example of what Hegel and Engels called the transformation of quantity into quality. In pure oxygen at six atmospheres there is thirty times as much oxygen in a cubic inch as in air at one atmosphere. And thirty times as much dissolved in a cubic inch of water. You don't taste sugar or salt dissolved in water till it reaches a certain concentration. Nor do you taste oxygen. Still it is rather striking that a gas with no sensory qualities at ordinary pressures develops them at high ones. In the same way ammonia and methane have quite a color if you look through enough of them. The first men to go to Saturn (and by the way they will have to wear self-contained diving suits) will notice this fact, for a spectroscope shows that the atmospheres of the outer planets are colored by these gases.

The greatest of all dangers to divers remains to be described. An average man has a little over a quart of nitrogen dissolved in his body. If he stays for six hours or so in air at two atmospheres, he will have two quarts, and so on. It soaks in rather slowly. Organs like the brain and liver, with a good blood supply, take it up quickly, but those, like the joints and fat, with a poor blood supply, take some hours to fill up. Now if you have a liquid in which a gas is dissolved at a high pressure, and suddenly lower the pressure on it, the gas comes out of solution and forms bubbles. Ginger beer and champagne contain carbon dioxide under pressure, and froth when a bottle is uncorked.

Much the same happens in a man or woman. If you have been for an hour at a hundred feet, that is to say at a total pressure of four atmospheres, and incautiously screw up the escape valve of your diving dress, it inflates until you suddenly leave the bottom. You shoot up to the top, and within a few seconds you are black in the face, and unconscious. If the attendant undoes your dress, you will die in a few minutes, and the post-mortem examination will show your blood vessels full of froth. As your heart cannot drive bubbles through your capillaries, you die of oxygen want. In such a case the only thing to do is to open the air vent and drop you back to the bottom again. The bubbles are at once compressed to a quarter of their size, and soon begin to dissolve again in your blood. A number of lives have been saved in this way.

Supposing, instead of coming up very rapidly, you do so in two or three minutes, the blood will have time to unload its spare nitrogen in your lungs on the way up. For on an average every drop of blood goes through your lungs about twice a minute. But within a short time you will be in severe pain. The commonest places for this pain are the joints, but one can get them elsewhere. You may also become paralyzed. The joint pain is called "bends" because when one has it in the knee or elbow one finds it difficult to straighten the limb concerned. The pain has been described as unbearable. I don't believe it. I have never seen anyone sweating with pain from bends, which I take as a good rough sign of severe pain. But it is quite enough to stop one working efficiently, and may go on for days.

Bends are probably due to bubbles in the bags of synovial fluid which buffer the joints. A bubble in the nervous system is more serious. I have only had one. This was in the lower part of my spinal cord. For several days I had a burning pain in the skin of my buttocks. This gradually died down to a tickle, combined with a loss of ordinary sensation. Both of these are still there after six years. If I had lost most of the sensation from my right hand, the result would have been more serious. Other people have had bubbles which interrupted the paths to muscles, and therefore caused paralysis, and some have died from this cause.

My father, Dr. J. S. Haldane, worked out the method which is universally used to avoid bends. He found that however long an animal or a man had been exposed to compressed air, it is always safe to halve the pressure. Thus even after many hours at thirty-three feet of sea water, or two atmospheres, one can come to the surface at once. But after a long time at sixty-six feet, or three atmospheres, it is only safe to come up to sixteen feet, or one and one-half atmospheres. Then one waits until one has got rid of some of the excess nitrogen, comes up a further stage, waits again, and so on. For example after half an hour to an hour at 175 feet, one comes up to seventy feet in three minutes, stops three minutes at seventy feet, three at sixty feet, seven at fifty feet, ten at forty feet, twenty at thirty feet, thirty at twenty feet, and thirty-five at ten feet. The total time spent in ascent is 181 minutes, or perhaps three times as long as one spent on the bottom.

Sir Robert Davis, of Siebe Gorman and Company, speeded up decompression by the following device. The diver comes up to the first stop, then gets into a chamber like a diving bell with an open bottom. An attendant helps him out of his dress, and gives him oxygen to breathe. In consequence almost all the nitrogen in the blood passed through his lungs comes out of it, and he can be decompressed a lot quicker than if he breathed air.

My father also recommended the use of mixtures of air and oxygen under water, so that the diver would take up less nitrogen. However no systematic work had been done with such mixtures. The matter became urgent in 1943. It was foreseen that when we captured ports from the Germans they would leave behind them mines and obstacles such as sunken ships, which would have to be removed. Now you must be a very brave man indeed to hunt for magnetic mines in muddy water, especially if you have seen some of your comrades go up. You must be a man of superhuman courage if you know that if you hear a mine beginning to tick, and go up to the surface quickly, you may be paralyzed for life if you are not blown to pieces. There is another reason why you should be able to come up quick. In an air raid on Le Havre or some other recaptured port in 1944 a man in a boat was in no greater danger than the average Londoner at the same time. But if he was underwater he might be killed by the shock wave from a bomb bursting in the sea several hundred yards off. For water is so incompressible that a shock wave must travel very much further than in air before it fades out. So divers should come up during an air raid.

Clearly if the diver breathes a mixture of air and oxygen he will absorb less nitrogen than if he breathes air. Hence he can come up safely from a greater depth. So one wants to cut the nitrogen down as much as possible. On the other hand if he gets too little nitrogen, and too much oxygen, he will have a fit. It is safer to have a fit when clearing obstacles with a comrade ready to haul you up than when crawling under the *Tirpitz*. But it is not 100 per cent safe. So my wife and I set out to find the safest mixtures to use at various depths and for various times. There were some calculations to be done first, for the mixture in the diver's lungs is by no means the same as that in his bottle. Then we had to try the mixture out. This meant going say to seventy feet pressure for half an hour. One of us would work while the other kept watch. Then we were rapidly decompressed. If there were no symptoms we repeated the experience the next day for three-quarters of an hour, and so on. If either of us got bends we generally took a day off to let the bubbles disappear.

These experiments were successful. According to the official tables, a diver who had been at a certain depth for a certain time was supposed to take forty-seven minutes to come up. We did it in two minutes without anything worse than itching, though I admit the naval officer who tried it next got a rather stiff shoulder. So the official time for an ascent from such a dive is, I think, seven minutes. But one could come up in one minute during an air raid without serious danger. The mixtures which we had tested in 1943 were used by the "P-parties" which cleared occupied ports in 1944. This was our main contribution to winning the war, though I gave a good deal of advice on all sorts of matters, from tanks to bomb-aiming, and some of it was accepted.

One of these matters was escape from submarines, and here Dr. Case and I had to deal with still another gas, carbon dioxide. Suppose a submarine is on the bottom and cannot rise. By the time this is clearly known the air is fairly foul. Now all the hatches of a submarine open outward, so that the water pressure outside keeps them shut. They cannot be opened till the air pressure inside is equal to the water pressure outside. Men can get out of a submarine one at a time from a small escape chamber, or twenty or thirty at a time from a flooded compartment. Suppose you are at three hundred feet, you let in water till the air in the compartment is squeezed into one-tenth of its original bulk. You then put on your Davis apparatus, open the hatch, and ascend to the surface. At least you are supposed to.

But there will certainly be some extra carbon dioxide in the ship's air from the crew's breathing, even if the air-purifying apparatus is acting well. At ten atmospheres there will be ten times as much in each cubic inch. We were asked to find out how poisonous this gas was at high pressures. The average man loses consciousness in about five minutes at ten atmospheres when there is as little as three-quarters of a per cent of carbon dioxide in the air breathed. This gives the same absolute amount per cubic inch as if he were breathing 7.5 per cent at atmospheric pressure.

The standard setup was an inquisitor (Dr. Case or myself) and a rabbit (somebody else, after each of us had acted as rabbit). The inquisitor wore a respirator to absorb the carbon dioxide in the air breathed. If he kept it on he had the fun of seeing the rabbit lose consciousness and finally fail to respond even when his or her eyes were touched. Sometimes however, the inquisitor got so intoxicated with nitrogen that he forgot to put his respirator on after taking it off to say something. Then there were two unconscious rabbits, and an observer outside gave the order to decompress when both appeared to have taken the count.

The Admiralty also wanted to know what happened if the water was very cold, as it is in the Arctic Ocean. So we used to lie in a shirt and trousers in a bath of water with melting ice in it until shivering became uncontrollable. This took about fifteen minutes for Case, and twenty minutes for me, as I am fatter. Then we were compressed, and any gas required was added. These experiments were not appreciably unpleasant. One feels a sharp pain round the neck at the surface of the water. The rest of the skin soon gets numb. One's resistance to high-pressure gases is slightly but not greatly lowered.

Dante said that the very worst sinners were frozen in ice. They were also exposed to compressed air ("*l'aer perso*" is his phrase, and the pressure would reach ten atmospheres at a moderate depth) and presumably to carbon dioxide from the flames. As one of the two people who have tried it, I can say that the great Italian poet exaggerated the discomfort of the sinners in question. I hope that if any reader has qualified for the eternal ice by the treacherous murder of a relative or benefactor, this may console him.

It now remains to draw the moral. The first point is that such experiments can and should be done on human volunteers. The Nazis did similar experiments on political prisoners and on Russian military prisoners. They killed many of them, but the information which they got was of little value. These experiments were, in fact, almost as futile as they were cruel. For the important practical question to be answered is how long a man can carry on with his work under unfavorable circumstances; not whether, after he has become unconscious, one can bring him round again. Experiments on animals are useful to show the kind of danger to be expected, but they do not tell exactly what a man can stand. This can only be done on human beings whose courage or curiosity will keep them going till they drop.

One of the three men who formed the first Aqua-Lung diving team in 1943, Commandant Philippe Tailliez has had a distinguished underwater career. Several times commander of the Undersea Research Group he helped to found, his naval service has taken him under the Pacific, Atlantic and Mediterranean, down in the bathyscaph FNRS 3 and to flights of inspiration for what man can achieve beneath the surface. Tailliez is now commandant of the French Navy free-diving school at Toulon.

The Fountain of Vaucluse

BY PHILIPPE TAILLIEZ

*V*aucluse, its coat of arms a field of azure with one trout and one grayling argent. You may have read Petrarch or you may not; you may have visited Vaucluse and its spring or you may not; the fact remains that no other spot on earth is so strongly evocative of springs, nymphs and woods. The Petrarchs, emigrants from Florence, had come to seek their fortune at Avignon. There on April 6, 1327, in the chapel of the Sisters of Sainte-Claire, young Francis Petrarch first saw Laura. She was seventeen and her hair was gold.

It is to Petrarch that we owe the first picture of the chasm of Vaucluse, "the most illustrious source of the long-since famous Sorgue," he wrote, "now even more celebrated through my sojourn and my songs."

At the bottom of the valley, hollowed out in the side of a tall cliff of over two hundred feet, the fountain of Vaucluse, at any rate during the dry season, is a sheet of still, crystal-clear water; in winter a boiling torrent, the flow of which is as violent as that of any upsurging subterranean water in the world. A legendary fig tree maintains a precarious hold on the walls of the cavern. Its bare roots are submerged when the water level reaches an exceptional height, and for the country people constitutes a tide mark. But the level of the spring can vary as much as seventy-five feet.

Frédéric Mistral, the great poet of Provence, explained the enigma of the flow as follows:

Having set out to make the girls of L'Isle-sur-Sorgue dance to his music, the old minstrel Basile fell asleep in the shade on a hot summer's day, somewhere along the road to Vaucluse. Appeared a nymph, who, beauteous as the clear waters, took the sleeper by the hand and led him to the edge of the basin where the Sorgue opens out. Before them the waters parted and allowed them to descend, between walls of liquid crystal, to the bottom of the abyss. After a long subterranean journey, the nymph, in a smiling meadow sown with supernatural flowers, brought the minstrel to a halt before seven huge diamonds.

Raising one of them, she caused a powerful jet of water to issue forth.

"Here," she said, "is the secret of the spring, the keeper of which I am. To increase its flow, I withdraw the diamonds. When I reach the seventh, the water rises to the fig tree, the roots of which drink only once a year."

She vanished, and Basile woke up.

Speleologists in their turn have tried, with the aid of fluorescine dye, to follow the track of rainwater and springs, the complex aqueous road system which from Mont Ventroux on the plateau of Luberon feeds the spring. In spite of all their calculations, they have not yet succeeded in fathoming its workings, which, to quote the words of one of them, still remain "the most exasperating enigma of subterranean hydraulics."

What, among other unknown quantities, is the shape of this siphon, the upstream branch of which may end in one of those immense caves dear to schoolboy imagination? The answer might be found by drilling, but this has not been done for fear of disturbing the delicate balance of the forces of nature.

There remained the possibility of exploration by divers. And twice helmet divers have made the attempt. In March, 1878, Ottonelli, from Marseille, descended into the chasm. It began as a tunnel, the angle of which he has estimated at fifty degrees; some thirty feet below the surface it was obstructed by an enormous boulder. He circumvented this and went on for another hundred feet. But then, overcome by fear of darkness and possible falls of rock, he stopped and lowered a weight, which went down another twenty-five feet. Ottonelli returned to the surface, thinking that he had established the maximum depth of the siphon. In September, 1938, Negri, also from Marseille, renewed the attempt. He apparently went a few feet lower, but his dives brought no new information.

It was not until 1946, two years after the French Navy Undersea Group had been founded, that we reckoned we had at our disposal sufficient diving and lighting equipment to be able to attempt an investigation, with the permission of the naval authorities. On August 27, at 4 A.M., the Group set out for Vaucluse with a lorry laden with carefully checked material for our task of underwater mountaineering. During the drive I sat next to Frédéric Dumas. To be candid, we were both deep-sea divers and preferred Neptune to Pluto, and we were feeling none too bold. I had never seen Dumas the prey of dark forebodings. That morning he was. As for myself, I had drawn up a table of dangers which awaited us, and as our lorry rolled on through the night I brooded over them in my somnolent state. There were seven dangers—not counting those unforeseen.

There was the instinctive repugnance to diving underground.

There was the cold, for the water in the spring was no more than 54 degrees Fahrenheit.

There was the darkness, which our electric torches could pierce but feebly—if they did not fail altogether.

The rope might part, leaving us to extricate ourselves from an uncharted maze.

There might be a fall of rock.

There might be suction, or underground currents might pin us in some corner.

And, finally, there was the danger of the intoxication of great depths.

Everywhere death would be prowling, Basile's diamonds glittering, the flitting shades of Laura and her lover. Beyond the bend of the siphon I could already see, in my mind's eye, the great hall that awaited us.

On our arrival at the village of Vaucluse, in the morning, we were greeted by M. Garcin, the mayor. Silently our caravan threaded its way along the admirable course of the Sorgue; two porters ahead with a canoe, then our team, each member carrying a heavy load; diving suits, compressed-air tanks, tools, coils of rope, bags of clothes, resuscitation apparatus, medical equipment, camera, compression chamber. . . . The breathing cylinders had been fully loaded the night before to three thousand pounds per square inch with the aid of a newly acquired air compressor. Several trips were necessary. We dumped our luggage, went down the slope, toward the steep face of the cliff with its fig tree, to the very edge of the fountain. The rainy season had not yet set in, and the level was at its lowest. Through the transparent sheet of water the bottom of the shallow basin could be made out, and to the left, to the right of the cliff face, our eyes were drawn to a large black spot, which was the siphon. That was where we would have to go down.

With the divers, who were beginning to get ready and to prepare the materials they had to take down with them, were Madame Simone Cousteau, a few friends from Sanary and Marseille, several speleologists interested in the attempt, and a growing cluster of villagers, whose curiosity by the afternoon would have to be forcibly restrained. The canoe was launched, and from the bows over the mouth of the abyss a heavy pig-iron weight was let down at the end of a cable. At a depth of just over fifty-five feet it stuck. To free it, Torpedo Petty Officer Jean Pinard went down, without protective clothing, thus being the first to enter the siphon, which he did by following the cable. Soon the weight dropped down to ninety-five feet.

Petty Officer Maurice Fargues was not in a state to dive, as the week before he had burst an eardrum while diving too fast. He stayed at the surface, therefore, and assumed the responsibility of guiding the divers, of paying out and raising the cable and of interpreting all signals. He laid the ropes out on a narrow earth beach in the right-hand corner at the bottom of the grotto.

By this time Dumas and Cousteau were ready. They wore protective clothing and were provided with heavy weights, for they intended to slide down the slope, believing that they would find it easier thus to combat any currents they might meet. Cousteau's clothing included a cowl, still in the trial stage, which allowed him to take off his mouthpiece under water and make himself heard over a very short distance. Each man had a knife, and two waterproofed torches were hooked onto their belts. Dumas had yet another load to carry—two supplementary air cylinders: the first as an auxiliary supply of breathing air, the second to allow him to inflate his diving suit and thereby increase his buoyancy. Finally, he also carried a pressure gauge for ascertaining the depth, and a mountaineering ice-ax.

The two men were linked by a thirty-foot safety rope. Cousteau had carefully coiled some three hundred feet of thin rope round his left forearm. Taking the weights down with them, they reckoned to let themselves sink to the bottom of the siphon. There they would give the rope three tugs, then one tug. Upon receiving this signal Fargues would pull the rope taut so that they would have it as a helpful banister for the return journey. Cousteau would then attach the end of his rope to the weight, after which they would go up the other arm of the siphon, Cousteau uncoiling his rope as he proceeded, hoping thus to reach the open surface of the water, if it existed.

At 11:10 A.M. the two divers entered the tunnel. Cousteau, ahead, came upon the triangular rock reported by Ottonelli; he lit his torch and slid past it on the right, following the wall. In doing so he reached Pinard's weight. Dumas, behind him, was very heavily encumbered by all his material; he had to brake himself, feet foremost, and caused an avalanche of stones to pelt down upon Cousteau.

Three times the latter tugged the rope and pushed the weight down into the abyss, forgetting, however, to add the second part of the signal. At the surface, therefore, Fargues did not tauten the rope. Within two minutes the descent was accomplished. They had landed on a sloping beach, which to Cousteau appeared to be the cone of detritus in the crook of the siphon. He approached Dumas and shone his torch on the depth gauge attached to his cylinders. The depth as revealed was over a hundred and fifty feet.

Cousteau now began to suffer from a violent headache. He did not yet realize that his companion, stuck on the shingle, was in difficulties and was gradually losing his lucidity of mind. Dumas, having discarded the useless ice-ax, was making vain efforts to turn the cock of his air cylinder and inflate his diving suit. His torch was leaking and gave only a feeble glow.

Cousteau, within the limit of the thirty-foot rope which linked him to his companion, now began to explore the terrain and rose vertically for about twenty to twenty-five feet. From there he shone his torch upward, then in every direction. Nowhere could he find a rocky wall. It was at this point that he realized that the coil had disappeared from his left arm. Down he went again, put his face close to that of Dumas and shouted, "Stay here a minute! I'm going to have a look up." Dumas was intoxicated, and misinterpreted: "Auxiliary cylinder. No more air." He let go the rope of the weight and attempted unsuccessfully to unhook the auxiliary cylinder from his belt. He lost his mouthpiece and only succeeded in replacing it after having swallowed a lot of water. On his right, Cousteau found a rocky wall, along which he rose again twenty to twenty-five feet. But the wall continued to rise vertically. He went down again, and Dumas, who believed Cousteau to be intoxicated also, seized him by the arm.

Then, suddenly, Cousteau realized the situation for what it was. Here were two divers, roped together, floundering in the dark through a maze of which they were both totally ignorant, a hundred and sixty feet, if not more, below the surface. Each was aware that the other was intoxicated and in distress, and both had lost the rope which was their life line. Several times Cousteau slowly swept the beach with his torch. At last he made out the rope, seized it and pulled it toward him. But it was slack, and merely gave, without resistance, fathom after fathom.

Above the surface, in the grotto, our nerves taut, we were crowding round Fargues. His fingers, practiced in holding a diver at the end of a cable, had not felt a single definite signal since they had gone down. Perplexed, he imagined the exploration was proceeding, and simply paid out more and more rope. The whole of one rope was uncoiled by now, and he knotted another length to it. On the other end Cousteau stood pulling, wondering why the rope, which was now piling up behind him, refused to tauten. Finally the knot which Fargues had made came into his hands. At that he gave up and attempted the ascent, towing Dumas, whose weight was growing heavier and heavier, and in this way he managed to rise some fifty feet. At the point of collapse, he began pulling the rope again, repeatedly giving the signal of distress, six sharp tugs.

Above, Fargues' fingers felt a peculiar tremor passing along the rope. For one moment he hesitated, then decided to pull. We hauled on the rope, which stiffened at last, and within two minutes Cousteau emerged from the tunnel. He was dragging Dumas, who was still feebly moving his legs, after him. I could clearly see, through the water, that he had lost his mouthpiece. Fargues threw himself in and we drew Dumas onto dry land, where he had a choking fit and violent nausea. Cousteau, very pale, was still lucid. Quickly, the warmth of a blazing petrol fire revived them. And in snatches they told us the story of the horrible twelve minutes of their dive. To Jean Morandière and myself it was of the greatest importance to know exactly what had happened, for it was our turn to go down next. The depth gauge was partly filled with water. They must have gone down considerably below the hundred and fifty-odd feet read by Cousteau. But, judging by the length of cable and the angle of the tunnel, they could not have gone beyond the two-hundred-foot mark.

There was one thing that worried us: the unusual form of the malaise suffered by the two divers. At sea, when on deep dives, our first experience would be one of exhilaration and not this loss of vigor, this agony they described, which had so nearly cost them their lives. As we gazed on the rough sketch which Cousteau drew for us, we could only see from the perpendicular wall along which he had ascended and the absence of any obstacles within the range of his torch after ten yards' climbing that they must have been to the bottom of an enormous mass of water.

While we were having lunch, which for the two of us consisted of a few bars of chocolate, the best tactics for clearing the "siphon" took shape in my mind. We must try to follow the walls of the vault as far as the tunnel. And we must be as light as possible, to avoid going down too deep. We put on light woolen underwear, which protected us very little against the cold but at least allowed us to move freely. Apart from the diving helmet and foot fins, we took only the most necessary equipment: a dagger, a torch held in one hand, another torch slung at our waist as a spare. The guide rope, which Fargues was gradually to let out, was secured to my belt, another ten feet of it linking me to Morandière. We arranged with Fargues that one tug on the rope meant "All's well," three tugs that we wanted to be hauled up. Morandière and I agreed that if one of us shouted, we should both return to the surface as quickly as possible.

At 4:13 P.M. we dived. The water felt icy. After we had passed Ottonelli's rock we were in complete darkness. We switched on our torches, but to our surprise could not see any light. The water is so pure that there are no particles to reflect the shafts of light, and it was only when we swept our torches to the right or upward that circles of light showed on the rocky wall. Clinging to that wall, which is smooth, with only a few projections and jutting ledges, roped together one behind the other, we swam slowly and rhythmically downward. In the silence our breathing was strangely loud and resonant. I directed my torch onto the ceiling and followed the luminous circle. At times it seemed to me that the vault was getting higher, but in fact we were going down all the time. Meanwhile the rope was being paid out smoothly. When it seemed we must be about twenty fathoms down, I stopped to analyze my sensations. The cold had not yet penetrated me, but I was filled with a subtle kind of anguish, which was yet not quite fear, and which I struggled to overcome.

There was no doubt that we must be in that vast mass of water the bottom of which had been reached by Cousteau and Dumas. A few yards from here the wall was sure to go up and lead us to the sheet of calm water on the other side of the siphon. Certain as I was of this, an instinct which is even stronger than my urge to go on makes me turn round. I give an involuntary cry and shine my torch on Morandière. He is trembling in every limb. I go past him, pulling on the rope. It is slack. Unless it is taut, we cannot send a signal to the surface. Suddenly I feel my breath quicken. I am conscious, but I feel strangely powerless, emptied of all energy. I try to force my hands forward to clutch at the rope. Morandière stumbles against me. I feel that he is pushing me, or that he, too, is struggling for breath. But in fact he is trying to save us. He passes in front of me, seizes the rope, and gives it three violent tugs. Then he goes back.

Up on the surface Fargues has repeated our signal and is beginning to haul up the rope. All of a sudden it tightens, and I realize that when it was being pulled a moment ago a loop must have formed behind us and caught up on something on the wall. Morandière cannot know this, and it is I, and I alone, who must make the gigantic effort of cutting that loop. I wind the rope several times round my left wrist and seize the dagger in my right hand. Then I hesitate, with the blade resting on the hemp. Should I cut the rope above or below my wrist? At last I decide and cut through it anywhere.

We're going up now. I grip the piece of cut rope in my right hand, but I have no hope any more. The blackness that surrounds us has numbed my brain. I tell myself that when I open my hand it will be two lives I shall be throwing away with that torn bit of rope.

Before long I see a faint glimmer of light, and very high above us, very far away, surrounding a solid dark block cut out like the map of an island, three little windows of sky. We rise up and up toward the beauty of God's light. In passing I catch sight of an unusual object, which attracts my attention almost as if it were a human being, and I realize that it is the ax which Dumas dropped this morning.

Scraping the sides of the wall, we come up into the pool. I get on my feet and stagger unsteadily to the shore. Behind me Morandière collapses. Somebody—Simone Cousteau—smiles at me. She holds out a glass which contains something strong. I drink it down in one gulp without feeling any effect. I look at my left hand, contracted round the blade of the dagger. The palm is deeply gashed and blood is streaming from it.

Like Dumas and Cousteau earlier, we in fact recovered rapidly. Our dive had only lasted nine minutes, we had paid out a full three hundred feet of rope, yet we certainly had not got down more than a hundred and thirty feet. It was difficult to understand why we, too, had been so near death. After that Pinard, and then again Cousteau and Dumas, made another attempt, in order to learn more about the details of the siphon in the immediate vicinity of Ottonelli's rock. And that night we left Vaucluse.

A few days later the analysis of the air contained in our cylinders gave us the key to the mystery. While they were being charged, the exhaust fumes of the compressor engine had passed too near the air intake and were sucked into the cylinders. We had been suffering from carbon monoxide poisoning, which prevents oxygen being absorbed into the blood stream.

*

The Invisible Eel

Thomas: They write here, one Cornelius' son
              Hath made the Hollanders an invisible eel
              To swim the haven at Dunkirk and sink all
              The shipping there.
Pennyboy: But how is't done?
Cymbol: It is an automa runs under water
              With a snug nose and has a nimble tail
              Made like an auger, with which tail she
                  wriggles
              Betwixt the costs of a ship and sinks it
                  straight.
Pennyboy: A most brave device
              To murder their flat bottoms!

Ben Jonson, STAPLE OF NEWS, *c.* 1627

(Ben is fancifying on an actual submarine, built by Cornelius van Drebbel, who demonstrated it under the Thames around 1621. King James I is reputed to have dived in it. "Costs" are ribs.)

In 1925 Fleet Admiral Ernest J. King, USN, then a captain, recommended a Navy Cross for a master diver who had worked for him in the salve of the sunken submarine S–51. He said of Tom Eadie, a civil service diver at the Newport Torpedo station, "In my twenty-nine years of service I do not remember having met anyone who so thoroughly deserves to have it said of him, 'He is a man.'" Two years later another S–boat was sunk in a winter collision off Provincetown. For the deed he reports here, Eadie won the Congressional Medal of Honor. After Michels' rescue, stormy seas prevented any attempt to help the entombed men, but the Navy, under public pressure, was forced to continue salvage operations that winter, long after they were dead. Eadie and his mates made 570 dives in frigid brawling seas, often with ice blocking their air hoses. Fred Michels came back and helped bring up bodies from the S–4. After three months of ordeal, the divers succeeded in bringing up the submarine.

The Story of Michels

BY TOM EADIE

*T*he U.S. Coast Guard destroyer *Paulding* struck the submarine S–4 at 3:37 on the afternoon of Saturday, December 17, 1927, and I first heard of it through a telephone message from the Newport torpedo station to my home in Newport at 6:15. I had been in Fall River with my wife and daughter that afternoon, doing Christmas shopping, and we had just come home and had had our supper. "Come to the station immediately," was the order on the telephone. "The S–4 has been sunk at Provincetown." I was in civilian clothes but I changed into uniform, got out, begged a ride to the ferry—which is about a mile from my home—and caught the boat that left at 6:25. I remember that, during the whirl of changing my clothes, my wife was standing by, wildly anxious, and I was trying to tell her what had happened and dress with speed at the same time.

At the station I was met by Commander Causey, the executive officer. Word had been sent to all the station's divers; they were even then coming in—Fred Michels, Bill Carr, Bailey, Burd, Brown, Winters, Anderson and Hawkes.

We left in three machines. The State Police met us at the Two-Mile Corner outside of Newport, and the motorcycle policeman pulled us along all the way to the outskirts of Fall River. A Massachusetts State Policeman met us in Fall River and took us as far as his authority and said, "You've got a hundred miles straightaway now. Good luck to you; I wish I could go with you." Lieutenant Matthews said, "All right. Now, boys, you can settle back for a sleep." Can you imagine anybody's sleeping with the thought of what we were coming to on our minds?

We reached Provincetown at 12:30 that night. The Navy Salvage Vessel *Falcon* was not due over the wreck until morning. The town was already swarming with reporters and photographers. They were all over us; they wanted to know who we were, where we came from, how many of us there were, and when we were going out. Even after we turned in, one man came into our rooms. He asked so many foolish questions that the crowd began kidding him. I was laughing myself sick, and I'd say after each story they'd tell him, "Tell him another." Later, I realized that when you kid a reporter you are really kidding the public.

A young gale had been blowing all the afternoon and evening, and next morning—Sunday—it was even worse. The only boat safe for us to go out in was a surfboat belonging to the Coast Guard at Wood End. They took us out, towing a dory astern. When we got out to the scene of the wreck, it was so rough we couldn't go alongside the *Falcon*. So we went to windward of her, and two of us got into the dory. When the surfboat slacked down alongside the *Falcon*, I threw my suitcase aboard, and when there was a chance, I climbed aboard myself. Captain Henry Hartley met me. "Eadie," said he, "you'll be the first man to go down." I said, "All right, sir, as soon as I get into my gear."

We were not even sure then that we had the S–4's position. The Coast Guard had grapneled some object on the bottom. But what it was could not be known until the catch was "proved" by a diver. The *Falcon* was anchored on the wreck buoy set by the Coast Guard. She wasn't moored out, for there was too much sea running, and it wasn't yet sure it was the submarine we had found.

I went over the side on the stage. It was bitter cold; the vessel was rolling, and but for the many hands that crowded to hold the stage ready, I should have been smashed against the *Falcon*'s side. They lowered me quickly, and I was soon below the send of the sea; for you get the forward motion of a sea only so far below the surface as its height above the surface. That is, a wave five feet high will give you a "send" five feet below the surface. When you get deeper than that, the only effect on the diver is the varying pressure when a wave passes over him. This is a serious effect—and in deep-sea work, where there is always more or less of a swell, it is always present. If a wave two feet high passes over you, you get a sudden increase of pressure amounting to one pound a square inch—really almost a ton on your whole body. As soon as I was well under the water, I tested everything, telephone, valves, and the suit for leaks, and then left the stage and slid down on the grapnel line. I wore a suit with gloves on it, and carried nothing but a hammer to tap signals on the various compartments of the submarine, though I never for a moment thought there would be such a thing as life aboard her.

I went down one hundred feet in less than fourteen seconds, and landed between the two periscopes. My shoes hit with a clang. And I thought I heard a signal. I said at once over the telephone, "It's the submarine." Then I looked round. The visibility was very poor. The current was running thwartships, and stirred up the mud, making the water terribly murky. To make it worse, the day was overcast, and so there was very little light there at all. I jumped down to the forward deck locker, and this time I heard another signal, and heard it plain. The men imprisoned in the torpedo room were pounding, and I said, "My God, a signal!"

I knew exactly where it came from; I had to climb over the gun, which was slewed round to port, and had its breech up and its muzzle down. As I walked—or rather, ran—along the narrow deck, I found loose pieces of wreckage lying about—bits of metal I picked up and threw overboard, and parts broken off the *Paulding* and off the *S-4*'s own superstructure deck. Larger twisted and bent pieces were all snarled up in a heap forward of the gun. The *Paulding* had ridden right over her, and I could see where she had cut across the superstructure deck to within four inches of its outboard edge. I climbed over the gun into a tangled mess of wreckage.

I picked my way over the mess to the place where the sounds were coming from, the torpedo loading hatch. This is the only opening from the deck into the torpedo room, and the way those men would have had to come out if they came at all. They were pounding on the torpedo-room hatch, which is just inside the loading hatch.

I banged with my hammer a number of times on the hatch, with my other hand on it to feel answering vibration. I got a response at once, and it seemed to hit right under my hand. They made six taps. Every time they signaled, it was six taps. The vibration of it was so strong that it was transmitted through my body to my telephone line. The man tending my telephone told me afterward that before I told him there was life aboard, he already knew it. He said, "I could hear your signal and their answer, and I could tell the difference between them."

As soon as I had their answer, I banged the hatch again a few times as a message of good cheer; I didn't know Morse code, but I just let them know we were on the job. I telephoned to the topside, "Life aboard in forward torpedo room." Then I headed toward the bow of the boat. It was covered with mud. This showed that the boat had gone to the bottom on a sharp angle and had scooped up the mud with her bow. She was lying on a level keel. The idea of going to the bow was so that the people on the topside could trace my bubbles and so know the boat's position as she lay on the bottom, and would know how to set the moorings as soon as it was possible to go to work. I reported every bit of information, as fast as I came to it. All this time the men inside never sent another signal. I figured that they knew what I was doing, and that I would try to signal other compartments. If I did, and they replied, they knew it would only confuse me, and so they kept still. "Gee, Eadie," I said to myself, "if you never do anything more in your whole life, inspire those men in there with the confidence that we on the topside are onto our job, and doing every last thing we can." I fully realized their predicament, and that because of the bad weather and heavy sea at the surface we had little chance to work quickly—and only speed could save their lives.

I got aft to the conning tower and tapped on it, but got no answer. Worse than that, you can tell by the sound when you tap a metal plate like that whether the space behind it is full of water or empty so that it sounds hollow. So I knew the conning tower was full of water.

Now I ran along the deck, going aft, until I was brought up by a sudden jerk. In my anxiety to cover the ground as fast as I could, I had not been as watchful as I should have, and I had run into the boat's tangled radio antenna, which had been carried away by the collision. It was fouled on one side of my helmet on the spitcock, and on the other side on the exhaust valve. They noticed on the topside that I had stopped, and that I hadn't traveled the length of the boat. "Are you in trouble?" the tender asked. "I'm foul in the antenna, but I'm all right and can clear myself shortly." I did get clear, and tried to move farther aft. Still I couldn't; I was held up somehow. I pulled at my hose and life line to get some slack, and it wouldn't come. Then, looking up, I saw that I was foul round the submarine's little yardarm. "I guess I can't get any farther aft," I told the topside. "I'm foul on the yardarm. But I'll lie down and stretch out as far as I can, and try a tap." I just did reach the engine-room hatch, and sent a few signals, without response. Then I was perfectly assured that there was nobody alive inside the boat excepting the men in the forward torpedo room.

I got back to the conning tower and climbed it to clear my lines from the yardarm, about seven feet above me. When I came down from the tower, knowing that what they would try next would be to blow the ballast tanks from the topside, I went to the side of the cutwater on the conning tower and opened the hatch there, though without any instructions to do so. There is a hatch on each side of the cutwater, containing the external connections to the ballast tanks and the compartments. These hatches and connections are placed there for this very emergency which had occurred. I told the topside then that I had completed my inspection and opened the hatch; what did they want me to do? They answered, "You've been down long enough. Stand by to come up; we have another man ready to go over."

This man was Bill Carr, and while I was going up, I saw him pass me. He was carrying with him an air hose, to hook onto the external connections, to blow the ballast tanks, and if possible to make her light enough and bring her to the surface. They figured that if the ballast tanks were flooded, it would be through the Kingston valves, and they could also be blown through that opening. There was a chance that the ballast tanks were not flooded, for the *S-4* was surfacing when she was hit. Her tanks might have been already blown. This would not help, however, if the compartments were all flooded and the ballast tanks dry; she would still be held down.

As soon as Carr had hooked up, the *Falcon* was moved a little way from the position, in the hope that the submarine would come up—and so as to be out of the way of her—and started blowing. They blew for half an hour. Then a big eruption of air was seen at the surface—and that attempt was a failure. One of the tanks must have been ruptured by the collision, so it was useless to carry on any further in that respect; and it wasn't possible to make an external patch on her, except by a long job.

The men in the *S-4* didn't signal to Carr at all. I figure they could hear him hitching up to the connection and hear the air going into her. It took him perhaps ten minutes to make his hitch, and it was just an hour and ten minutes from the time we started that the air was going into her. Those men, being experienced, undoubtedly knew what was happening. On the topside, as soon as they knew there was life aboard the submarine they got the oscillator of their submarine signal system overside and sent Morse signals, to ask what the conditions were. The answer was, "There are six men here in the torpedo room with fifteen inches of water and a slow leak." This was close to noon on Sunday. Carr came up before the *Falcon* started to blow the tanks, and nothing else could be done until this plan had been tried and found useless.

The next thing was to put air into the compartments. This meant taking the gags off the lines at the connections inside the hatch on the cutwater. The diver, instead of taking off the air hose already set on the tank connection, to save time would take down another hose line and set that onto the connection to the compartments. By this time, it was dark, and the sea was getting worse all the time.

Let me say right here that diving has never been attempted before under such desperate conditions as we had, and it never will be tried again unless by a man of the United States Navy. No commercial diver would think of doing it. Every time you went over the side, it was an attempt at suicide. There was a ten-foot rise and fall of the waves; with one pound pressure to every two feet that meant five pounds additional pressure, suddenly applied and as suddenly taken off again, to the square inch of your body. A man's body is approximately two thousand square inches of surface, and that means five tons of pressure for the five pounds per square inch. It causes intense waves of pain in the eardrums; it may burst them, and it can quite simply kill a man.

It was bitter cold. The seas were by this time coming aboard the *Falcon,* and the tenders standing along the rail and holding a man's lines, or watching his air or handling his telephone, were hit by the spray and solid water that came over the rail and were rapidly coated with ice. Before a diver could get under water, the spray and wind had made him a mass of ice. The cold lets up a little when you actually get under water, but if you have got chilled before that, you stay chilled. But Captain Ernest King said, "We must get air in there tonight. It's tonight or never." So they looked round for the best man to send, and decided on Fred Michels. He went down, taking the second hose.

I was decompressed and slowly got warm again, had something to eat, and went below and turned in. In the meantime, Mike was down on the *S-4*. Forty-five minutes after he dived, the tenders realized he was very indistinct, but he seemed to be saying, "Send Eadie. Cutters—Eadie—cutters." Captain Hartley himself came down and woke me. "Mike is foul," said he, "and it looks kind of bad. Will you go after him?" I said, "Yes, sir. As soon as I can." I was in such a hurry that, instead of putting on the usual three sets of underwear for cold weather, I put on only one. Topside I asked for a suit without any gloves, for I knew I should need the freedom of my hands. The temperature of the water that night was thirty-four degrees Fahrenheit, and putting your hands into it was like putting them into freezing brine, and was extremely painful.

The seas were coming well over the rail and giving everybody a good ducking. In fact, they had to put up a canvas shield to make a lee where I could get dressed without getting sopping wet before I even went over the side. Captain Hartley said, "We are still talking with Mike, but we can't hear him very well, but it seems to be cutters, wire cutters, so I'm giving you a heavy pair." "All right," said I, "but put a hammer, a chisel, and a small crowbar in the bag."

I went down on Michels' own line, carrying a thousand-watt lamp, and landed close by Mike, who was lying face down in the wreckage.

He was pinned under a web of his own heavy air hose and life lines —at least eight turns of lines woven back and forth, 150 to 175 feet of hose and line. The loops were caught in the wreckage on both sides of him, on one side, in a piece of the *Paulding*'s bow driven into the *S-4*.

Mike's pickle was due to the storm blowing on the surface. The *Falcon*, lying to anchor, naturally would yaw. As the vessel went off to one side, Michel's lines came taut and his tenders gave him slack to keep from hauling him off the submarine. When the limit of yaw came and the *Falcon* swung the other way, his lines became a bight— a long narrow loop. And so, as the *Falcon* yawed, the lines were paid out, and one bight happened to land on Mike's shoulders and pressed him down on the deck. He didn't know what was happening, as more turns were laid on top of him. Mike was not to blame, nor was it any inattention by his "bears" (line tenders) above. It was the result of weather on the surface, that's all.

I tried to clear him. I saw one bight that was caught in a U-shaped angle iron, down on the side of the boat, and I realized that if the line could get into that U, it could get out. So I got down over the side. I couldn't see, even with the light, but I felt down below the angle iron, got hold of the line, braced my foot and pulled. But with all my strength I couldn't get it out. I wasn't talking to the topside much. I simply told them, "It's quite a mess here. Don't bother me." I never saw such a mess.

I realized that the wire cutters were absolutely useless. They couldn't cut the angle iron. I came to the conclusion that the best way would be to saw through the angle iron, through the bight of the U, and let Michels stand up on his feet. So I telephoned up for a hacksaw, and told them to shackle it onto my light wire. I hadn't spoken to Mike for the topside had told him I was coming. I was close to him, and he knew I was there; he kept pointing to where he was foul, and I would make a motion that I understood. He was really only a dim outline in that muddy water. But I wasn't paying any attention to him whatsoever. I wasn't concerned with him, but with what held him.

I had been down fifteen or twenty minutes. The hacksaw came down very quickly and I took the light over to Mike, put it in his hand, and told him to hold it on the U-shaped iron, but he couldn't get over to it. He was so held down that he could not even get his hand to his air-control valve. Had it been shut off—for instance, to telephone—he would have suffocated. That was why they couldn't hear him very well; he couldn't shut off his air, and you have to shut it off to be heard on the telephone. He held my light, but in less than a minute it flared up in my eyes so I couldn't see a thing. I got kind of angry and shook him, and said, "Hold it there!" Then he dropped it.

I realized something was wrong with him. He would have helped me if he could. As a matter of fact, he was unconscious; his suit had become cut and was full of that ice water—and he couldn't move to keep his circulation going. So then I took the light and put it against the gun mount and finally I got to work sawing that angle iron.

It was a miserable job. The iron was loose, and I had to hold it with one hand and saw with the other. It was in an awkward place, near the edge of the superstructure, and I had to lie right down by Michels and go slow and carefully, for a hacksaw blade is brittle, and, if I broke it, it would cost time to get new blades. And time was the breath of life. I could last only about so long, and Mike could live only so long.

It took me forty to forty-five minutes to cut through that stout angle iron. Inside the boat they never made a sound; they undoubtedly thought that whatever we were doing was toward their rescue. It was very cold, and my hands were aching terribly. Finally I got through, but here was a new misery: a sharp angle in the wreckage had cut my suit now, and I was wet to the neck.

The bight I had freed, however, was the end nearest to Mike, and as soon as I had worked the slack back and forth and got some more, I stood him up. He didn't help me. As a matter of fact, he was out—and I didn't know it. I could hardly see him at all; there was a lot of mud.

By this time I was taking the turns out of his lines, and telling the people on the topside to haul it in slowly. I thought I had got it all clear, when I noticed a bight leading over the side and another on the port side. I put my line and hose in Mike's hands, for him to hold me. When I went over the side, he let me go entirely. So I secured my life line round part of the wreckage, and started in to clear him down there. His line was just hung up by the strain and didn't take long to clear. I telephoned the surface. "Take in the slack on his life line and hose," I told them, "and tell Mike to follow me to the descending line."

As I was going along toward the descending line, I felt myself becoming buoyant. "Stop pulling me up," said I. "We aren't pulling you," they answered, and I turned round quick and saw Mike's feet floating about level with my face plate. I grabbed them and pulled him down.

Our life lines had become entangled and his buoyancy was pulling me off the deck. I tripped his spitcock to relieve his buoyancy. Then, I pulled down the lines till I saw the turn and passed him under the lines to clear him. I closed his spitcock again; then I motioned to him to come toward the descending line, and held the light behind me to show him the way. Even then I didn't realize that he was out. I simply wondered why he didn't work with me.

I didn't know how bad things were on the surface. The *Falcon* had begun to drag anchor in the gale. She had drifted 450 feet, even though two other ships had their moorings out and had lines on the *Falcon* trying to hold her in position. The *Falcon* has anchors one thousand pounds heavier than ships of a like size—so you can see it was blowing some on the topside. Mike and I were at the extreme end of our lines. Captain Hartley figured that in five to twenty minutes longer, if I didn't get Mike clear, he should undoubtedly be forced to leave us down there. So time was even more precious than we had any idea.

When I got to the descending line, I told them on top that I couldn't see Mike. "All right," they said, "stand by to come up."

"All right, haul me up—I'm wet to the neck," said I.

They rushed me into the recompression chamber. There were already three attendants in there, waiting for us. They took my suit off. They were still at it when Mike was passed in. It was just the same as you'd pass in a broom; he was stiff as a board. They had found him floating in the waves.

His eyes were rolled up into his head, he was frothing at the mouth and making a gurgling sound, and we had to cut his clothes off him, diving suit, underwear, and all. He had a pair of woolen gloves on, and, even though we cut them, his fists were clenched so tight that it took all the strength of two men to open his hands and make him let go of them. According to the decompression tables, we should have been under a pressure of thirty pounds, but when I saw his condition I ordered the pressure run up to sixty pounds, to relieve the "bends"—for it looked as if he might have a serious case. However, he didn't; it turned out to be only a bad case of exposure. I said to the other fellows, "Men, you've got to work," for it looked as though we'd lost Mike after we thought we'd saved him. We massaged his body, slapped his face, and in general gave him a beating. Cold as I was myself, I never felt it until I noticed that Mike was apparently coming round. Then I began to shiver. I lay down by Mike, both of us naked under blankets, to share the heat of our bodies. It was 11:40 when we entered the tank; it wasn't until 3:30 that Mike regained consciousness. The first man he recognized was Lieutenant Commander Edward Ellsberg, who had volunteered his services and had just arrived on the job. And ten minutes later we got down to atmospheric pressure. I left then, and went down, turned in, and slept. They kept Mike in the tank. In the morning he sent for me and told me he could remember very little after I came down. He had put his hand out for the hacksaw, he said, because he had the idea I wasn't working fast enough and he wanted to help.

He was still very weak and it was thought that to save his life he ought to be taken to a hospital. The only safe way to get him there was in a decompression chamber, and as the *Falcon* was the only ship that had a decompression chamber, she had to be used. That was the reason she left the scene, and I think it was a thing worth while doing; it saved Mike's life, and the conditions at the wreck were so bad that diving was impossible. This was Monday morning, and we had one more signal from the submarine before the *Falcon* left.

All through the storm, the only line the *Falcon* had on the submarine was the descending line. As the ship yawed or dragged, this line had to be tended by hand. Before the *Falcon* left for Boston, she buoyed the line and let it go. This was the buoy that carried away and lost the *S–4*'s position for us.

The *Falcon* transferred Michels at the navy yard at Charlestown to an ambulance from the Naval Hospital, and stayed only long enough to take aboard supplies that were urgently needed. I managed to get out on the pier and send Mrs. Michels a telegram to say that Mike was in the hospital as a precaution, that he was perfectly all right, and that she was not to worry.

Epilogue: Two Months Later

We got to the White House and were escorted by Secretary of the Navy Ray Lyman Wilbur to be introduced to President Coolidge, who said to me, "I'm glad to know you, and I thank you for your services." I said, "I want to assure you, Mr. President, that everything humanly possible was done on that job, under the circumstances." He nodded. By this time my little procession was moving on. He shook hands with all the gang that was following me, remarking, "Quite a large gathering." I said, "I come of a large family, sir."

On the lawn a flock of cameramen were waiting. All hands stood to attention and the Secretary read the citation. He handed the President the Medal of Honor, and the President fastened the ribbon around my neck. Next the cameramen had their turn and they ordered the President of the United States around like a rookie. These cameramen are quick to grab a chance for sentiment. I said, indicating my wife, "Here's the one that deserves the medal," and one of them said, "Kiss the wife"—and I had to kiss her and the kid for the pictures. A reporter wanted to find out how I felt during the presentation: "With the President waiting on you, didn't you get a thrill?" "No," I said, "I expected it: I didn't think about it at all." He looked disgusted. I told him, "The thrill I'll get is when the boat comes up." Lieutenant Weickhardt volunteered to write the story. Though he didn't quote me, he insisted that I was thrilled.

The Australian writer James Aldridge traveled broadly before he took to submarine ambulation, and is now a hard man to find without a mask and snorkel. He has dived in the Black Sea and the Red Sea. To reach remote reefs in the latter, he drove to the Sudan in a land rover with his wife, baby, compressor, and antishark cage aboard, lugged his air-lung across the tortuous coral and dived alone among the sharks. We think Jim is a bit crackers about diving. Here are some Mediterranean notes from his book Undersea Hunting for Inexperienced Englishmen.

From a Novelist's Diving Log

BY JAMES ALDRIDGE

*Y*ou are in another world—absolutely—the moment you put your head under the water. This thought will occur again and again, and you will never become tired of saying this trite thing to yourself. *It's another world, it's another world....*

Unlike space, or looking up into the sky, you will find that looking down into very deep water is like looking into confinement rather than into freedom. Yet the moment you are under and in it, the depth and the solidity of the water around give you a feeling of freedom which even flying cannot yet satisfy above, for no man has yet devised wings for the body itself which is what you feel like under water; a man with wings, free, in a free element.

To dive and zoom, with no other power but your own legs, is finally to free the body of the need of a single line of gravity running from head to toe. Sometimes, after a few hours diving in the water, you will return to land and immediately feel like a drawing pin that has to be stuck into something, point down, to be of any use at all.

Conversely, if it is gravity that sticks you by two feet to the ground, then underwater it is an air bubble that attaches you to the surface. The need for that bubble of air in your lungs makes the world a very desirable place; and nothing under the sea can yet equal the physical joy of that first deep breath of air after a dive below, which also reminds you of what you are: a creature who lives on warm gas rather than cold liquids.

Each year I try diving and fishing without flippers to see how it feels. Naked is the only word; naked and helpless; for the feet seem so bare and powerless without them that I feel indecent.

A bass (*loup*) is certainly the loveliest fish to see in action. Off Théoule and Miramar, which I fish often, they are usually lone specimens. Their lovely, speedy, effortless motion, their long slender shape, their useful professional olive-green coloring: these things are the summation of the ideal fish. They always seem to be badly scarred, as if often in combat. I have an idea that the lone *loup* near rocks spends much of his time trying to scrape the lice off his back. To see a *loup* swimming and zooming and rolling over to brush a rock, as if in play, is delightful; and one imagines him practicing acrobatics; but a closer view reveals the reason in that black devilish thing that clings to it and sucks the blood: the sea louse (*Anilocra*) is a rotten thing made of high-quality steel rather than flesh and bone, for its grip on a fish is by hooked legs which are practically unbreakable. You tear one off a fish and usually a lump of flesh comes with it. On smaller fish they are usually seen just near the tail joint, which means that a free-swimming fish is often slowed down by this nuisance. In fact it is very pathetic to see a small bream lagging behind his fellows because he has a giant louse on his tail. One longs to catch the fish, get rid of the louse, and then give the bream a fighting chance. Actually, many of the lice are simply too big for the small fish to get rid of, and sooner or later it will make the fish too slow to survive, so that it is either seized by a predator, or simply wastes away. The latter is an assumption, however, and could not be considered a real observation.

One late evening, just before dark, I was swimming near the shore over some fairly deep rocks, near Miramar. The pale blue deep was whitish and opaque over the mixture of bald rocks and black grasses, and great white valleys running between these high formations made me feel very much like a man alone on the moon. You are really alone, in these circumstances; but what saves you is the quick look up which will restore you in a second to a solid everyday world over your head. Even so, I became rather mesmerized with this pale blue space isolation, and I began diving down into it and rolling over and looking up at the surface to see the silk curtain on top change from rose pink to a thin black. Soon I became very depressed with the feeling of isolation it gave me, and I had to get out and sit on a hard rock and undo my loneliness before I could swim back the long way home.

Swimming with the mask at night is gloomy and frightening, for the sea is only alive with flecks of phosphorescent light, and all else looms and threatens you. Fish are dull shadows which flash for a second as they turn and whip away from you. Your instinct is to get out of the water and leave the sea to its own, no matter how much your mind tells you that you know every rock and stone below. The sea has too much of primeval night in it, and civilized man is a bit soft for it.

The sea is full of debris, all of it fascinating, some of it embarrassing. Also informative. I was lying on my stomach in the shallows one day, reading an abandoned newspaper which lay on the bottom. It was an article on the ancient Minoan water systems. I had to dive to read the small print. I was called away before I had finished the article. Next day I returned to pick up where I had left off, but the paper was gone with the sea. I spent a little time looking for it, diving on every scrap of paper in the area. I didn't find it: but thereafter in that area I could never see a sheet of newspaper below without diving to see if it was my unfinished article.

*

This Great and Wide Sea

O Lord, how manifold are Thy works!
In wisdom has Thou made them all;
The earth is full of Thy riches.
So is this great and wide sea,
Wherein are things creeping innumerable,
Both great and small beasts.

Psalm 104

In April, 1941, one of the first reserve officers to be accepted in H M Submarines, a book editor, Edward Young by name, born in the West Indies, sailed as Third Officer on the maiden voyage of HMS Umpire *from Chatham, down the Medway to the Thames, into the English Channel. What happened then he recounts in the following extract from* One of Our Submarines, *an undersea-boat combat memoir which acclimates us more surely to this inexorable experience than do some of the wham-boom books about it. Young had already served in the North Sea in the submarine* H–28 *before* Umpire *was lost. He was later in* Sealion *in the Baltic and Bay of Biscay and in* Saracen *in the Mediterranean. In his own first command,* Storm, *which campaigned at the North Cape, Ceylon, the Malacca Strait, the Andaman Islands, Sumatra and Australia, Commander Young won the Distinguished Service Order and the Distinguished Service Cross. He is now a partner in a London publishing house.*

Submarine Disaster

BY EDWARD YOUNG

Umpire's dockyard trials had been successfully completed, including the usual static basin dive to prove that the hull was watertight. The last welding leads had been removed, the bunks, cupboards and other wooden fittings were a bright mahogany gleam, new curtains hung in the messes, and the whole boat was resplendent with fresh-smelling paintwork, white inside and battleship gray outside.

Mervyn Wingfield was plainly delighted with his new command, though he tried to conceal his pleasure behind a demeanor of severity and icy reserve. The First Lieutenant, Peter Bannister, I had not met before; he was tall, energetic and humorous, easy to get on with. Tony Godden, the navigator, had been in the same training class with me at Fort Blockhouse; I was delighted now to find we were in the same boat, for he was a most amusing and endearing shipmate, and we had many good evenings ashore together during our stay in Chatham.

Umpire moved out at last into the River Medway on a day toward

62

the end of July, spick and span, a brand-new white ensign flying, bound north-about for the Clyde, where we were to carry out sea trials and training with the Third Flotilla based at Dunoon, before setting forth on a "working-up" operational patrol in the North Sea. After that, the Mediterranean.

We stopped overnight at Sheerness to wait for a convoy of merchant-ships leaving the Thames the next day. In the morning we got under way early and found the convoy congregating off Southend under an escort of motor launches and Admiralty trawlers. We took up our station astern, and by the time we turned the corner at Shoeburyness the convoy had more or less sorted itself out.

All day we moved up the East Coast, passing Burnham, Clacton, Walton-on-the-Naze, Harwich, Felixstowe, Orfordness, and when we were somewhere off Aldeburgh a German bomber came in low from seaward and began attacking the leading ships of the convoy. I was officer-of-the-watch at the time, and in accordance with our convoy instructions gave the order to dive.

Now, we had never dived before at sea and under way. Normally a brand-new submarine carries out numerous dives in slow motion, with the crew already at diving stations, before it is committed to a full-speed dive. We had to make our first dive on the klaxon, and it is to the great credit of all concerned—the Chatham men who built her; Wingfield, who as Captain had thought ahead and trained his officers and men to his satisfaction; Bannister, who as Number One had organized the crew in their duties and had also worked out the first trim; and the crew, who went calmly to diving stations and performed their jobs correctly—it is to the credit of all these that *Umpire's* first dive was a complete success. Within two minutes Bannister had caught a trim and the Captain was able to concentrate on the periscope. We did not want to stay down longer than we need, because the convoy was drawing ahead of us. Five minutes later the Heinkel seemed to have vanished, so we surfaced and pressed on to regain our station in the convoy, which had sustained no damage from the attack.

We felt very pleased with ourselves, and boyishly proud of our boat that had behaved so well. Then, about nightfall, one of the diesels developed trouble and had to be stopped. At first this did not affect our speed, our propulsion being diesel-electric, and we continued to maintain our station. But as the evening wore on, the engine-room staff were unsuccessful in their attempts to get the defective engine going. The other one produced insufficient power by itself to balance the batteries' output when driving two propellers, and we were obliged at last to reduce our speed. The Captain flashed a signal to the Commodore of the convoy, reporting the situation. A motor launch was detailed to drop back and act as our escort, and we were to catch up as soon as possible.

We knew from the latest wireless situation report that, some twenty miles to the north of us, a southbound convoy was approaching down the same buoyed channel. The two convoys were due to meet somewhere about midnight. The international rule at sea is that in a channel-way ships must keep to the starboard side. Ships meeting in a channel should therefore pass port-to-port. It was revealed afterward that when the two convoys met, some miles ahead of us, they passed on the *wrong* side, starboard-to-starboard. So when Tony Godden, the officer-of-the-watch, presently sent down a message that the southbound convoy was approaching, Wingfield was surprised to find on reaching the bridge that the oncoming convoy was not on our port bow, as he expected, but right ahead, with part of it actually extending across our starboard bow. It was a calm night, very dark, but with reasonably good visibility; lights could have been seen at a fair distance. But the German E-boats were raiding the East Coast convoys nearly every night, and no one was showing any lights. Our escorting launch had lost touch with us sometime earlier. We were quite alone and almost invisible to other ships even at close range.

The normal action would have been to alter course to starboard, but this would have taken us across the bows of the approaching merchant-ships and we might not have had room to get clear. Wingfield altered a few degrees to port, and the first six ships of the convoy passed safely down our starboard side about two hundred yards away. Although we did not know it, our own convoy, now several miles ahead, had taken the same action.

Suddenly a dark shape appeared ahead of us, detached from the nearest column of the convoy. Examining it through his binoculars, Wingfield saw that it was a trawler, presumably part of the convoy's escort, and that we were directly in its path. In the next second he realized that it was alarmingly near to us and apparently unaware of our presence. He had to decide quickly what to do. The trawler was fine on his starboard bow and seemed certain to pass dangerously close. By the rule of the road it was the trawler's right of way and our duty to keep clear. According to the rules Wingfield should have altered course to starboard, but only two hundred yards to starboard was the endless line of southbound merchant-ships forming an impenetrable barrier. With every ship fully darkened, this was a predicament not visualized by the authors of the Regulations for Preventing Collision at Sea. Wingfield ordered, "Hard-a-port." But, even as we began to turn, the trawler seemed to see us, low and dark in the water, and turned instinctively to starboard. This made collision inevitable. Wingfield yelled his last order down the voice pipe, "Full astern together!"—but before the order could be carried out, the bows of the trawler struck *Umpire* with a sickening metallic crash, some twenty or thirty feet aft the starboard bow. The submarine lurched to port, and for a few seconds the two vessels stayed locked togeher, held by the impetus of the trawler's headway. During these seconds Wingfield clutched the trawler's side as it swung in toward him, and shouted furiously, "You bloody bastard, you've sunk a British submarine!" Then the trawler fell away, and Wingfield found his boat sinking under him by the head. In less than thirty seconds she plunged under, leaving Wingfield, Godden and the two lookouts in the water. In the darkness there was shouting and confusion, but the four kept together. But presently, one and then the other, of the lookouts dropped out of the small circle. Tony Godden, who was wearing long fur-lined seaboots, gasped out that he could not kick them free and that he was sinking. For a while Wingfield helped to support him, but Tony finally let go and sank out of sight. It seemed a long time before the trawler's boat appeared, and Wingfield was unconscious when he was hauled on board. When he came to and realized that he, the Captain, was apparently the sole survivor, his feelings can be imagined.

When Captain Wingfield had left the wardroom to go up on the bridge in response to Tony's message about the approaching convoy, Peter Bannister and I were sitting at the wardroom table, decoding a routine wireless signal. The wardroom was divided from the control-room only by a thin steel partition, and by curtains from the passage-way; at sea these curtains were drawn back, and Peter and I could hear the helmsman repeat the orders which came to him down the voicepipe from the bridge.

When we heard him repeat the Captain's emergency order, "Hard-a-port," we pushed back our chairs and stood up, our eyes meeting in question and alarm. We stumbled out into the passageway, and Peter at once gave the order to "Shut watertight doors!" Almost immediately we heard another urgent yell down the voice pipe, but before this last order from the bridge could be repeated by the helmsman there was a violent crash for'ard in the torpedo-stowage compartment, followed by the blue-white flare and muffled thump of an electrical explosion. The boat rocked to port, stayed there a few seconds, and then slid drunkenly forward and over to starboard as she began her plunge to the bottom. If the water were deep here, its weight would crush us like an eggshell. Most of the lights had gone out. Then men were running past us from the forward compartment, Peter was yelling "Shut that door!" and I had my hand on it, letting the men run through, disobeying Peter because I hadn't the courage to deny any of them a chance so long as the water was not yet actually at their heels. Somehow the further door to the damaged compartment had shut, whether blown to by the explosion or deliberately shut from the inside by a last nameless act of self-sacrifice as the sea came flooding in, we shall never know. "Shut that bloody door!" repeated Peter in a fury, but by now all the men from the intervening compartment were through. With some difficulty, because of the angle of the boat, I pulled the door up toward me and clamped it shut.

I turned, and struggled up the tilting deck into the control room. The boat was listing to starboard and sloping forward at an angle of about ten degrees. Water was pouring in from what seemed to be a hundred places. Peter was struggling with the outboard battery-ventilation valve overhead, desperately seeking an explanation for this inrush of water, and acutely aware of the fatal danger of chlorine gas if the sea water should find its way into the battery cells under the deck. I reached up to help him, glad in my numbed state of something positive to do. But the valve was already shut, as we knew it should have been, and we must look elsewhere for the breach in our defenses. To my paralyzed brain it seemed that the shock of the collision had cracked the hull and started rivets along the whole length of the ship. Surprisingly enough, no water was coming down the conning tower; presumably the upper hatch had fallen shut when the boat took on a list immediately before she went under.

Peter was now calling for more light, and one or two of the men searched about for the emergency hand lamps. I remembered that I had a flashlight in my drawer in the wardroom, so I retraced my steps, moving with difficulty down the wet and sloping deck. In the passageway the water was already knee deep. I sloshed through it and pulled myself up into the wardroom. Streams of ice-green water were cascading from somewhere overhead, drenching the beautiful new curtains and bunks in a universal deluge. If I had brought a conscious intelligence to bear on the source of this waterfall, I should have hit on something that ought to have been obvious to all of us. But not until the whole thing was over did I realize that all this water must have been coming from the *ventilation shaft*, now open to sea pressure through the damaged torpedo-stowage compartment. By reaching up my hand over the Captain's bunk I could have shut the valve on the bulkhead quite easily, and the flow of water would have stopped. But my brain, as though stunned by the catastrophe, had become incapable of constructive thought.

I found the torch and splashed my way back to the control room. As I did so, it occurred to me to wonder what depth we were at. I shone the torch on the depth gauges and found, to my surprise, that they were both reading only a little over sixty feet. This meant we were in very shallow water, with the bow presumably resting on the bottom at something like eighty feet. I asked Peter whether it was possible to *blow* her up. It seemed unlikely, since we had been at full buoyancy at the time of the collision, and a vast quantity of water must have entered for'ard to have overcome that buoyancy so suddenly. It was obvious that a large gash had been torn at the top of the pressure hull in the torpedo-stowage compartment, and that the compartment had filled up in a matter of seconds. We should never get her up with all that weight of water in her. However, Peter thought it would do no harm to try, so one by one he opened up the valves of the high-pressure air panel until all five ballast tanks and the two main internal tanks were blowing. But it was no use: the depth gauges did not even flicker.

The sea continued to pour in on us, with a terrible and relentless noise, and the water in the compartment grew deeper every minute. As the level crept up the starboard side, live electrical contacts began spitting venomously, with little lightning flashes. Vaguely I wondered if we were all going to be electrocuted. In the half-darkness the men had become anonymous groping figures, desperately coming and going. There was no panic, but most of us, I think, were suffering from a sort of mental concussion. I discovered one man trying to force open the watertight door that I had shut earlier. "My pal's in there," he was moaning, "my pal's in there." "It's no good," I told him; "she's filled right up for'ard and there's no one left alive on the other side of that door." He turned away, sobbing a little.

For some reason we decided it would be useful if we could find more torches. I knew there must be one or two others somewhere in the wardroom, so I made yet another expedition down the slope, wading through the pool that was now waist-deep and already covering the lowest tiers of drawers under our bunks. I spent some time in the wardroom, shivering with fear and cold, ransacking every drawer and cupboard, pushing aside the forsaken paraphernalia of personal belongings—underclothes, razors, pipes, photographs of wives and girl friends. But I could find only one torch that was still dry and working. Holding it clear of the water, I returned to the control room.

It was deserted.

The door into the engine room was shut. Had I spent longer in the wardroom than I thought? Perhaps they had all escaped from the engine-room escape hatch, without realizing that I had been left behind. Even if they had not yet left the submarine, they might already have started flooding the compartment in preparation for an escape, and if the flooding had gone beyond a certain point it would be impossible to get that door open again. I listened, but could hear nothing beyond the monotonous, pitiless sound of pouring water. In this terrible moment I must have come very near to panic.

I could at least try hammering on the engine-room door. Looking around for a heavy instrument, I found a valve spanner and began moving aft toward the door. As I did so I heard a voice quite close to me say, "Christ, who's that?" I looked up and found I was standing under the conning tower. In it, to my infinite relief, I saw Peter with an able seaman and one of the Engine Room Artificers. "Where the hell have you come from?" said Peter. "Where the hell's everybody gone?" I retorted. "Any room for me up there?" He said, "We ought to be able to squeeze you in. The others are going to escape from the engine room."

I climbed up through the lower hatch, grateful as never before for the company of my fellow creatures. Four of us in the tiny space made a tight squeeze. Peter at the top of the ladder with his head jammed up against the upper hatch, the A.B. halfway up the ladder with his bottom wedged against the side of the tower, leaving just room for me and the E.R.A. standing at the foot of the tower, with our feet on the edge of the lower hatch opening. The Artificer was in a bad way, vomiting continuously and hardly able to stand.

In the center of the upper hatch was a small port, or round window, made of glass thick enough to withstand tremendous pressure. Number One said that he could see a glimmer of light through it, and supposed it to be caused by a searchlight from some vessel waiting overhead. This encouraged him to think we ought to be able to swim to the surface and be picked up without much difficulty. We knew the control-room depth gauges were reading just over sixty feet; the upper hatch was something like fifteen feet higher than the normal surface water line (the point of reference for the depth gauges) and was therefore probably only about forty-five feet from the surface, say the height of eight men standing on top of each other. It ought to be easy.

"Shut the lower lid," said Peter, "and let's just think this out." I bent down, shut the hatch and pulled the clip over. We then discussed exactly what we were going to do. We agreed that to wear Davis escape gear (D.S.E.A.) would be an unnecessary complication in the confined space. One of the dangers was that on our way up we might crack our skulls on the crossbar between the periscope standards, but we decided there was little chance of this owing to the starboard list. We hoped (vainly, as it turned out) that we might be assisted in our rise to the surface by the bubble of air which would be released from the conning tower as the hatch opened. The drill was simple. Peter would open the hatch, and as the water came in each man would fill his lungs with air and climb out as fast as he could. Except for the poor Artificer, who was sick beyond comfort or encouragement, we were by now quite calm, even cheerful.

How long we considered the situation I cannot remember; but at last Peter said, "Well, the next thing is to see if we can open this hatch against the sea pressure." Bracing himself against the side of the tower, he pushed upward with all his strength. The hatch remained firmly shut. Somehow we must raise the pressure inside the tower. It occurred to me that while we had been talking the pressure had still been building up in the control room below us, owing to the continuing inrush of water. I eased off the clip of the hatch under my feet, and sure enough there came the sharp hiss of air forcing its way into the tower. I allowed the air to come in until, after a minute or two, I became aware of a peculiar, faint smell. Perhaps it was merely the odor of fear, but my first thought was that the sea water had at last found its way into the batteries. "Hullo," I said, "I think I can smell chlorine gas." "All right," said Peter, "Shut the lid again and I'll have another shot at opening this one." This time he managed without much effort to lift the hatch slightly off its seat, allowing a trickle of water to come through.

"O.K.," said Peter. "Well, boys, take your time. There's no hurry. You say when you feel you're ready." I said I was for having a go at once, before we weakened ourselves any further by breathing foul air, and the others agreed. We stripped down to vest, pants and socks.

"Ready?" asked Peter.

"Ready," we all replied, though I think the Artificer had reached the point in his sickness where he wanted to die more than anything else. "Right. Stand by," said Peter cheerfully. "Here we go for fourteen days' survivor's leave. We're off!"—and he pushed up the lid with all his strength.

I took as deep a breath as I could, and then the sea crashed in on us. There was a roaring in my ears, a blackness everywhere, and there was nothing for it but to fight for life with all one's primitive instincts of survival. Hauling myself up by the rungs of the ladder, I found my head obstructed by the A.B.'s bottom. With the strength of a desperate man I pushed up at him, his heel struck me in the face, I pushed again, and then we were through the hatch and clear of the submarine. I swam upward with quick, jerky breaststrokes. It seemed a terrible distance. Time stretched out of its normal span until I thought my lungs must surely crack before I reached the surface. And then suddenly I was there, coughing, spluttering, gasping in great drafts of the sweet night air and drinking in the blessed sight of the stars shining in the immensity of space.

The sea was fairly calm, with no more than a gentle popple. Seeing two heads in the water not far away, I called out and found they were Peter and the A.B., both in good heart. Of the Artificer there was no sign. We could make out the dark shapes of several ships around us, so we began shouting to attract attention. Some of them were throwing searchlights on the water, and one of these seemed to be nearer than the rest. "Come on," I said, "let's swim to that nearest one," and began swimming toward it with my rather feeble sidestroke. I pressed on for a few minutes, imagining the other two were following me, but after a while I turned and could see no sign of them, although I heard them shouting at intervals not far off. The vessel I was making for was farther away than I had thought. I am not a strong swimmer, so I turned over on my back and relaxed into an easy backward leg stroke, calling "Help!" at the top of my voice from time to time. Sometimes a wave lopped over my head and I swallowed a little more water. I seemed to be swimming for a long time. Whenever I looked around, the ship seemed to be as far away as ever. Surely, after all this, I was not going to drown in sight of safety? I began to feel rather exhausted.

Suddenly I heard voices shouting, the churning of propellers going astern, and I turned to find a searchlight blazing in my eyes and below it the shape of a launch quite close, with a scrambling net down over the side and men running along the deck. A heaving line shot out, I grabbed it and was hauled in. A sailor clambered down the net and helped me onto the deck, where I fell into the arms of two R.N.V.R. officers. Exhausted and groaning for breath, with my lungs half-full of sea water, I must have appeared in a worse state than I was, but while they wrapped me in blankets and hustled me below I managed to tell them that there were some more of us out there in the water and many others still down in the submarine trying to escape from the engine room.

In a cabin below they rubbed me down, gave me dry clothes, and put me into a bunk, where I lay shivering from delayed shock. About half an hour later they came and told me our men were starting to come up from the bottom. I couldn't bear to stay in my bunk while this was happening, so I wrapped myself in a blanket and tottered along to find out what the situation was. They were coming up at fairly frequent intervals, strange Martian creatures with their D.S.E.A. goggles and oxygen bags, and rendered almost unrecognizable by black oil which had floated up from the bilges when they flooded the engine room for the escape. But they were in extraordinarily good spirits, half-intoxicated with their unexpected return to life. Every one of them was full of praise for the way in which the Chief E.R.A. and the Torpedo Gunner's Mate had organized the escaping party and carried out the escape drill. When finally these two reached the surface, the Chief E.R.A. last of all, they reported there was no one left in the engine room. There had been enough Davis sets for all but two of the party. Two men had volunteered to go up without them, each holding on to the legs of one of the others; one of these was never seen again. A final roll call showed that the only other casualty of the engine-room party of twenty was a civilian technician from Chatham dockyard, who had joined *Umpire* as passenger for the trip north: the Chief E.R.A. had fitted him with a Davis set and patiently explained its simple operation to him several times, but the man was so unnerved by the catastrophe that, although he succeeded in getting out through the hatch, he failed to reach the surface. But altogether the engine-room escape was a remarkable justification of the submarine escape drill.

It was only afterward I discovered that, halfway through the escape, the Chief E.R.A. thought it would be advisable to make sure none of the escapers was getting caught up in any obstruction outside the hatch. He therefore clipped on the oxygen mouthpiece of his Davis set, made his way up through the hatch, walked about on the outside casing of the submarine in the vicinity of the hatch, and then, although he could easily and without shame have made his ascent to safety, he climbed down through the hatch into the engine room once more and carried on with the business of supervising the escape of the remaining men. Not until every other man had left the compartment did he make his own getaway. For his part in the escape Chief E.R.A. Killen was later awarded the British Empire Medal.

It was not until the launch landed us at Yarmouth that I heard Peter Bannister was missing. I had been told that another vessel had rescued some survivors from the water, and I had assumed these were Peter and the A.B. who had been with us. In fact only the A.B. had been picked up. When I saw him later at Yarmouth, he said that he and Peter had swum together for some time and that when they were rescued he had thought Peter was immediately behind. A long search failed to find him. I was staggered by this news, for Peter was a strong swimmer and had seemed in excellent fettle when we spoke together on the surface. To have got so far and be lost at the last moment was an appalling tragedy.

It was daylight when we reached Yarmouth and were met by Lieutenant Commander J. F. B. Brown, who had flown up from submarine headquarters in London to get the facts at first hand. During the day, in the intervals of answering questions, we enjoyed the generous hospitality of the Naval Base.

That evening I strolled alone after dinner in a small grassy courtyard. A gentle drizzle of rain was falling, and it was what one would call a miserable evening, but to me the sound of the soft rain falling like a benediction on the living grass seemed inexpressibly sad and sweet, and life itself so desirable that I could not imagine myself ever again being dissatisfied with it. For the first time I knew the delirious joy of not being dead.

At the same time I felt that in the emergency I had failed to act in the manner expected of a submarine officer. Running over again and again the sequence of events following the moment of collision, I was tortured by two nagging thoughts. First, why had I not had the sense to realize that all the water coming into the control room had been pouring in through the ship's ventilation system? Secondly—and this has haunted me ever since—I knew that I should have been in the engine room with the men. At first I was sure I never wanted to see the inside of a submarine again. But the conviction grew in me that to ask to leave the submarine service would be such an admission of defeat that I should never recover my self-respect. For the purely egoistic reason of patching up my pride, I therefore decided to remain in submarines—if I was allowed to.

With thoughts like these crowding my brain, I was still awake when Wingfield walked into my cabin about midnight. He had just landed, having stayed on the scene of the collision until nightfall. He was looking ten years older, gray and haggard from worry and lack of sleep. He told me how Tony Godden had been drowned, and asked about Peter Bannister. I told him the story up to the point where we had separated after reaching the surface. He said the final casualty total was two officers and twenty men, almost half the ship's complement.

The next day, after further interrogation, they sent us off on fourteen days' leave. In the middle of it we were recalled to attend the official Board of Inquiry at Chatham, a dreary and grueling experience. At the end of my leave I reported to HMS *Dolphin* at Grosport, and in answer to my request for an early return to sea I was appointed to relieve Freddie Sherwood as Torpedo Officer of the submarine *Sealion*, then based on Fort Blockhouse and operating off the French coast under the command of the famous bearded Ben Bryant.

*

Childlike Wonder

When we think of the sea bed, abandoning ourselves to its fantasy, we become poets of childlike wonder. We roam around like divers in colored shadows overhung with liquid skies.

Paul Valéry

The World Below the Brine

BY WALT WHITMAN

The world below the brine,
Forests at the bottom of the sea, the branches and leaves,
Sea-lettuce, vast lichens, strange flowers and seeds, the thick tangle, openings, and pink turf,
Different colors, pale gray and green, purple, white, and gold, the play of light through the water,
Dumb swimmers there among the rocks, coral, gluten, grass, rushes, and the aliment of the swimmers,
Sluggish existences grazing there suspended, or slowly crawling close to the bottom,
The sperm whale at the surface blowing air and spray, or disporting with his flukes,
The leaden-eyed shark, the walrus, the turtle, the hair sea-leopard, and the sting-ray,
Passions there, wars, pursuits, tribes, sight in those ocean-depths, breathing that thick-breathing air, as so many do,
The change thence to the sight here, and to the subtle air breathed by beings like us who walk this sphere,
The change onward from ours to that of beings who walk other spheres.

Diving With and Without Armor, Containing the SUBMARINE EXPLOITS of J. B. Green, The Celebrated Submarine Diver *was published in 1859 by Faxon's Steam Power Press in Buffalo, New York. It may well be the first autobiography of a diver: the editors know of no earlier one. The first successful closed-helmet dress of Augustus Siebe had appeared in England only a decade before. After he was crippled by the bends, Green had his life's story printed on the steam press and sold it in the streets for twenty-five cents. We wish to thank John Scofield for lending the rare original edition of* Diving With and Without Armor.

Diving With and Without Armor

BY J. B. GREEN

*I*t was in the spring of 1841, as I was walking leisurely along the dock in Oswego, that I first saw diving for lost property. Two men were plunging to the bottom of Oswego River for a box of soap and a clock—which had been stolen and thrown into the water. As the weather was fine and diving a sport in which I greatly delighted, I at once decided to try my art in the search. I divested myself of my garments, and dove for the bottom of the river. I sank about fifteen feet—halfway—when I began to feel a little timid, and I instantly rose to the surface of the water. I again observed with what ease and apparent unconcern, the divers sank even to the bottom of the river; and I decided not to be outdone in my favorite sport, and I plunged down again, and swam to the bottom; and with me as I returned to the surface, I brought a bar of soap.

Encouraged by this prize, though simple, I continued diving with renewed vigor, and was soon rewarded by finding the clock; and, in doing so, my last submersion lasted one minute and a half, a longer time than I ever remained under water before. To the spectators on the wharf it seemed two times two and one half minutes. They supposed I had strangled, and in my desperation clung to some protruding object below the surface of the water.

Elated by this success, I at once conceived the idea of following diving for lost property as a vocation; and during the same season, I

75

recovered large quantities of freight which had been lost in the harbor and lake about Oswego; the sale of which was so remunerative that I resolved to follow Submarine Wrecking in the future, as a business.

It was along the shore of Lake Erie that I first saw scientific diving. A party of divers and wreckers, who used submarine armor, were exploring the wreck of the steamer *Griffith,* which was burned in the summer of 1850. The wreck lay in about fifteen feet of water. The divers went down, and remained from twenty to thirty minutes. I expressed my desire to try the armor; but I was only scoffed for my boldness. I was gravely informed by those experienced divers, as they termed themselves, that none but those who had the greatest skill were ever allowed to use the armor, and it would be hazarding my life to undertake it. I replied, "My sins upon my head," and dove down to the wreck, and remained under water almost three minutes. This satisfied those "old divers," that I knew something of diving, at least, without armor, and they allowed me to encase myself in the strange habiliment.

This armor was constructed of copper and India rubber. That part constructed of copper was to protect the head, and termed the helmet. It was of oval form, quite large in comparison with the head, and had a window in front, and one on each side, for the diver to see through. The rubber covered all the remainder of the body, except the hands, and its dimensions were sufficient to admit an ordinary sized man, with three suits of woolen clothes, which amount was necessary to keep the body warm while under water. At the top of the helmet was attached the pipe, through which air from the surface, by means of an air-pump, was forced into the armor, keeping it constantly inflated. At the waist of the helmet in front was the escape pipe, for letting off the impure air into the water. There was also in the helmet a valve, which would, in case of leakage of the supply pipe, instantly close and prevent the air from passing out; and another on the end of the escape pipe, which the water would instantly close on rushing into the pipe.

I dove for the wreck, and, on my first submersion, I had far stranger sensations than ever before experienced under water. It resembled that timidity which attacked me when first I dove for the lost clock and soap. But in that case I was master of my own ability, and if I wished to emerge, I could instantly return to the surface. Here it was not so. The thought that I might suffocate—that my signals would fail to be understood, or, if they were, would they draw me to the surface before I should die, awoke feelings which I cannot describe; nevertheless, I ventured down to the wreck. To add to my discomfiture, I was attacked with symptoms of seasickness, which were increased by every movement of the water. Nothwithstanding, I was determined to show the old divers that I could remain down as long as they, for on emerging, I found I had been down about thirty minutes, which was equal to their stoutest boasts. The instant that I began to ascend in the water, my sickness increased, and by the time I was on the boat, I felt as disagreeable as ever a "land lubber" in a gale at sea. About half-past one o'clock, I sank again to the wreck, and remained down until seven o'clock—about six hours. At this date the time was unprecedented in the annals of diving.

We raised some parts of the engine of the steamer, but besides this we found very little of value; and, after two weeks, I proposed to our company to remove to the wreck of the steamer *Erie*, burnt August 9, 1841. I was unanimously opposed. Some of the most learned, scientifically, informed me that philosophy taught, and that any man of learning would tell me, that a person could not live in such a depth of water as that of the *Erie*—that it would press him to death instantly. My experience in diving had taught me differently, and I still advocated a search for that wreck, stating my willingness to go down to it. By this assurance, I was successful in changing their minds. We had now formed ourselves into a mutual company, with the understanding that the spoils should be divided pro-rata.

We found the hull in seventy-one feet of water, yet I found but little difficulty in reaching the wreck. On going down I struck on the bow, where my first attempt was rewarded by five dollars in silver, which I picked up almost on the very spot where I first struck. Here again I was beset with a myriad of fishes, which came around me in such numbers as to darken the water, and retard my work. But the *Erie* proved a more wealthy mine to us than the *Griffith*. I sent to the surface large sums of money, which strange to record invariably proved to be less than when under water. I called the attention of the company to this discrepancy, but was politely informed that it was "very deceiving down there, you know." Perglich, a land shark belonging to our company, came to me privately, saying that I was about right on that point, and if I would agree to hide a part of the treasure below, he would come with me some night, and help secure the same, and we would divide the booty among ourselves. I gave a feigned consent, and kept my eyes open, and ears awake. But a few nights after, I heard this pretended friendly thief relating to a comrade his plans, and said he, "I will hide it thus and so. You carry off the booty when I place it there, and I will make it appear it has been stolen. You shall have half." To hazard my life, and then to be robbed by those who were to share in all I found was a provocation more than I had virtue to take, and still live in reverence of the golden rule. I sent up only a part of the money, and stored the rest away for some future emergency. I also found what to me at that moment seemed equal to the fortune I had just lost. It was a mass of metal weighing about seventy pounds, as if five or six thousand dollars in gold had melted, and run into one solid mass. This I cast into my submarine vault, and locked the secret in my heart. Some of my party complained because I did not send up more money. I replied, "It is very deceiving down there, you know."

My various exploits in diving had been made known to the public through the columns of newspapers in every part of our country. Various parties addressed me at this time, for the purpose of obtaining my services. Among these were the American Express Company, for the purpose of raising the safe containing thirty-six thousand dollars, which was on board the steamer *Atlantic*, sunk off Long Point on the nineteenth of August 1852—in a collision with the propeller *Ogdensburg*.

The gentlemen had also made arrangements with two submarine operators from New York City, who had been employed in diving in the ocean. While on our way to the wreck, these persons were constantly boasting of their great exploits; that they had gone down in one hundred and fifty, and two hundred feet of water—often; and remained down—how long I will not attempt to say. They termed me "the fresh water diver"; that I played in shallow water, and like a boy who could not swim, dared not venture where it was too deep.

On arriving at the place of the accident, we found that the steamer lay in *one hundred and sixty-two feet of water;* and my suspicions were verified; for both of these "salts" positively refused to go down to such a depth; myself alone must undertake the dive. I resolved at once to reach the wreck if it was possible. The armor owned by these New York divers was far superior to the one I had been using, and I selected it to make this trial.

I sank on my first trial one hundred and five feet—deeper than I ever before had been in water. The pumps failing to supply the armor with air sufficient to prevent the water from pressing my body, I at once arose to the surface. Having arranged that difficulty, I again submerged, and sank to the depth of one hundred and twenty feet, when the air pipe commenced leaking, and I was again compelled to emerge. On repairing this difficulty, I went down again, and was successful in reaching one of the smokepipes of the steamer, my body passing into it, while one of my arms dropped outside the pipe, the top striking my armpit. To extricate myself, it was necessary that I should be drawn up a little distance, and I again arose to the surface. I immediately went down again, and this time struck upon the walking beam, and by feeling my way still down, as I was in perfect darkness, I stood upon the deck of that ill-fated steamer, one hundred and fifty-two feet below the surface of Lake Erie. The air pipe again burst, and I had to be instantly drawn up. We were obliged to return to Buffalo in order to get it repaired. Where now were the "salt sea divers"? Where their gigantic boasts of exploring the "vasty deep" two hundred feet below the surface? These crestfallen fellows were as silent as a couple of day-overtaken owls.

At the time I first became acquainted with the submarine armor, for a diver to remain down thirty minutes even in twelve to fifteen feet of water was a great adventure. At the time I remained down at the *Griffith* about six hours, it was the longest time on record, and when I went down to the wreck of the *Erie*, it was the greatest distance. These circumstances convinced me, that I was the first person who tested the expedient of *having all the air that could be constantly forced into the armor, and consequently, it would be safe for the diver to go down to any depth as long as the air kept the armor inflated.*

The winter of 1852–3 at length broke away, and as there was a prospect of resuming navigation on the lakes, I began to make preparation for drawing on my bank in Lake Erie, of which I had so often boasted. No one with a deposit in one of our free banks, could feel surer of his checks being paid, than I did of having mine when I presented my face at the counter of that bank—the hull of the *Erie*.

With the first favorable weather, I set sail for the scene of the wreck. On going down, I found the massive chunk just where I had placed it the previous year. I at once rose with it to the surface; and you can have but a feeble conception of my mortification and chagrin, to find that, after all my high anticipations, I possessed a portion of the bell which once belonged to that ill-fated steamer.

I secured, however, about seven hundred dollars, mostly in five-franc pieces. But I was soon disturbed by others, who pretended to have a claim on the same. A party of divers, who were with me at this wreck the year previous came with the determination of dispossessing me. They cut away my buoys, and threatened to drown me if they found me down to the wreck. One of these divers, a braggadocio of a fellow, was particularly boisterous, with this threat, "If he met me down at the wreck, I never should come up alive!" I gave him an immediate opportunity to carry his threat into execution, by going down to the wreck; for I had possession of that part of it where I had reason to believe that the greater portion of the money was to be found, and I was anxious to maintain it. He immediately followed, but struck at such a distance from me that we were both unaware of the precise locality of the other. At last I saw a dim form in the water moving toward me. I made at him with all my power, my uplifted bar ready to strike, and the specter at once ascended from my view. The boaster had signaled and been drawn up. But he was not to give the battle up thus, for I learned by a signal from above that he was again descending. I stood on my guard, and the fellow came down directly over my head. The instant he came within reaching distance, a punch from my crowbar caused a retrogression in his movement, and he soon reached the surface, contented, having fought as much as he thought would be prudent under water.

The spring of 1854 had now arrived, and I commenced business by forming a partnership with Messrs. Wells & Gowen, of Boston. Mr. Tope, the celebrated English diver, and myself, went to the location of the Steamer *Erie*, with the intention of raising her hull. We succeeded in getting chains under her bow and stern, and under the cylinder, securing the chains above by means of a buoy. We then returned to Buffalo and erected derricks for raising her to the surface. During the construction of this apparatus for raising the *Erie*, Mr. Tope wished to test a new armor which he had constructed on principles different from that of the old. It consisted in having the tube for the escape of foul air extended to the surface of the water. In company with three others he started from the mouth of Cattaraugus Creek, in a small vessel, and selecting that locality where the water was about forty-five feet, Mr. Tope went down some fifteen or twenty feet, each time signaling to be drawn up, and complaining that the foul air did not escape fast enough to allow free breathing. Previous to descending the third time he removed a spring which he had attached to a valve on the escape pipe of his new armor, to prevent too great an escape of air; and observed to the man holding the signal line, to answer the slightest signs of a message, as he should signal the moment he reached the bottom. He then entered the water and sank some forty feet, when those above thought that he felt unusually heavy. The signal line was at once worked to ascertain if anything was wrong; but receiving no answer, they at once drew him to the surface, and on opening the armor, to their horror, found him quite dead; although he had been down but about one minute. The corpse presented such a dreadful spectacle; blood was oozing from the eyes, nose and mouth. Detaching the spring from the escape pipe had allowed the escape of air to equal the amount pumped into the armor, and consequently did not inflate it in the least, and the pressure of water forced all the blood in the system to the head, bursting blood vessels and causing instant death. Although he had not been submerged one minute, on opening the armor we found the head very badly swollen, the face and neck so filled with blood as to resemble liver, while the remainder of the body was as white as unclouded marble.

On going to the wreck of the *Erie* again, we raised it some fifteen feet, when the cylinder broke away and sunk to the bottom, we again made fast to it, and commenced raising again when the hull broke about forty feet from the bow. We were successful in holding the smaller portion, which we towed to Cattaraugus Creek. When off Cattaraugus, I came very near losing my life, while down to the fragment we had in tow. In some way the signal line and air pipe became entangled in the purchases lowered to raise the wreck. I could not make my signal understood above. There I was, chained down as it were in some forty feet of water, and to add to my peril, it was sunset and fast growing dark. Death seemed to stare me in the face. But I did not lose the presence of mind which is of all importance to the diver. I put forth every nerve to extricate me from my fettered situation. By great effort I climbed up about six feet, where I cut my signal line. I made it fast to my wrist, and examined the head line (the line by which the diver is drawn up); which I also found entangled, but by cutting it I was enabled to get it free; and I fastened it to my body. I then examined the air pipe, which I found like the signal line, was entangled in such a manner as to make it impossible to extricate it. To cut this, I knew would be death unless I was instantly drawn up. I again examined the head line— that I was sure was free. Something I knew must be done at once.

I was nearly exhausted from toil, in endeavoring to release myself, and the anxiety attending my situation. I began to feel sleepy, and with that symptom the diver knows that he must instantly be drawn up. I was now free except the entanglement of the air pipe, and I resolved to sever that. I gave signals by means of the signal line, a jerk from which always was understood to raise. I waited until I was drawn up as far as I could be, at that instant I with one slash, cut the air pipe, and in a moment was on the surface. My effort alone saved me from a watery grave. Had I been so much frightened that I could not work or have sent up signs of distress to those above, I might have lost my life.

My services were engaged by the "Boston Wrecking Company" to go to the West India Islands, for the purpose of exploring the wreck of the British man-of-war *Sovereign*, which was lost on the Silver Banks as long ago as 1773. These Banks are seventy-five miles east of Turk's Island, and north of the Island of Hayti. The frigate, when she sunk, was on her way to the West Indies, and had on board eighteen tons of Spanish milled dollars, intended for paying the British soldiers stationed there.

We found the wreck, but there was not a vestige of her wood-work remaining, for it had long since been destroyed by worms. The only indications of the wreck were her cannon balls, and various other implements of war, which were strewn around the place. They lay in from ten to twenty feet of water.

On going down the first time, I found one Spanish milled dollar. It was so imbedded in the coral as to require considerable effort to extricate it. After heating, we found the date to be 1772. We also found some silver plate, belonging to the ship. It bore the inscription "Frigate." We were not successful in procuring anything of value, the coral having grown over the silver to such a depth that it could not be got at without submarine blasting. We were obliged to abandon the place. Every spot where the silver lay could be distinctly recognized, as the coral over it was of a dark hue, having been stained by the decomposition of the silver.

On diving to another wreck near by, we obtained a quantity of quicksilver, which, as it lay on the bottom of the ocean, was very brilliant when the sun shone upon it. There must have been a large quantity of it on board the vessel, for it filled the crevices in the coral in every direction. Here we found some champagne bottles, dated 1770, in the glass, which gives a faint idea of the date when this vessel rode the seas. The date of cannon, which we found here, showed them to have been manufactured one hundred and thirty years ago. These we could see from the surface of the water, sixty feet beneath, lying among the pillars of coral. Here is presented to the diver one of the most beautiful and sublime scenes the eye ever beheld. The water varies from ten to one hundred feet in depth, and is so clear that the diver can see from two to three hundred feet.

The bottom of the ocean in many places on these banks, is as smooth as a marble floor; in others it is studded with coral columns, from ten to one hundred feet in height, and from one to eight feet in diameter. The tops of those more lofty, supporting a myriad of pyramidal pendants, each forming a myriad more; giving the reality to the imaginary abode of some water nymph. In other places, the pendants form arch after arch, and as the diver stands on the bottom of the ocean, and gazes through those lofty winding avenues he feels that they fill him with as sacred an awe, as if he were in some old cathedral, which had long been buried beneath "old ocean's wave." Here and there, the coral extends even to the surface of the water, as if those loftier columns were towers belonging to those stately temples now in ruins.

There were countless varieties of diminutive trees, shrubs, and plants in every crevice of the coral. They were all of a faint hue, owing to the pale light they received, although of every shade and entirely different from plants I am familiar with, that vegetate upon dry land. One in particular, attracted my attention; a sea-fan of immense size, of variegated colors, and of the most brilliant hue.

To enumerate all the kinds of fish that I beheld while diving on these Banks, would were I enough of a naturalist so to do, requires more than my limits will allow. The sun-fish, saw-fish, star-fish, dolphin, white shark, ground shark, blue or shovel-nose sharks, were often seen. There were also fish which resembled plants and remained as fixed in their position as a shrub. The only power they possessed was to open and shut when in danger. Some of them resembled the rose in full bloom, and of all hues. There were ribbon-fish, from four or five inches to three feet in length. Their eyes are very large, and protrude like those of the frog. Another fish was spotted like the leopard, from three to ten feet long. They build houses like the beaver, in which they spawn, and the male or female watches the ova until it hatches. In diving here, we were often surrounded by sharks. They would swim cautiously toward me, as if to ascertain what I was, and I found it necessary to wear hoops of iron for just the opposite purpose of that for which ladies wear them at the present time. It was to protect me from sharks, not attract them.

We were often obliged to defend ourselves from this ravenous fish with our pikes. As they came near me I would strike them beneath, the hook penetrating their bellies and, as they wheeled to swim away, it would often rip them half their length, and their innards dropped out into the water; as they fell, this ravenous fish would turn and devour its own offal. The blood staining the water would attract others of the same species to the place; and these voracious monsters would at once devour their wounded comrade. A specimen of the white shark which we killed, measured twenty feet, and five feet across the head; but, I did not receive the least harm from any animal while diving on those banks; nor did any of our crew.

That wealthy safe at the bottom of Lake Erie had been rife in my mind, during all my adventures on the "Silver Banks." I made immediate preparations for raising it, and returned to Buffalo for that purpose. I chartered the schooner *Yorktown* with which to proceed to the wreck of the *Atlantic*. With eighteen men, I started for Long Point, where I arrived on the fourteenth of August. After several days spent in taking bearings, and in sounding, we succeeded in finding the spot where the wreck lay—five miles south of the extreme point of the Peninsula. Here we let down grappling irons to both bow and stern, and secured them above with buoys. I then commenced diving; and, as in my former trial, I found it was total darkness at the depth of the wreck. Her decks were covered with mud some ten inches in depth; but what was more marvelous, she had changed her position. Her bow, which was headed southwest when I first went down, now was southeast, having changed nearly a quarter of the compass. She lies on a smooth slate bottom, and I thought I could see her move at times; and I presume she does move considerably in rough weather.

After diving five or six days in succession, I found, my only way to get to it without great impediment, was to strike on the wheelhouse, and follow this down to the deck, and then follow the deck along to the third window from the wheelhouse aft. One morning I reached the spot, and placing my arm through the window, I laid my hand on the much sought for safe.

I immediately arose to the surface, obtained a line, went down again, and fastened it to the railing to enable me to descend at once to the place. I also attached a buoy to the line, ten feet below the surface, that it would not be carried away by passing vessels.

I could safely stay down no more than twenty to thirty minutes. I experienced much pain from the pressure of the water. A sensation was constantly felt between the eyes, as if a needle was piercing there; sparks flashed before my eyes, and the drowsiness, as in my former attempt, constantly attended me, all of which was occasioned by the insufficiency of air in the armor, as, with our pumps, it was almost impossible to force the air down to such a depth.

At noon, I unguardedly partook of a hearty meal. I was at the same time very warm, and much elated at the prospect of success. That thirty-six thousand dollars, thought I, before nightfall would, in all probability, be mine. That safe was found, which had so long baffled my skill, and to procure which I had hazarded money and almost life. On going down again, I took with me an iron bar and a saw, and I succeeded in cutting away so much of the cabin that it allowed me to drag the safe out, and I left it between the cabin and the railing.

I then arose for a rope and hook, and found that I had been down just forty-seven minutes, but notwithstanding, felt perfectly well, and would have instantly returned had the rope and hook been at hand. As they were not, I removed the face of the armor, and sat down to wait for the implements. I had sat but a moment, when a sharp pain shot like lightning through my lower extremities, and the next instant it went through my whole system, so prostrating me that I could not move a limb, or even a muscle. I was immediately taken to Port Dover, where I had medical attendance. After lying two weeks, I was brought to Buffalo, where I received every attention. The best physicians pronounced me incurable. I remained in Buffalo ten days, but I did not improve in the least. I was then removed to my home in Boston, where it was five tedious months before I could step; and in the spring I was only so far recovered as to walk a very little with crutches.

Even in this crippled state, I was loath to give up the trial, which, in the moment of success, sickness had obliged me to abandon; and, bidding defiance to sickness itself, I again repaired to Buffalo in June, 1856; and, after fitting out another vessel, I sailed for the wreck, where I arrived on the first of July. I found that the line which I had taken so much pains to make secure the previous season, was missing. On again finding the location, I was not a little mortified to find that the divers whom I had engaged refused to go down to the wreck, the farthest they sank being not over sixty feet. But I was not to submit tamely to this unexpected barrier, and, putting on the armor myself, I at once went down, striking on the upper deck. I found it dangerous work in my crippled state, and being quite weak, I could remain down but a short time. I reached the spot where I left the safe the previous year, and imagine my disappointment, when I found that the prize for which I had almost lost my life once, and risked it again, was gone. Crippled as I was, I worked myself along to the next door—a stateroom—in which there was a trunk containing seven hundred dollars in gold. The trunk was also gone. I felt for the safe again. It was gone. All—all my efforts for nothing! Never—never did I rise to the surface with so heavy a heart! On emerging, I was again paralyzed, prostrating me equally to my former shock. I was immediately brought to Buffalo, and by treatment I was restored to my present disabled state.

At Buffalo, we ascertained that a Mr. Harrington succeeded in raising the safe on the twenty-seventh of June, the very day we started for the wreck. My buoy was there, attached to a cord leading directly to the spot; and all Mr. Harrington had to do was only to descend to the boat, and remain down perhaps ten or fifteen minutes.

In the spring of 1857, I again started with a small vessel, which I had constructed with a view to submarine wrecking. I proceeded to Lake Huron, but not having good divers, and being too disabled to dive much myself, I found the business unprofitable; and I returned into Lake Erie, and proceeded to the wreck of the propeller *City of Oswego*. The water was so rough that I could not work, and I was obliged to endeavor to make the port of Cleveland, in doing which my little craft struck the pier, and with that disaster, ended my Submarine Diving.

*

The Uttermost Parts of the Sea

O Lord . . .
If I take the wings of the morning
And dwell in the uttermost parts of the sea;
Even there shall Thy hand lead me. . . .

Psalm 139

Noel Monkman lives in Brooklyn—New South Wales, Australia, that is—on Dangar Island and "plays the wag" as a scientific wanderer in the jungles and coral kingdom of the Great Barrier Reef. He is a concert cellist and internationally known microscopic cinematographer. He shot half the footage in the film The Sea Around Us, *and has published a fine naturalist's autobiography in* Escape to Adventure. *Here is one of his extraordinary experiences in the marine wilderness.*

I Found Undersea Insects

BY NOEL MONKMAN

*I*t seems strange that we humans should have lost so completely all ability to be at home in the sea from birth. Each and every one of us begin life, as did our ancient ancestors tens of millions of years ago, as a single-celled organism living in a sea. Each fertilized human egg cell lives for months completely immersed in the salt sea of the amniotic fluid of the mother's womb. Here we race through our embryonic past, evolving from the protozoa (the single-celled) to the metazoa (many-celled) reliving those times when we lived in the ancient seas of the world's beginning. For a brief period we sport the gill clefts of the fishes, then long discarded characteristics of the amphibians are hurriedly built by our busy cells, only to be torn down again to be rebuilt into the more highly evolved structure of the organism called man. Only nine months to travel millions of years; yet we can read the stations as we flash past to the destination where we are born as squalling landlubbers drawing air into our lungs to be carried through our arteries by the red blood corpuscles floating in the salty remnants of the ancient seas which aeons ago were locked away in the swirling currents of our closed blood stream.

Why then, since the sea is in our blood, should all these centuries have been necessary for man to invent a satisfactory method of returning even for a short visit to his ancestral home, the sea?

Insects and spiders have been using self-contained diving suits for many thousands of years. The water beetles lift their domed wing covers to take in a supply of air beneath them, then dive into the

87

water to search for their living prey in the underwater world. Here they courageously attack creatures often much larger than themselves. Down in the depths they fight their desperate battles, relying upon the air stored beneath their wing cases to enable them to breathe during the struggle. Even the modern invention of the submarine snorkel is ancient history to the larvae of the water beetles, which each possess a slender tube that is protruded and pushed above the surface of the water when their air supply needs renewing.

And what of the diving bell of the water spider? Unlike man, this spider has not forgotten how to live in the underwater world. The spider uses the hairs growing on its body to trap and hold an air supply when it dives down into the ponds. Here, in the cool depths, it spins a diving bell of cobwebs. Returning to the surface it enmeshes a fresh supply of air. Diving down again it scrapes the air bubbles from its body, allowing this air to be trapped in the cobweb. Trip after trip is made to the surface until all the water is forced out of the cobweb dome which now gleams in the pond like a tiny, silver bell. The spider now takes up residence in its underwater home. Soon a web is spun around the submerged dwelling, and the spider becomes a busy fisherman, harvesting a bountiful living from the small water life ensnared in the silken net. If this spider is a female she will not long remain alone. A male spider, wearing his Aqua-Lung of air bubbles, is sure to sight her villa and spy on her until satisfied that she is a lass he could love. Busily he builds another tiny diving bell alongside her residence, with the walls in actual contact —semidetached, as it were. Driven by consuming love for the girl next door, the male bites through the adjoining walls and enters her home. Does she run screaming out the front door? No. Almost certainly she makes a quick rush at her impetuous suiter—and eats him. There may be many silken tents vacant and forlorn around the citadel of the proud lady before life brings gentleness and understanding. But passion wanes. The honeymoon is over. She eats her husband to gather strength for her confinement. Soon, a loving mother, she moves serenely about her duties in her crowded nursery beneath the water.

But this is in fresh water. Are there, then, air-breathing inhabitants of the sea? The largest animal in the world is an air-breathing land animal that has returned to the sea, the whale. It is only one of many —turtles, seals, and walrus are amongst the others. These are large and powerful creatures that can contend with angry seas; but do any insects live in the sea? My Aqua-Lung introduced me to an insect living in the tropic sea sixty miles from the northeast coast of Australia. Here, in the wet season, devastating cyclones rage, yet here lived these tiny insects. The new-found joy of using the Aqua-Lung had coaxed me into the sea on a day when stormy skies made undersea photography impossible. I had been swimming through majestic canyons, and exploring coral caves along an isolated reef, when I realized that I had been submerged for an hour and my air supply was running low. When using an Aqua-Lung it is much easier to swim underwater than it is to plod ahead on the surface where the apparatus is a definite hindrance. I decided it would be easier to surface, then signal to the boat crew to come and pick me up. Pulling the release that set free an extra five minutes' emergency air supply, I swam toward the exit of the cave. It was like approaching a magnificent painting. Perfectly framed by the stalactite and stalagmite coral formations of the cave entrance was the lovely translucent blue background of the sea, with a big shoal of yellowtails swimming past in stately formation. Ducking under a swaying festoon of stinging hydroids that fringed the mouth of the cave like delicate curtains of lace, I sped upward past a mountainside clothed in a patchwork quilt of rainbow-hued corals. Reaching the surface I signaled the lookout man on deck to come and get me, then swam toward the top of the coral mountain which the falling tide had uncovered for a few inches. As I started to clamber up on the coral I saw a sudden movement. A number of small creatures scuttled across the exposed coral into the sea, and continued running down the mountainside under the water to disappear beneath a stony ledge some distance below. In the fleeting glimpse they had looked like insects, not sea creatures, but surely that was impossible away out here in the open sea. Unstrapping the empty air bottles, I placed them on top of the coral as a marker for the boat crew, and dived down after the mysterious creatures. I slid beneath the ledge and looked up. There they were rapidly scrambling along the underside of the ledge toward a number of deep and roomy crevices. With my face-plate only a few inches from them I could see every detail. Two-four-six legs, all other observable characteristics added up. Yes, no doubt about it— they were insects! But how could they live and breathe beneath the sea? Then I solved the mystery. Many of the crevices under the ledge were actually diving bells. At low tide the ledge was above water; as the tide rose again the air was trapped in these crevices making homes for these hardy seafarers. Here, while storms shrieked and raged above, they could safely shelter in their secluded, air-locked caverns. When low tides left the coral exposed, they wandered about the mountaintop looking for food or basking in the tropical sunshine. With my air bottles refilled I dived down again and lay under the ledge watching these queer little insects going about their daily lives. Always they clung to the coral reef and never attempted to swim—a very sensible habit. If they trusted themselves to the water, the swirling currents would almost certainly prevent them returning to the safety of the reef, and they would be swept into the open sea where they would soon become exhausted and drown. I watched them stroll down to the shore line of their undersea villages, where they would gaze fixedly into the sea beneath them. Suddenly they would make a quick grab into the water and haul out some almost invisible prey which they would devour with quite dainty table manners.

The ledge had many well-populated villages, and as these creatures were strange to me I captured two and sent them for classification to an entomologist of the Australian Museum. In return I received a letter asking for more specimens, preserved in tubes of spirits, as these were insects of a species new to science. By the time that the letter reached me I was exploring another reef hundreds of miles away from the courageous little inhabitants of that outpost of insect empire. I admit I was happy to be unable to fulfill the further requirements of the entomologist. After all, they were now properly recorded in the census of world population, and since their ancestors and my ancestors down through the ages had managed successfully to adapt themselves to all the tremendous changes in world conditions, we held certain rights in common. The first of these rights was to live; the second, to enjoy the freedom of the sea.

*

Diving Bells: Fourth Century B.C.

So that sponge fishers may be supplied with air for respiration, vases are lowered in the water with the mouth downward so they fill not with water, but with air; these vases are forced steadily down, held perfectly upright, for if tipped slightly, the water enters and knocks it over.

Aristotle

In 1904 an American archaeologist, Edward Thompson, dredged the cenote, or sacred well, of Chichén Itzá in Yucatan and brought up a hoard of Mayan gold and jade sculptures, which are now in the Peabody Museum at Harvard. Thompson brought in a helmet diver, who found it impossible to work in the well. Cenote archaeology languished until the free diver came along. Luis Marden is among those now working the cenotes. He is, in our opinion, the finest underwater still photographer in the field. He will go to any lengths after a picture, as his story demonstrates. It was written for the National Geographic Magazine, *of which Mr. Marden is a writer-photographer on the Senior Staff.*

Up from the Well of Time

BY LUIS MARDEN

When I dived into the cenote of Dzibilchaltun, I took a plunge into history. Even as I sat on the edge of the big natural well, I felt that my rubber-flippered feet had already crossed the frontier of the ancient Maya world. I slipped the mask over my face and clenched the Aqua-Lung's rubber mouthpiece between my teeth. My Indian helper patted me on the head; I took a breath of bottled air, slid into the water, and thrust downward toward the yawning black depths. Cenote Xlacah (pronounced Shla-cah, Maya for "old town"), one of hundreds scattered over the face of the Yucatan Peninsula, is shaped like a sock, with a foot and toe that extend back under a rock ledge. The pre-Columbian Maya built their cities close to the sources of fresh water. I had come to the archaeological site of Dzibilchaltun to dive and search for artifacts that might have been dropped or thrown into the deep sinkhole by the inhabitants of the old city.

I have often dived to the sea bottom, but this was the first time I had ever dived through it. I was plunging into a hole in an ancient ocean bed that slowly emerged from the tepid sea perhaps as long as a million years ago. Rain falling on Yucatan percolates through the porous limestone, so that there are no streams or surface water of any importance on this hot, dry peninsula. Instead, fresh water stands

91

in cenotes, or natural sinkholes, that reach the subterranean water table. Hundreds of these water holes, deep or shallow, clear or green with algae, pock the flat face of northern Yucatan. Through the passing centuries the slow rain of Maya pots and gourds, spears and lances, jade pendants and carved bone hair ornaments, even the bones of men and women, sifted softly down to their beds of rotting ooze. Here they were held, safe from the erosion of sun and wind, inviolate in the green twilight until man found a way to take his air with him into the aqueous world.

Cenote Xlacah is 100 feet across at its widest point and at least 140 feet deep. Twenty feet beneath the rock lip at the deep end, the bottom plunges steeply into blackness. Schools of flat-bodied silvery characin fishes darted round my head as I stared into the darkness. Beneath me the green carpet of tufted water weeds stopped abruptly at the limit of sunlight. Under the overhang the darkness seemed almost total at first. I paused to clear my ears and to turn on the flashlight that hung from my wrist. As my eyes adjusted to the gloom, I could see the vast curve of the roof and back wall receding in a dim semicircle. Under me the rubble-strewn slope dropped at an angle of fifty degrees.

I expelled the air from my chest and, with arms extended straight before me, sank silently down the slope. Below me, the jumble of limestone fragments bedded in black ooze slid upward, seemingly reversing in slow motion their age-old fall into the depths. Here and there in the rubble lay squared and carved stones, evidence of human handiwork that had tumbled into the cenote centuries before.

At sixty feet I paused to look upward. Against the lambent blue rectangle of the entrance Bates Littlehales, my diving companion, swam in black silhouette like some space-suited alien suspended in a void. Bates swam down to me, wagged his lamp reassuringly, and we continued to sink. At eighty feet the slope came to a flat landing of velvety mud, then plunged abruptly into blackness between two up-thrust pylons of rock. At the foot of the slope a big rectangular lintel of stone stood on end between a tree trunk and the drum of a column. Head downward, I carefully fingered it for possible hieroglyphs, but all four sides were smooth. We edged over the drop-off between the leaning rock pinnacles. Our lamps threw cones of light on the back wall, which curved abruptly down to the toe of the cenote. At the foot of the rocky columns we came to another landing, and then the bottom dipped again, flattened, and slid into a low-arched black tunnel. At the mouth of the tunnel the depth gauges read 120 feet. The exhaled air bubbled noisily from our regulators, and when I held my breath, I could hear the expanding silver mushrooms of air glucking and tinkling as they streamed to the rocky vault far above our heads. I looked upward. Under the curve of rock the surface opening glowed faintly green, its dim arch of light slashed brutally by the diagonal masses of leaning rock, like monstrous jambs at the gate of some cold and silent hell.

Littlehales and I finned our way into the tunnel's mouth. We had to swim close to the floor of ooze to pass under the low arch, and the muck swirled in the wake of our fins. Suddenly the oily black stuff whirled up before my mask, and I turned to look for Littlehales just in time to see the green disk of his lamp wink out. I turned my own light full in my eyes and could see nothing. I was in utter blackness and could not tell up from down, or which way led back to the tunnel opening, to the surface, and to air. For ten seconds I felt black panic. Then reason returned. Inhaling deeply, I rose to the arched roof of the tunnel and clung there like a fly. As the roil gradually subsided, it left a foot of relatively clear water under the roof. The green firefly of Bates's light wavered toward me. We touched hands and started up. We had been down about twenty minutes.

When we emerged into the dazzling sunlight, I asked Littlehales if he knew why the mud had boiled up so suddenly. "It was this," he said, holding up one arm. He wore an oversize armlet of terra cotta. It was the broken neck of a jar, our first artifact. "I saw it lying half buried in the mud," said Bates, "and when I tugged at it, the ooze spurted up in a black cloud that obliterated everything."

Our first task was to take a life line down as far as we could and anchor it, so that we should always have a link with the surface. We had engaged two experienced Mexican divers, Fernando Euan and Earl Becht, to work with us. The season before, Fernando had made several dives into the cenote. Earl could build anything, with or without tools. In a few days he had constructed, with the help of two Mayas, a diving platform just under water, where we could sit while putting on our Aqua-Lungs, as well as a kind of shear legs, or derrick, of slender logs, that leaned out over the cenote. We made fast the line to the derrick head; then Littlehales and I put on our breathing apparatus and submerged. Each of us held one side of a sixteen-pound mushroom anchor, which dragged us down so fast that we had to keep swallowing and popping our ears. We dropped the anchor just inside the black tunnel and watched it disappear in a cloud of ooze. On our way up we followed the white nylon line which stretched in a glistening catenary curve to the surface, a reassuring link with the upper world.

On the north rim of the cenote stands a great mound of rubble. As we dived day after day, we became convinced that much of the worked stone from the facing of this pyramid had at some time in the past slid down the slope into the deep waters of the well. Beginning at sixty feet, carved and shaped stone flowed in a cascade to the foot of the slope: squares and rectangles of white limestone with sharp uneroded edges, blocks faced with intricate geometric carving, columnar drums, and finally the great door lintel at the foot of the slide. An "Engulfed Cathedral" of pre-Hispanic Yucatan. Manuel, the camp caretaker, heard diver Fernando Euan and me discussing the enigma of this cataract of carved stone. It did not puzzle him. "That's the cacique's castle, *jefe*," he said. "Our people say that a king had his *castillo* standing where the cenote is now. One day his mother came to him asking for water, and he sent her away, saying he had none. God in His anger caused the ground to give way under him and his fine house, and they all sank together into the cenote. He had plenty of water then."

At sixty feet we struck our first rich lode. Pieces and whole necks of earthenware pots lay thick among the tumbled rubble. In one dive we could easily fill our wire baskets. Lying head upward on the slope, moving as little as possible to conserve our air and to avoid clouding the water, we could stay down forty to fifty minutes on a single tank of air. We sent pail after pail of potsherds to the surface. The ancient clay was soft and crumbly when it first came out of the water, but after a day's drying in the fierce Yucatan sun, the pieces became quite hard.

Sometimes we inadvertently moved a key stone; the rubble would tremble and shift, then start to tumble down the slope in slow motion. Usually we heard a warning click, or saw an uneasy stirring of the mass of rock, which barely gave us time to inhale a chestful of air and rise safely above the underwater landslide. Such landslips threw up clouds of ooze. This excited the few venturesome finger-length fish that had followed us down from the sunlit shallows, and they would dart through the water, snapping at bits of organic matter. When the cloud had subsided, we would search the new working face minutely. For days we mined pieces of pottery. Then one day I heard Bates hooting through his mouthpiece. He held a slender tapering object toward me. I took it, thinking it was an abnormally long thorn; when I turned my lamp on it, I saw that it was a bone awl engraved with a vertical row of hieroglyphs. We shook hands and started up the slope. Like nearly all nonnumerical Maya hieroglyphs, some of these carvings proved undecipherable. Actually, the awl may have been a hair skewer, thrust into the glossy black hair of some Maya girl who lost it while drawing water. The leader of our National Geographic Society–Tulane University cenote expedition, Dr. E. Wyllys Andrews had always maintained that the objects found in the cenote had been accidentally dropped into the water by women who had come to draw water, or by other persons. But from the discovery of the awl onward, we began to find things that were not entirely utilitarian. We found a clay flute, a miniature molded head finished in the mysterious "Maya blue" pigment, obsidian flakes, bone noseplugs, and human bones. Interspersed with the bones of cows and small rodents we found human jaw bones and crania. The skulls were so flattened that the top of the cranium was very little higher than the ridge over the eyes. Bishop Diego de Landa, the misguided zealot of the sixteenth century who burned all the Maya manuscripts he could find, partially atoned for his cultural crime by writing his *Relation of the Things of Yucatan*. In it he says: "They had their heads and foreheads flattened, and this was also intentionally done by their mothers in their childhood." The infant heads were flattened by binding two boards tightly to the cranium. Possibly the bones were victims of drowning or even the *corpora delictorum* of pre-Columbian murders. But the increasing numbers of nonutilitarian objects, in addition to the bones, made Dr. Andrews think that Xlacah may have been the center of a cenote cult, like that which centered round the celebrated Cenote of Sacrifice at latter-day Chichén Itzá. At the foot of the slope we found bigger bones. One enormous femur must have belonged to a giant of a man, perhaps a conquering Spaniard who either fell or was thrown into the sinkhole. Other thighbones were smaller and more delicate, and one pelvis was, I am convinced, that of a Maya maiden. My skeptical companions asked me how I could be sure, and I could only reply that I felt it in her bones.

At the end of two weeks of extensive digging, our rich vein at sixty feet became exhausted, and we moved down to the landing at eighty feet. Here we worked standing on our heads, groping in ooze up to our armpits. While we probed in complete darkness, Newton's third law of motion—"For every action there is an equal and opposite reaction"—was graphically borne home to us. If we made a violent effort to thrust our arms deep into the ooze, our bodies would move back an equal distance, so that to penetrate the stuff we had to kick our fins constantly. Under a tree trunk we found a dozen buried pots, some of them entire. It was frustrating to feel the rounded shape of a whole jar in the ooze, only to have a section come away in the hand despite the most careful digging. At this depth the walls curved down to meet smooth side slopes of mud. We worked up these slopes, our right arms buried like plowshares. Ahead of our questing arms the quivering aspic of clinging muck heaved and erupted in geysers of cloudy smoke that shone brown and oily in the light of our lamps. On this slope I found the handsomest whole jar of the season. Fortunately it lay mouth down, and so was easier to extricate in one piece. I left it for Fernando to dig out while I prepared to photograph him as he emerged with the magnificent specimen.

One day, while probing deep in the muck at ninety feet, I grasped something that felt like a branching twig. When I shook it free of its coating of mud, it shone too smooth and hornlike in the circle of light to be a tree branch. It looked familiar, and suddenly, to my astonishment, I recognized it. I held a piece of sea fan, a gorgonian such as I had swum among so many times on coral reefs. How did it come to be in the cenote, ninety feet down, under three feet of ooze? Later I found more sea fan fragments, and these finds, more than any others, convince me that there must have been a cult of some kind connected with the cenote. Of no known use, the gorgonians must have been deliberately thrown into the cenote in some rite, perhaps a cult of the sea.

While we dived to sixty feet or less, we had little cause to worry about the physiology of diving. We rarely had to decompress, because we stayed within the limits of the no-decompression tables, and so had no cause to fear the bends, that unpleasant ailment that hovers over the head of every diver who dives too deep and stays too long or comes up too fast. When we moved down to the eighty-foot level and beyond, we had to keep close watch on our time below. Complications confront a free diver when he makes several deep dives in one day. Then, even though he may adhere carefully to decompression times for each dive, the nitrogen which dissolves in his body under pressure slowly builds up to the threshold of danger.

One day Littlehales and I decided to see how far we could penetrate into the cavern at the bottom of the cenote. We dived to where the palely gleaming life line plunged into blackness between the rock pinnacles. I had rigged two lines tied to bronze snap swivels. We snapped them to the life line and swam down into the murk. The swivels slid to the end of the life line and clicked against the shank of the buried anchor. Unwinding the lines as we went, we swam slowly into the black tunnel. In the cone of light from my lamp a single black catfish, its eyes gleaming dull ruby, trailed its whiskers in the mud. Above us the vault rose gently. Soon the cloud of ooze swirled around us. I looked at my depth gauge; it read 140 feet. Here, more than fifty feet into the tunnel, the floor ran nearly level. Our gauges were calibrated for sea water, which is denser than fresh water by 2.5 per cent, so that the actual depth was nearer 144 feet. We remained at this deepest point only fifteen minutes, then swam back to the outer amphitheater and rose at the then-prescribed rate of twenty-five feet per minute. We had dived twice before that same day, decompressing carefully both times on ascending. Within five minutes of emerging, I felt a slight pain in my right upper arm. Quickly I put on a fresh tank of air and went down to sixty feet, where I stayed for ten minutes then came up by decompression stages. Still I felt the pain, and so went down a second time to eighty feet for twenty minutes. When I rose, again by stages, the pain returned. By now I was blue with cold, having been under water so long that I was chilled through.

By coincidence an engineer friend, Melvin Art, who was building a new power plant in Mérida, had mentioned the night before that he could rig an emergency recompression chamber if ever we needed one. During the twenty-minute ride to town, the pain became almost unbearable. There was no doubt now; for the first time in seventeen years of diving I had a case of decompression sickness—the bends. We telephoned Art from Dr. Andrews's house. "See you at the plant in ten minutes," he said. When we got there, workmen already were swarming over a square-sided oil storage tank the size of a small room. A pressure gauge and air hose had been connected, and men were cutting an airtight gasket of linoleum for the manhole atop the tank.

After briefing Mel on the use of the recompression tables in the U.S. Navy diving manual, Bates and I climbed up the ladder and lowered ourselves into the tank. Littlehales felt no symptoms but decided to take the treatment too. Mel handed down a flashlight and hammer, and then the men slammed down the cover and began to twist home the nuts. The clangor inside was ear-splitting. Air began to hiss into the tank. We lay on our backs in pitch darkness. The hissing grew into a roar so deafening that we had to cover our ears. We began to sweat, because the compression of air raises the temperature sharply.

The roar fell, and died into silence. The tables called for a pressure of three atmospheres, the equivalent of one hundred feet of water. We had popped our ears a couple of times, but I could feel that we were not under very great pressure, so I banged three times with the hammer, signaling "more air." The valves opened and air roared in. Almost immediately the roar died to a hiss. Still my ears told me we were not at one hundred feet, but we lay quietly, knowing that Mel was doing his best. After twenty minutes we signaled for more air but none came, so we hammered six times, the signal for "take us up." The air screamed out, and the temperature dropped until we shivered. The manhole cover clanged aside, and we climbed back to the fresh outer air. My arm still ached dully.

"What happened?" I asked Mel. "The tank wouldn't take any more pressure," he said. "We hadn't reached two atmospheres when the sides began to bulge." If the tank had exploded, the men standing round it would have been seriously injured, if not killed, and I should probably have had a permanently paralyzed right arm from the explosive decompression. "I've got a cylindrical oil tank that should stand a lot more pressure," Mel said. This tank was big enough for only one man. Bates still showed no signs of bends, so I entered it alone. So much time had now elapsed that we decided to try a recompression to five atmospheres, equivalent to a depth of 165 feet, and a total time in the chamber of ten hours and forty-eight minutes. For the long wait I took with me flashlights with extra batteries, paperbound books, my diving watch, a copy of the treatment tables, and a hammer.

When the manhole cover was bolted fast, I was in Stygian darkness. The air hissed in, the temperature soared, and sweat streamed off my body in rivulets. Standard recompression chambers are ventilated every few minutes. We had no such provision, and what I feared most was asphyxiation in my own exhaled carbon dioxide. I had asked Bates to "crack" the inlet valve periodically, to let in a little fresh air, and I lay quietly, to avoid building up excess CO_2.

My time in that steel coffin was one of the least pleasant experiences of my life. I would not recommend it to anyone with claustrophobic tendencies. The books soon wilted to the consistency of limp lettuce, and I made no attempt to read. Now and again a hammer blow would startle me, and I replied with a single bang. Faintly, as from a great distance, I could hear Bates say, "Well, at least he's still alive!"

When, after centuries of time, I heard the six-blow hammer signal "We're bringing you up," I felt as though I were emerging from a dungeon in which I had lain for years. I looked at my watch; to my surprise, I found I had been in the tank only six hours and twelve minutes. Never had the air of Mérida, so hot and sticky at that time of the year, smelled sweeter or felt cooler. Blinking in the blaze of light, I saw long faces all around me. "We couldn't get you down to 165 feet," said Littlehales. "The tank wouldn't stand more than one hundred feet." The treatment had temporarily alleviated, but not cured, the bends. That night I slept under strong sedatives. When I awoke, Littlehales had not yet come downstairs. I found him stretched stiffly on his bed. He complained of a pain at the base of the spine and could not sit up. Now I was truly alarmed. If this was also the bends, Littlehales was in danger of complete paralysis.

There was no choice. Allen McLean, Jr., the United States Consul, telephoned Mexico City, and with the U.S. Ambassador's approval, the Naval Attaché sent out a radio call. Within the hour we received word that an aircraft would arrive that afternoon to evacuate us to Florida and a Navy recompression chamber. The four-engined airplane was a welcome sight as it circled Mérida airport. The Navy had sent the big aircraft because it could pressurize its cabin fully. We flew at only nine thousand feet across the Gulf of Mexico, so that sea-level pressure could be maintained. High flying in an unpressurized cabin would have expanded the bubbles in our blood streams, causing permanent injury. Less than three hours later we landed in Panama City, on the northwest coast of Florida. At the Mine Defense Laboratory, it seemed that the entire base, headed by the commandant, Captain Richard Anderson, had turned out to meet us. We were hustled straight to the recompression chamber. Because of the long delay between the onset of the bends and treatment, we spent forty-four hours and twenty-six minutes all told in the gray tank. At the end of that time, thanks to the expert care of the Navy, we emerged completely cured.

I should like to express here the deep gratitude of Littlehales and myself for all that the United States Navy did for us. They took care of two unshaven and ailing civilians with unfailing good humor, and we shall always remember them with heartfelt thanks.

I planned to return to Yucatan to finish the job. A Navy specialist in diving medicine, Dr. Charles Aquadro, offered to go to Yucatan with me. I was delighted, because Lieutenant Aquadro is an experienced underwater swimmer, and he would bring the latest and as yet unpublished U.S. Navy tables for repetitive dives. When I returned to Yucatan a few days later, I was warmly welcomed at the cenote.

Some of the Indians seemed rather surprised to see me back, and I asked Fernando why. "They fully expected to see you get in trouble," he said. "They say their patroness, St. Ursula, lives at the bottom of the cenote and resents anyone digging up the bones and household goods of their ancestors."

Fernando handed me a clipping from a Mexico City English-language daily newspaper that was headlined: "Ancient 'Curse' on Mayan Wells Strikes National Geographic Divers." The Indians of Chablekal settlement at Dzibilchaltun say that the image of their patron saint once stood in the ruined Spanish chapel on the east side of the cenote. When she was moved long ago to the church of Chablekal, her "little sister," or another manifestation of the saint herself—it was not clear which—remained behind in the cenote. "It is dry down there where she is," they insisted. I had been to the bottom many times and had been wet all the way. Whenever the feast day of St. Ursula is celebrated in Chablekal, music and fireworks can be heard issuing from the cenote, they told us.

My wife had come to dive with us for a few days. One morning Ethel went down with Fernando and me. She halted at sixty feet while we sank to the slopes below to make photographs. As I worked, I hummed "Adelita," Pancho Villa's old marching song. Fernando, who could hear me quite clearly, recognized the tune and looked up from digging to grin. Later, when we had come up, my wife said: "You know, while I hung there waiting for you, I heard a high, thin singing. It was very faint but quite clear." "Impossible!" I said. "You have been listening to too many old Indian's tales." "I tell you I heard it," Ethel insisted, "and what's more, the melody sounded vaguely familiar. I can't explain it, but I know it was not imagination." "You must have heard the singing of Santa Ursula," Fernando said with a straight face. My wife did not know the answer to her mysterious singing until she read these lines.

We had gradually worked our way down the slope, and finally we moved into the black tunnel at the bottom. The floor is nearly level here, and anything that rolled down the slope must have been caught long before it reached this point. We found nothing. Returning to more productive levels, we opened up another vein at sixty feet. On my wife's last day of diving, she made a unique find. Fernando and I were searching the slope when we heard an urgent hooting. Ten feet above us, Ethel waved her lamp violently. Gently, in order not to raise clouds of ooze, we pulled ourselves hand over hand along the stones. She held out her hand, and there in the beam from my lamp lay a little clay jaguar, not quite five inches tall, the first figurine from the cenote.

The days slipped swiftly by toward mid-June and the rains. Charlie Aquadro, Fernando, and I worked our new mine. The potsherds were smaller and fewer now, but of better quality. We found nearly all of a beautiful orangeware dish. Its glowing pieces felt as silken to the touch as jade. For nearly two weeks we had a phenomenal run of luck; not a day passed that we did not turn up some odd or striking piece. Once Fernando held something out to me that shone white in the light. It was a spatulate bone hair skewer, with four hieroglyphs carved on its triangular face. That same day I found a small cylinder of rock crystal; Fernando next found the only bit of jade to come out of the cenote, a grass-green bead. One of the most unusual finds was a small wooden mask. The puff-cheeked face, with its curious double-topknot hairdress and wide-open mouth, looked more African than Maya. In the laboratory we experimentally inserted the rock-crystal cylinder I had found into the mouth; it fitted perfectly, and may well have been fastened there when the mask was tossed into the cenote centuries ago. My own best find came nearly on the last day of diving, when I saw a yellow circlet embedded in mud. It was a bone finger ring, incised with glyphs and a zigzag design, as fresh and sharply outlined as if carved yesterday.

On the last day Fernando and I retrieved the anchor and life line. As we neared the surface, we heard a sudden rattling. I looked up. A myriad of silver rods punctured the surface, dimpling and starring the water mirror. The rattling became a loud sizzling; the first heavy rain of the season was falling. As we emerged, the pelting rain felt cold and wet. When a naked diver comes up into heavy rain, he feels much as a fully clothed man does when walking into a thunder-shower. If he can, the diver ducks down under the surface again to keep "dry."

With the suddenness of the Tropics, the rain passed and the sun came out, washing everything in a pale champagne light. In the distance the sky lowered black, but near at hand the trees and rocks shone with the newness of a freshly made world. The bush, awakened by a week of tentative raindrops, burgeoned with spring green. Clouds of butterflies, pale chartreuse, sulphur yellow, and white, clustered on the rims of the rain pools. I thought of the archaeological treasures that surely lay still hidden beneath my feet. All over Yucatan cenotes hold in their cool grasp secrets as yet unprobed by earthbound archaeologists. One day, with St. Ursula's permission, I should like to dive once more deep into the centuries of ancient Yucatan.

Here is the historic account by the zoologist Professor Louis Boutan of how he took the first underwater photographs ever made. He began his experiments in 1892 at the Arago Marine Station at Banyuls-sur-Mer in the Mediterranean. He continued developing underwater photographic technique for seven years and in 1900 published La Photographie Sous-Marine, *the first book on the subject. By that time he was making "instantaneous" exposures of ten seconds. In 1899, he succeeded in taking remote-controlled arc-light photos at the then incredible depth of 165 feet. The founding of underwater photography was only one of Boutan's achievements. He was the first to learn how a mussel anchors itself to the bottom, which is by placing its foot on a rock and pumping a glandular secretion down a groove in the leg. When the fluid hardens, the mussel withdraws its foot, leaving a sort of mooring line. The inquisitive scientist was also the discoverer of how to grow perfect round cultivated pearls in oysters, which he reported in an open scientific paper,* The Real Origin of Fine Pearls, *in 1903. Japanese cultured pearl firms immediately put his findings to work. During the First World War, Boutan and his brother, Auguste, designed a one-man submarine to be launched from a mother sub, which they gave to the French Navy without cost or royalties. It was better designed than the first such chariots to go into action in World War II.*

The First Underwater Photographs

BY LOUIS BOUTAN

The first attempts at undersea photography were made in the neighborhood of the Arago laboratory with a camera that I designed and had built.

I used two boats that Professor Henri de Lacaze-Duthiers had generously put at my disposal for the pursuit of my experiments. One was a felucca of four or five tons, decked and fitted with a lateen sail. It had been a gift to the laboratory at the time of its founding by the inhabitants of the region. The second boat was considerably larger. *Le Roland* was a steamboat of about twenty-five tons,

which had been liberally offered to the director by a scientific Mae-
cenas. (Prince Roland Bonaparte—Ed.)

In the stern was a large cabin where different observations could
be carried out. This cabin could, in turn, be transformed into a
workshop, dining room, or dormitory. Three bunks provided sleeping space in this minuscule dormitory. In the middle were the steam
engine and boiler room as well as a tiny kitchen for the preparation
of light meals. In the bow was located the steam winch for lowering
or raising equipment without fatigue for the men in the crew.

I first sought to explore the Bay of Banyuls with my lens. This
stretch of coast is not the most favorable for this purpose; the bottom
is made up of a mucky sand because the river, emptying at this level,
washes down considerable silt in the winter. Subjects for photography,
however, are numerous and varied; beaches of sand, prairies of seaweed, rocks with deep caves are represented in this bay. But when
you go down in a diving suit, the silt or muck I talked about above
constitutes a serious obstacle to good undersea shots. The first disadvantage presented by the silt is to give the landscape a uniformly
grayish color; the contrasts are not accented enough to give sharp
blacks and whites and the pictures obtained are necessarily dull.

The second disadvantage is that it is impossible to move on the
bottom without troubling the surrounding water. At each step the
diver raises a cloud of mud which stays in suspension for several
minutes and darkens the water through which the light rays have to
pass. I persisted, however, in spite of these unfavorable conditions,
until I obtained a series of pictures which if not entirely satisfactory,
were at least adequate.

But I lost no time in looking for a spot better suited for my experiments and I found it a little south of the laboratory in a small cove
briskly washed by the swell and called Barter Bay. Sandwiched between two rocky hills, it is one of the most picturesque spots on the
coast. In spite of the violence of the north wind, the bottom is car-
peted with undersea meadows which dip in a gentle slope toward the
high seas. Violent currents produced by the swell when the prevail-
ing winds blow have brought about the formation of sandy patches
that crisscross the meadows and constitute real paths where one can
circulate freely, when one is dressed in waterproof gear. Nothing
is more impressive than to follow one of these roads traced by the
current; on each side, on the shelves worn by the tide, stretch tall
stems of *Pocidonie*, whose luxuriant growth and aspect recall the
plants of a tropical country. The diver finds himself surrounded by a

green wall, for the stems of these singular plants reach as high as his helmet.

To walk in the meadow itself, after having crossed the shelves I have just spoken about, you must push aside the tall grasses which reach only to the level of the chest. In addition, in this cove you find large rock formations covered with algae and showing large openings inhabited by numerous animals. The depth of the bay is variable, and you can operate from six to thirty-six feet by going down the slope.

Here is the procedure that I adopted to get my pictures with the quite rudimentary camera I then had at my disposal. The boat being anchored securely to the bottom and kept stationary with the help of a series of cables fixed to the rocks of the coast, I put on my diving suit and went in at the point chosen in advance as the center of operations. After having landed at the desired depth, I signaled the captain to lower the different parts of the photographic equipment. On the end of a line I received the iron platform, the copper-covered camera, and a weight to anchor everything.

The view chosen, I would set up the base of the apparatus at leisure and arrange the camera in such a way as to have only to press a button to open the shutter. This done, I sent another signal to the captain who held the life line in his hand. This signal indicated that the exposure had begun, and I would wait patiently for the captain to indicate the end of the operation.

You understand, of course, that it is impossible or, at least, very difficult without a special gadget, to take a watch down in a diving suit to time the exposure. Thanks to the method that I had adopted, this difficulty was overcome; the captain's job was to consult his watch and warn me in time.

It was thus that the photographs were obtained, after exposures that lasted up to a half-hour. The chief disadvantage of the process I used then was precisely the length of the exposure. Undersea landscapes are far from immobile; even in the calmest weather at my operating depth the swell always makes itself felt and the plants, disturbed by the movement of water, oscillate and make the pictures fuzzy. But, with the first camera that I had built, I had to expose the plate for a very long time and, to get more sharpness in the pictures, I tended to close the aperture more and more which forced me to increase the exposure even more in order to get an impression on the plate.

These first pictures were far from good. They were, in any case, a point of departure; however, I was far from being satisfied with them. Why did these first attempts furnish only mediocre pictures? Is water an unsuitable medium for getting good photographs? The experience of these last three years has proved to me that the medium of water was in no way guilty and that if the camera were improved, the resulting pictures would be improved.

*

Cleopatra's Joke on Marc Anthony: 40 B.C.

Marc Anthony went out fishing one day with Cleopatra, and being able to catch nothing in the presence of his mistress, he gave secret orders to fishermen to dive under water and put fish that had already been caught on his hook. He drew them in so fast, Cleopatra perceived the reason. Pretending great admiration, she invited everyone to come out next day and see how skillful he was. While they watched from the boats, as soon as he threw in his hook, she had a diver put a salted fish on it. Feeling a tug, Anthony drew it in and great laughter ensued. Cleopatra said, "General, leave the fishing rod to us poor sovereigns of Pharos and Canopus: your game is cities, provinces and kingdoms."

Plutarch

The author of this breezy tale of real underwater treasure was born in 1932. Anderson is an accomplished diving technician, having worked on development of several compressed-air devices. He has also been adviser on underwater movies and has several times descended more than two hundred feet in the Pacific. Donald "Red" Carter, his noisy colleague in the Mother Lode, is a veteran of the Second Armored Division, who packs into the remote creeks in the summer, seeking gold.

California Gold Divers

BY RICHARD ANDERSON

Since gold was first discovered in California during the 1850's, thousands of eager prospectors have descended upon the Mother Lode country seeking their fortunes. The early miners traveled up the rivers and streams taking the easily accessible gold, leaving behind a fortune for those who were to follow.

The Mother Lode is the richest gold field ever found anywhere on the face of the earth. During the great California gold rush miners extracted approximately three billion dollars in gold from all types of mining operations. Geologists estimate that thirty billion dollars remains at the present time. The Placer gold in the Mother Lode comes from an ancient river channel which, due to prehistoric volcanic eruptions, now lies on the western slope of the Sierras. When erosion formed the Feather, Yuba and American rivers, they cut through the ancient river channel. The free gold from the channel was deposited in these rivers in great quantities.

With the increasing popularity of skindiving in the last decade, a new figure, the underwater prospector, has appeared in the rivers of the rich Mother Lode country.

Present-day prospectors are quick to say that "all the easy gold is gone," and indeed it is, for them. For after the forty-niners came the Chinese and others, who by sheer manpower moved entire gravel bars and even diverted rivers into new hand-dug channels to work the river bottoms unencumbered. There are areas though, where the old-timers couldn't work the river bottom by any means. It is here that the skindiver with his light, portable equipment can dive and find gold that was impossible for the early miners to recover.

My good friend Jack Reynolds and I decided to take a weekend trip to the American River to examine the diving possibilities. On the American, we met a picturesque old-timer, who was amazed by our portable diving equipment. He claimed to have studied the "riffle action of the river" for twenty-eight years and assured us that under his guidance we could all be rich. He told us of underwater crevices that were lined with gold nuggets. All he needed was a couple of divers and a little suction equipment. Since Jack and I were both more or less virgins at mining, we decided to team up with him. We agreed to build two underwater "suckers" according to his specifications and also send him two lightweight engines to power a revolutionary Vortex sucker he was inventing. We returned to Santa Monica, already counting our fortune, and began building the equipment we needed.

By the time we left Santa Monica, we had assembled a huge mass of diving and mining equipment consisting of: ten diving cylinders and a compressor, two hookah regulators, a lightweight diaphragm diving compressor, four hundred feet of diving hose, several types of wet and dry suits, one hundred pounds of weights and a variety of miscellaneous diving gear. For the mining operation we had: gold pans, picks, shovels, pry bars, crevicing tools, a lightweight pump and engine to run the two-inch and four-inch suckers. We were going to stop in Stockton and borrow a 2½-inch dredge from a friend. All this, plus camping equipment, we loaded into a trailer hooked to Jack's trusty Volvo, and we were off (off our rockers).

In Placerville, the old-timer was still as enthusiastic as ever and we went right to work on the river. The old-timer's revolutionary Vortex sucker didn't suck. In fact, it discharged water at both ends. Our two suckers were useless as well. The old-timer was a wonderful liar but didn't know much about gold. These failures were quite disappointing, to be sure, but we still had the dredge, which worked very well. With it, we found more gold than our old-timer had ever seen. Besides having studied the "riffle action for twenty-eight years," he was also an expert on "swirling action": "Yuh go in there an' turn over them stones an' watch the swirling action an' pick up the nuggets," he said.

We turned over them stones and watched the swirling action but found no nuggets. When Jack or I would pan out the clean-up from the sluice box he would give us a suspicious look and say, "Hmmmmmm, I see it's all there but some of the larger nuggets."

I was getting fed up with hearing about riffle action, swirling action and eighteen-pound nuggets in his secret holes, so I told him I thought he was giving us the runaround. First, he called me everything but a good guy, then assured me that he knew where pounds and pounds of gold were in rivers, but he'd be damned if he'd ever tell us. I forget exactly what I said to him then but anyway he missed me with the tire iron.

Jack and I parted company with him. The month we spent diving on the three forks of the American was by no means wasted. We knew now just what equipment we needed to recover the gold and where we were most likely to find it. We didn't even regret the time spent with the old-timer, for although he didn't show us any gold, we had learned enough good tall tales to be a success in any Mother Lode barroom.

Jack and I accumulated a considerable amount of gold on the American River but stories of gold found on the Yuba aroused our interests. We met a gold buyer in Placerville and from him we obtained the only real factual information we have heard on gold. He showed us samples of gold from every river, stream and creek in the Mother Lode, told us where they came from, and the quantities that came from the different areas. After talking with him, we agreed that it would be to our advantage to move to the Yuba.

We had to return the dredge and we found ourselves in need of a new-type suction device. On the way to the Yuba we stopped in Grass Valley and bought material to build a new underwater sucker. We prospected on the south and the middle forks of the Yuba without finding anything that fulfilled our expectations, so we headed for Downieville on the north fork.

Highway 49 parallels the North Yuba between the Indian Valley Outpost and Sierra City and in this area the California Forestry Service has installed and maintains public camp grounds. This is not like roughing it, but if that's where the gold is, why not take advantage of it? We set up camp in the Indian Valley Camp Ground. Surprisingly enough, it was in this area that we made some of our largest strikes. Often, only a stone's throw from the highway.

Our first day on the North Yuba, I discovered a long underwater crevice in the bedrock and began knocking out the wedged-in rocks with my prospector's pick. I fanned away the sand underneath and what I saw was really a sight to behold. The crevice was lined with small nuggets. It is difficult to detect fine gold underwater, but when you uncover nuggets, they shine like gold. I was still picking them up when I ran out of air and had to surface.

I asked Jack to hold out his hand. I poured the gold into his palm. "Hmmmmmm, I see it's all there but some of the larger nuggets," he joked. We went right back to camp and began building our new sucker, so we could finish cleaning out the crevice. Our new (2½ inch) sucker worked like an underwater vacuum cleaner, sucking in at one end and discharging at the other. The sand and gravel, drawn through, ran over the riffle tray, and the gold, being heavier, was deposited in the riffles. It took a lot of prying, pounding, picking and scraping to clean out the crevice, but at the end of the day we had four more ounces of gold. We felt we would do all right on the Yuba.

When we arrived back at camp, a curious vacationer looked over our diving gear with great interest and said that he knew where we could make a lot of money. Jack and I were all set to listen to another fantastic tale of gold. "You guys," he said, "could take that gear of yours and make a pile of money diving for frogs around Marysville." Our mouths dropped open. This was sure a switch from the usual stories. Jack told him that it was a great idea because besides making money, we could call ourselves frogmen.

From our permanent camp at Indian Valley, Jack and I explored points all along the three forks of the Yuba and its converging streams. Somehow we couldn't resist checking some of the more reasonable-sounding tales that came to us in a constant flow. Most were just stories but sometimes we would hit a good spot. One such tip came from an honest-looking summer prospector. He told us, after three six-packs of beer, about a place near Goodyear's Bar, where a few years before he had taken a lot of heavy gold out with a gravel pump. We were there bright and early the next morning. Jack hadn't been in the water ten minutes when he came up with two small nuggets weighing about a pennyweight each. I fired up the engine on the pump and he took the sucker down with him. By noon he had cleaned out all the crevices in the exposed bedrock. We had several nuggets weighing one and two pennyweight and a generous quantity of "fine." When our benefactor came around to our camp that evening, we gave him more beer and showed him the coarse gold we'd found at Goodyear's Bar. He looked at it suspiciously and asked where we got it. "Aw, don't kid me," he said, "this isn't Yuba gold. This is Klondike gold." Even after six beers he wasn't convinced. Which just goes to prove that even the best gold stories are questionable.

At one point on the Yuba we found a rich area on the opposite side of the river. We purchased two hundred feet of stainless cable, some ⅝ chain, a three-foot turnbuckle, some shackles and material to build a small cable car. With this setup we could transfer our gear and ourselves across the river with ease. Jack volunteered to try it first. Just as he reached the middle of the river, the cable slipped off the rock on the other side. The car hit the water with a resounding splash, and Jack sank out of sight inside it. This scared the hell out of me because if there's anything I hate it's going into that cold water without a suit. But he came up finally with about ten fathoms of wire rope around him. We rerigged the cable and used it successfully for about a week. After that we didn't have to worry about any more accidents. We took a day off and some bandits stole the whole works.

One evening while Jack and I were quenching our thirsts at Paul Viles' Indian Valley Outpost we noticed a letter on the board addressed to Don Carter. I asked Paul if this could by any chance be a red-haired, wild-type Carter we knew. He said, "Oh, no, you're not friends of that bunch; three of them is enough." Despite his misgivings he told us where they were holed up and how to get there.

The next morning, armed with a case of beer, we set out to find them. We got lost and they found us. Our reunion took place in an old ghost town called Brandy City. Jack and I went with them down into the canyon where their cabin and claim were located. Carter and Gillbank showed us their mining operations while Jim Brown whipped up a pot of something they called Zapata stew. It was lousy.

We discovered later that "Zapata" was the name of the cat they used in the stew. This was a bad enough shock but in the middle of the night we were awakened by the roar of gunfire and found the boys having a rat-shooting contest in the cabin. Carter ran up the highest score with his .44 magnum and they all celebrated by having a party on chocolate pudding. Their only luxury. These guys had been in the canyon too long. Jack and I bid them farewell early in the morning before they had a chance to fix breakfast.

We continued diving on the Yuba and our pile of gold grew and grew. One evening we returned to camp and there was Gillbank frying a rattlesnake on our stove. (Strangely enough, they skinned it first.) Carter and Brown were just basking in the comfort of our camp. They had their snake and we had our steaks. Those guys would eat anything if it'd hold still. It seems that things in the canyon had taken a turn for the worse. The boys were at each others' throats and they decided to call it quits before the quiet seclusion was shattered by a roaring gun battle. Gillbank and Brown went on a tour of the gold country. Jack ran out of money and decided to go back to Santa Monica and get married. He did. Carter teamed up with me to work the rivers for a few more weeks.

That night we all went to Grass Valley to have a parting celebration. We entered the Gold Center Club with over a pound of gold in small nuggets. In the course of the evening Jack poured it all out on the bar and announced that we had hit a ninety-thousand-dollar pocket in the Yuba at Indian Valley. What an excellent liar he had turned out to be in only three short months! I was sure proud of him.

The very next afterhangover—I mean afternoon—we got the same story back from Paul Viles at Indian Valley. Carter and I heard it everywhere. About a week later we met an old-timer who lived way up in a remote canyon. While Carter was busy stealing his plums he told me about this ninety-thousand-dollar strike at Indian Valley made by some "diver fellers from Los Angeles." Carter asked him if he was sure it wasn't just a rumor. "Why, hell no, sonny," he said, "I seen it *myself*. They had nuggets as big as your head." He suggested that we try diving ourselves. We told him we would.

The first few days we didn't find much and Carter wasn't too sold on diving for gold. He changed his mind one morning when I came up and handed him a nugget as big as his thumb. After that he'd pull me out of the tent in the wee hours of the morning, and prop me up in front of a plate of steak and eggs, shouting gold, gold, gold.

There was hardly a place on the river where we didn't find some. I went in first and explored the areas with a prospector's pick and a pair of long tweezers. If I found a concentration we'd rig up the sucker and clean it out. Our one big problem was overburden. In some places we had to move it to get to the crevices in the bedrock. Since our sucker couldn't move much sand we did the job with short-handled shovels. Quite often we had to abandon very rich crevices because we reached a point where the overburden came in as fast as it was thrown out. Of course, we logged these places and can finish cleaning them out whenever we go in with equipment to move the overburden.

One afternoon I was working twenty feet down in a hole when I felt a jarring concussion. I looked up and saw rocks splashing into the water. Carter came into the water almost at the same time, with all his clothes on and a gold pan over his head. We climbed out of the river. A guy appeared on a rock high above us and shouted

"Fire in the hole." I guess he figured better late than never. Carter gave him a few pointers in Blaster's Etiquette while I taped a hole in the air hose caused by a falling rock. (Whenever I run out of air underwater I remember what René Bussoz said in his book *Self-Contained Diving:* "While it is important to see underwater, breathing is vital." How true.)

Carter and I were going great until one night we arrived back in camp after dark and it was my turn to cook. Whipping up a good meal was no problem but all I had for light was a kerosene lantern. (Carter shot out the Coleman lamp one night after reading a Western.) I fixed rib steaks, vegetables, a salad, and fried potatoes. When we were almost finished eating, Carter let out a roar and spit out a mouthful. While I was being assaulted by his verbal abuse, he pieced together a cigar butt out of his potatoes. I remembered having misplaced it while I was cooking and wondered where it had gone.

I finally quit laughing and Carter quit swearing but things just weren't the same after that. Carter wanted to do all the cooking. We were about to call it quits anyway because he had to get back to college and I had commitments in Los Angeles. We borrowed a scoop shovel and divided the gold we'd found. (How was that?) With his pick-up loaded high with diving and camping gear, Carter disappeared from camp in a cloud of dust. I followed shortly in my Volkswagen. I had more gold with me than most people in the gold country had ever seen, even though Carter had "some of the larger nuggets." The Mother Lode had done all right by us.

*

A Turkish Frogman

Sultan Ghazi Chelebi was a brave and audacious man, with a peculiar capacity for swimming underwater. He used to sail out with his war vessels to fight the Greeks, and when the fleets met and everyone was occupied with the fighting he would dive under the water carrying an iron tool with which he pierced the enemy's ships, and they knew nothing about it until all at once they sank.

Ibn Battuta, TRAVELS, 1332

The most unusual thing that has ever been said about the great speleologist Norbert Casteret was Eduard-Alfred Martel's remark that he is "a man of tact and good sense." Is it tact to abandon one's clothing and penetrate alone for a mile into an unknown cave? Is it good sense to plunge through two drowned passages inside? Martel must have referred to Casteret's scholarly attainment, which is eminently sound, tactful and sensible, and not to his daring methods of cave exploration, relentlessly pursuing the story of "ages vanished in the night." Here is the account of the youthful exploit that made Casteret famous. More than a third of a century later he is still leading cave expeditions.

The Oldest Statues in the World

BY NORBERT CASTERET

*I*n August, 1922, my explorations in the Pyrenees brought me to the village of Montespan, on the slope of a hill crowned by a feudal castle. The ruins, dominating the Garonne, draw the eye from afar. They go back to the Lords of Montespan, who ruled there for centuries before the celebrated Mme. de Montespan conquered the heart of the Sun King. Near the castle is the Grotte de Montespan, which I was to explore.

After a visit to the castle, I headed for the supposedly impenetrable cavern in the neighboring mountain. At the base I found a crack in the rock, with running water coming out. The villagers claimed that in exceptionally dry summers one could wade deep into a natural corridor, but that after sixty-five yards the grotto ended, the ceiling dipping into the water.

This description I found correct. Undressing, and slipping through a hole the size of a man's body, I got into a horizontal gallery from ten to thirteen feet wide, and six to ten feet high. I waded in running water on a sand and clay bottom. One hundred and thirteen feet in, the gallery turned right and a sudden dip of the ceiling forced me to stoop far over. After twenty yards of this uncomfortable locomotion the water deepened, and the roof touched the surface. This was an uneasy and discouraging stopping place. But memories of previous explorations elsewhere reinforced my habitual obstinacy. Instead

113

of leaving immediately, as was natural, I stopped in my strange posture to reflect. The limestone rock around me indicated that the stream might have excavated the interior of the mountain. On the other hand, geology tells us that the climate at the end of the glacial epoch was cold and dry, rather like modern Lapland. If the cavern existed, then it would have been dry for a long time in the early quaternary era, and so might have sheltered the wretched cave dwellers. Uncertain as it was, this theory appealed irresistibly to a prehistorian. I decided to dare the underground river, and push into the bowels of the mountain.

Neck-deep in the water, I considered the rashness of persevering alone in so hazardous an undertaking. Several possibilities came to mind: I might find water bathing the ceiling ahead indefinitely, run into a cul-de-sac, get to a pocket of foul air, fall down a shaft, be entangled in branches carried down by the stream, or possibly go down in quicksand. . . . After weighing these various chances in the awful silence and loneliness, I decided if possible to force the barrier, impregnable though it seemed.

Putting my candle on a rock jutting from the wall, I inhaled air for an immersion of two minutes. Then I plunged, one hand ahead, the other touching the ceiling. I felt the bumps and contours of the roof with infinite care; I was blind, with finger-tips for eyes. I had not only to go ahead, but to think about getting back. Suddenly, as I was going forward in this fashion, my head emerged; I could breathe. There was no telling where I was; the darkness was complete. Obviously, I had forced a siphon, a tunnel with a submerged ceiling. I turned tail at once, and plunged in the opposite direction, for in such circumstances nothing is more dangerous than to lose one's sense of direction. I sighted my candle through the black water. Despite the slender and purely sporting result of this first attempt, I was already anticipating the excitement of a second expedition, which I hoped would be long and fruitful.

The following day, back at the entrance to the grotto, I undressed, hid my clothes in the bushes, and slipped into the underground stream. I had a lighted candle in one hand, and a rubber bathing cap full of matches and spare candles in the other. This simple container, kept tightly closed, would enable me to relight my candle after each dive or after one of my numerous tumbles into the water.

In the siphon I swam exactly the same course as before, so as to find the air pocket. I came up safely with my eyes and nose just out of water. I shook my dripping bathing cap to dry it before lighting a candle; my caution was equal to my impatience. The flickering light reached but a few yards; it showed me the ceiling parallel to the water, with only a thin air space between. I went on, pushing my nose up into shallow air spaces to breathe. After a hundred yards I reached a clay bank at the entrance to a vast chamber; there I could recover somewhat from my excitement, but not from the freezing cold. The ceiling rose to a height of thirty-five or forty feet, and the stream was half buried under great boulders fallen from above. The hall was adorned with beautiful stalagmite cascades. I crossed it, and started wading again.

Familiar though I was with difficult caverns, I had never known such a feeling of isolation, oppression and terror. The most commonplace accident, such as losing or wetting the matches, can be fatal underground.

Passing an enormous pillar in the brook, I faced a new and deadly-looking siphon. The water was deep, and the ceiling spiked with black, needle-pointed stalactites. Repeating a maneuver already familiar but none the less breath-taking, I dived through this siphon as well. It seemed longer than the first. I was now locked in the bosom of the shades by a double barrier. The loneliness was tremendous; I struggled against an uneasiness slowly turning to anguish. I momentarily considered retreating: luckily the spot was unsuited to even the briefest reflection. Harried by cold and apprehension, I found I might as well go ahead as to retreat. I crawled on in the stream course, in a cramped and dripping gallery which kept snuffing out my candle. Bumping and scraping against the rough stones, I emerged in a hall much vaster than the first, where an indescribable chaos of huge blocks testified to some past upheaval. I performed frantic gymnastics to restore circulation in my limbs, numbed by the glacial water. My guess about the underground river had been amply confirmed; now I began to wonder how far the succession of corridors and chambers would take me. The water flowed endlessly, now smooth and silent, now murmuring noisily on little spillways.

First making sure of my candle supply, I scrambled on across the piled-up boulders. I made my way through with some difficulty, and entered a long, monotonous water gallery. At various narrow places, where I had to wriggle between limestone columns, I thought I had reached the end of the grotto; but always my feeble light opened further perspectives. I walked sometimes in the water, sometimes on slippery, sticky clay banks, where I left my footprints as precious signposts for the way back.

The cave narrowed and I began to crouch and crawl onward, lost to all sense of time and distance, the ceiling and walls narrowing into the watercourse. Then I saw no way ahead. I had been struggling for hours to reach the end of the cave, the source of the stream, and here was an impassable bottleneck. I could only get my head and arm through the opening. There was a pool of water. I gave a shout of triumph. I felt mud and tree branches and a colony of tadpoles. The brook of Montespan Cave had left the sun, fields and woods only a short way above. Tadpoles do not venture far into underground waters: air was close by. But I could not break through to the little frogs and go back where they came from (later I climbed the hill and saw they had fallen through a fissure in the brook, impassable to man). Although I had traversed this underhill grotto, root to branch, I had no choice but to return by the way I came. This I accomplished with increasing exhaustion, with agonizing doubts of direction at forks in the cavern. I passed the worst of the two siphons only on my second attempt, having dived at too great an angle the first time. I had entered the cavern in broad daylight, under a hot sun; I came out into the world chilled to the bone, with night upon me. I had been five hours inside the earth.

In the next days I made further expeditions through the cavern, inspecting new halls, an upper level, and a maze of low galleries. I kept hoping to find some trace of prehistoric habitation, which I thought rather probable from the period when the cavern was dry. Then a rainy spell swelled the brook, and shut off the entrance, so I had to put off my investigations to the following year. My booty from the cave in 1922 was limited to one bison tooth. This discovery confirmed my opinion that the cavern had been frequented by primitive man, and I waited impatiently for next season to go on with my search.

That time I brought along a friend, Henri Godin, a great swimmer and lover of underground expeditions. The summer of 1923 was unusually dry, and the water was lower. The roof of the first siphon, a flat arch, was not wholly submerged; the top was a couple of inches out of water. We were able to see and keep our candles lit as we went to the enormous pillar which seems to bid the visitor, go no farther. Beyond was the second siphon, which I had forced with such difficulty the year before. Abandoning its arctic caresses for the moment, we selected a dry tunnel 650 feet long, behind the calcite pillar.

This gallery, never more than sixteen feet wide by thirteen high, looks magical at first sight. The walls and ceiling are covered with limestone ridges and glittering stalactites. The floor is a succession of hollows whose waved and fluted edges form a natural staircase. Each tread is filled with clear water. Beyond, a bulging and granular floor of lovely yellow recalls the madrepore coral of submarine landscapes. Then the luxuriance of form and color comes to a sudden end. Beyond a sharp bend is a dark gallery of bare rock, its floor covered with soil.

We went down the corridor in Indian file; there was no sound but the slap of our bare feet on the clay. We covered the last hundred feet flat on our stomachs, between a misshapen ceiling and a cold, muddy floor. We turned back to a place where we could almost stand upright. I chose a nook which looked promising and attacked the solid clay with a small pick. My companion viewed me with disappointed eyes, wondering whether my sudden enthusiasm for excavation would keep us long in this unattractive retreat. After each blow I had to scrape sticky clay off the pick.

Suddenly my hand gripped a hard object, and even before I had freed it from the surrounding gangue (earth or stony matter in a mineral deposit), I knew I held one of those chipped flints which sometimes make the layman smile, but which delight any archaeologist. This simple flint, barely formed, but indubitably chipped and used, proved that primitive man had lived here. Small as the find was, it started a long train of thought, and more than ever I was struck by the resemblance between the grotto of Montespan and other Pyrenean caves rich in traces of the past.

In prehistory man lived in small grottoes or in the vestibules of great caverns, but avoided the deeper mazes in fear of darkness and wild beasts. Yet almost all prehistoric engravings and paintings occur in remote and inaccessible parts of caves. Evidently magical or religious customs compelled primitive artists to create their strange works far from daylight and profane eyes.

As soon as I found that chipped flint hundreds of yards underground, this proof that primitive man had been in the gallery, I stood up to search the walls by candlelight for the rock engravings which I thought must be there. Godin, interested by now, lifted the pick, and started to dig. Suddenly I stopped. Before me was a clay statue of a bear, which the inadequate light had thus far hidden from me. In a large grotto a candle is but a glowworm in the inky gloom. I was moved as I have seldom been moved before or since. Here I saw, unchanged by the march of aeons, a sculpture which distinguished scien-

tists of all countries have since recognized as the oldest statue in the
world.

As I yelled my companion crawled over, but his less practiced
eye saw only a shapeless chunk where I indicated the form of the
animal. One after another, as I discovered them around us, I showed
him horses in relief, two big clay lions, many engravings. For more
than an hour, discovery followed discovery. On all sides we found
animals, designs, mysterious symbols, all the awe-inspiring and por-
tentous trappings of ages before the dawn of history.

The rock engravings and clay statues were from the beginning of
the Magdalenian era; they date back, according to scientifically authenticated chronologies, about twenty thousand years. There are
fifty pictures of various animals (some species extinct or emigrated),
deeply incised in the walls by flint gravers. There are thirty clay
specimens, in the round, from statues forty inches high down to small
reliefs swallowed by the drip.

Leaving the water at the great column, we came back to the
vestibule where the long procession of Magdalenian relics begins.
Large animals of that epoch are engraved in the rock; the mammoth,
the horse, the bison, the stag, the dziggetai (*Equus hemionus*, a relative of the donkey), the wild goat, the hyena, the chamois, all drawn
with the skill and striking realism one usually finds in the works of
early man; his adeptness at animal portraiture is astounding.

Certain details are striking in their originality; others interest
us because the artist's intention is so puzzling. For instance, one of
the horses has a human hand with outspread fingers, deeply im-
printed on its shoulder. Another horse was engraved with a rocky
ledge as a natural spine, while an expressive chamois head is drawn
around an oval pebble (part of the pudding-stone rock), forming the
animal's eye. Two horses' heads, face to face, are so unlike that there
can be no doubt of the artist's intent to show their difference. One has
a massive head, prominent lips, dilated nostrils, and encroaching mane
and beard, while the other has a fine, slender head, no beard, and a
thin mane. Several of the animals' bodies show wounds, arrows, and
unknown symbols. One of the bison has an oval design on its neck,
and a dziggetai has on its rump a sharp V. A hyena engraved on the
ceiling of the passage at the end of the gallery, a spot to be reached
only by crawling, measures but two inches in length. I believe this
is the smallest rock engraving ever found. Finally, among this collection of animals contemporary with the cave man, I discovered
a curious human profile with a round head, large nose, enormous

round eye, and short beard. The most fascinating room in Montespan, however, is the low-roofed one where I found the first chipped flint. Our feeble candles had not shown its expanse, which is encumbered with a whole museum of Magdalenian work. The most important is a statue of a headless bear, forty-three inches long and twenty-four inches high, standing on a pedestal, crouched in the posture of the Great Sphinx at Gaza, and facing the entrance of the grotto. The figure is monumental, befitting the animal it represents, with massive hindquarters hunched upon folded paws, and the right forepaw outstretched, clearly showing its five claws. *The statue never had a sculptured head.* The neck is finished clean and covered with age-old water concretations. The body is mutilated with many spear holes, sealed in a hard film of calcite drippings which proves its great age and contemporary abuse beyond doubt.

Between the forepaws, there lies the calcified skull of a bear cub, proportionate to the size of the model. There is a vestige of a wooden peg in the neck, where the bloody head of the cub was once mounted. The ceremonies which took place there in the bosom of the rock are almost nightmarish to imagine.

In the Hall of the Bear is a little font-shaped rock cavity, evidently a catch-all; rummaging, I found it full of chipped flints. We found on the rock at the very end of the tunnel a series of radiating engraved lines, and heaped on the floor just below, a quantity of little pencil-like stalactites.

We can follow every step; the Magdalenians scooped up the clay by the handful, drew complicated networks and curlicues with their finger-tips, and planted or hid the flints. All these little operations whose meaning still largely escapes us, have been obliterated in spots by living bear clawmarks on the floor and walls. At Montespan, in fact, there are intermingled many footprints of bears and of naked human feet. Sometimes the claw marks are on top of the footprints, sometimes the other way round; man and beast struggled for possession of the cavern. One can hardly think without shuddering of the fearful combats which must have taken place, nor ever cease to admire the courage of our distant ancestors who ventured into this lair of the wild beasts armed only with spears, stone axes, etc. The marvelous preservation of such curious remains is, of course, due to the fact that the cavern has been inaccessible from prehistoric times to the present day.

Of all the traces of a vanished age, the prints of claws and feet are perhaps the most impressive. I shall never forget my awe at first seeing these marks, intact after two hundred centuries of solitude. Such an experience repays in a moment all the hardships, risks, and countless disappointments which await those who would rob the jealous past of its secrets.

A study of the art at Montespan indicates that this is a sanctuary, one of those sacred grottoes where the sorcerers of hunting tribes in the reindeer age performed their magic ceremonies.

*

A Hindu Temple

It appears that the temple of Shree Mahalalakshmi was built after the construction of the Worli causeway. It is further said that a member of the Prabhu community was intimated in a vision by the three Holy Goddesses, Mahakali, Mahalalakshmi and Mahasaraswati to take them out from the sea. He was asked to throw a net in the creek of the sea where they would be found out to him. The result was that he found the three stone images of the Holy Goddesses from the sea. There are many stories about these Holy Goddesses. It is all a divine mystery and will remain so forever.

History of Mahalalakshmi Temple,
BREACH CANDY, BOMBAY (1761)

Laurentic Gold

BY JAMES DUGAN

*O*ne arthritic winter morning in 1955, I walked down Haymarket to Pall Mall to meet the man who salvaged twenty-five million dollars in gold from a sunken ship. He had written me from his cottage on the Isle of Wight, "I am coming up to London tomorrow for a meeting of the Physiological Society and shall be stopping at the United Service Club—G. C. C. Damant." I checked my figurative umbrella with the bemedaled commissionaire in the marble lobby of the club and asked for Captain Damant. He appeared in the grayed light—a trim man with faded red hair, halted a trifle by seventy-four years, many dark depths of ocean and the English clime. He looked a good deal like U.S. Supreme Court Justice William O. Douglas, given a couple more mountains.

Captain Damant ushered me to a corner of a big lounge and ordered tea. I was aware of a beetling oil portrait hanging overhead of a former member, an admiral in knee britches, sashes and starbursts of several orders, and saw behind his white-stockinged calves a burning city. The brass legend on the frame said he was Rear Admiral Sir George Cockburn and the city he'd burnt was Washington, D.C. I did not feel that Captain Damant had deliberately selected such a rendezvous with an American, but it introduced a cautionary note, which his first remarks bore out. "I don't like personal publicity," he said firmly. "Practically everything I know is in Sir Robert Davis' book, and, if you are interested in diving physiology, look up Professor Haldane in the *Journal of Hygiene* for 1906." I said, "I read them. I got a lot out of them. But they are by great experts and the public can't follow all of it. My idea is—" Captain Damant said, "It wasn't like this in the old Navy. No publicity, no nicknames. We hadn't a journalist in sight the seven years on the *Laurentic*. Look here," he said, "there's no use writing about what we did. It's

121

over and done with. Why don't you write about these new chaps, the frogmen, all lashed up with TV sets?"

Having burned a bit of Washington, Captain Damant drank some tea and amiably discussed diving. I put away my notebook. It was difficult to keep on the Damant epic, because he quizzed me about Cousteau's salvage of the Greek argosy off Marseille. "Those eighteen inch bronze treenails, imbedded in charred oak dowels," he would say, "how do they account for them?" While I tried to ask him, "Who introduced the idea of percentage bonuses for the divers on the *Laurentic?*"

I was able to gather his story from that talk, the record, and amusing letters he wrote on a typewriter, "with a conical roller that makes radiating lines like a radio coming out of an antenna," as he described it. "I began diving as a gunnery lieutenant in 1904," he said. "I'd gone to the *Excellent*, the principal gunnery school. Diving came within the province of the gunnery lieutenant at sea, and we were given fourteen days' diving instruction, just enough to know what we could expect from divers and the necessary precautions for safeguarding them. Few of the young officers took any interest in the subject. We did not appreciate that war would bring submarine disasters, sunken treasure ships, emergency repairs or mine clearance to increase the importance of the craft. All that naval divers expected to be used for was clearing an inlet valve or a fouled propeller, scraping barnacles off a ship's bottom or searching for something lost overboard.

"I made a dive under the instruction of Warrant Officer Andrew Catto. He was a first-class officer and an experienced practical diver. I found going under water to be a delightful experience and infinitely preferred Catto's fatherly instruction to the study of ballistics and field gun drill. I loved it. Diving amused me. In those days, we knew that pressure was dangerous; divers wore under their dress a wickerwork frame to keep the fabric expanded. We called it the crinoline. We wore red tassel caps. They were comfortable, but if one slipped off your head it was a damn nuisance. The tassel might get in the outlet valve. One time in Liverpool there was an inquest on a diver who drowned on a dock job. They asked a chap from the docks, 'What first led you to suspect the diver was in difficulty?' He replied, 'When I saw his red cap floating, I guessed something was wrong.'" Captain Damant chuckled.

One of his first salvage jobs was in 1907, on Torpedo Boat 99, sunk in 150 feet of water four miles off Torquay in the English

Channel. Damant was in command of a torpedo gunboat, HMS *Spanker*, with six divers. The boat was ill-fitted for salvage diving. Walter Trapnell, a shipwright diver, was on the bottom in a stiff tide, when the current swept his life line away and snagged it on the wreck. His air pipe was carried in the opposite direction and fouled the propeller. Trapnell's best friend, Sydney Leverett, dived to his aid, but discovered that his air pipe was too short to reach the distressed man. Leverett signaled to be pulled out. Young Lieutenant Damant had no extra pipe and no boat to send ashore for more. And a man was pinned below in nearly six atmospheres of pressure. Trapnell had already been down an hour.

There were two hand pumps aboard, one for each diver. The lieutenant acted. He had the tenders strip rubber pipe out of the idle pump and splice it on Leverett's air hose. They tapped both divers' hoses into one pump and Leverett dropped into the water. The men on deck pumped furiously to supply them both. Leverett reached Trapnell, who reached out his bare hand and squeezed his friend's. The rescue diver struggled for hours in the darkness and cold current to free Trapnell. When they hauled them up, Trapnell had been down for five and a half hours. He was barely conscious. He had lost his hearing and rambled incoherently. In a few hours he was dead.

Damant retired from the Navy at the end of his statutory hitch in 1911. He worked with Professor J. S. Haldane on mine rescue apparatus and on diving physiological experiments with his great friend, Dr. A. E. Boycott. The war hastened him back into the Navy. "I fought two wars on the retired list," he said. (In World War II he was salvage officer in the Mediterranean and Suez Canal.) "In 1914 submarines began sinking, especially enemy submarines." A U-boat sank off Dover and Damant was sent with two divers to have a look at it. "We had none of your diving ships," he said. "We went out in a rowboat." Damant dived to the shallow wreck. It was only twelve feet down to the conning tower. He found twelve mines still in the wet tubes. This type of German mine layer carried its mines outside in silos exposed to the water. He tried to open the conning tower hatch. "I couldn't get it open," he said. "I decided to try a very little gelignite to jar the hatch open. Took about seven hundred yards of circuit wire on a reel made of handspikes, a very temporary rig. Set the gelignite, fastened the priming wire and got back in the rowboat. The idea was to row to the end of the wire and set the charge off, due to the possibility that the mines would go up too. About a hundred yards off the charge went off prematurely and the mines went, too. We were not hurt, but there was a huge wave coming off the explosion. I could swim, but the two divers were in their heavy boots and would drown. The wave arrived, but our little boat rode over the crest without spilling. Bit of luck, that. There wasn't enough left of the U-boat to learn anything."

Soon after that a U-boat deposited a mine off Malin Head, Donegal, which made one of the luckiest contacts of the war—the White Star Liner *Laurentic*. She was bound from Liverpool to Halifax without passengers. After the explosion the big ship sank quickly in the bitter January Atlantic, and 354 of the crew drowned or died of exposure in the boats. It was a heavy score for a dumb mine, but the ship-building struggle would make it up and more men would come forth to sail the ships. It was only a passing incident to Damant, rushing here and there on salvages and demolition.

It was not, however, a light matter in Whitehall. Damant was called to London, where several admirals received him in a solemn atmosphere. The Director of Naval Ordnance impressed on him the high secrecy of the facts they were about to tell him. The enemy did not know his mine had taken the *Laurentic*, and more certainly did not know what had been sunk in her. Very few persons in England knew and Lieutenant Commander Damant was about to become one of this select group. The *Laurentic* carried in her second-class baggage room five million pounds in gold bars. They had been dispatched to Canada by the government to pay for war materials. The loss was a blow to the national economy. The admirals asked Damant if he thought recovery practicable. He said yes. They said, therefore, would he kindly go get the gold? He was to have all the men and equipment he wanted "*if they were available.*" "I walked on air," Captain Damant told me, "I knew just what I wanted and where to find old diving allies. It was quite a change for a dugout lieutenant commander gunner to be responsible to the Admiralty only."

It was an unprecedented thing to face. The wreck lay 120 feet down in the cold open Atlantic, in surging tides and currents. The position was swept by northers and westerly gales of the ocean and behind it was Lough Swilly which piled high with water in a storm and unpiled in high waves. The man who loved diving set about the job. There was still no proper diving tender in the Navy. The best Damant could find was a little mooring lighter, the *Volunteer*. It had no crew quarters. He rapidly made for Malin Head six weeks after the sinking. A reconnaissance diver found the *Laurentic* lying heeled sixty degrees to port. It was impossible for the heavy-footed man to walk either on her deck or high side. It was an unusual position. Most merchant wrecks land upright, given a level floor, which was the case here. The ship was intact, however, and the drop to the high starboard rail was only sixty-two feet. Moreover there was a cargo port on the high side on the same deck as the gold room. A dangling man could make this big entrance without fouling his lines on davits or top hamper. They blew the steel hatch off the cargo port and prepared to enter. But they had to step aside for a weird jailbreak from Davy Jones' locker—buoyant casks and cases, which rumbled out in a stream and soared to the surface.

The divers went in with crowbars and unpacked more debris in the passageways, including sacks of flour, most of whose contents were dry and loose, protected by the outer casing of wet flour. They blasted an iron gate which barred the corridor to the gold room, and Diver E. C. Miller phoned up to Damant, "I've got to the strong room, sir." He faced a steel door, behind which were 250 tons of gold bricks. Miller felt the door hinges and lock in total darkness, inserted his chisel and banged the steel door loose. He lumbered into the strong room, kicking wooden cases of gold, each six inches high and a foot square. Lifting one was almost beyond him. It weighed 140 pounds in air and about 85 pounds in water. Miller pushed and crawled one of the cases out to the port and slung it. He suffered an attack of bends for his overexertion, but was cured in the decompression chamber. They took £32,000 in the first two weeks' work, before a norwester drove them to shelter in the lough. They were jubilant; at this rate the "impossible" job would be cleaned up in ten weeks.

Damant kept his eye on the sea, and noted that a lot of fresh wreckage was piling up on the beach. He took a walk around the lough with the rescued boatswain of the *Laurentic*. The debris was widespread. Damant came to a litter of rubber floor tiles. "Where do those red and white tiles come from?" he asked the survivor. "Second-class smoking room, sir." Damant said, "Oh, where is that?" The bosun said, "Amidships. Three decks down." Damant knew the wreck was working to pieces. Soberly they returned to the wreck and found their big mooring buoys carried away. They staked out on new ones and lowered a man to the open port. Damant watched the pressure gauge on the compressor, which gave an estimate of depth. The needle did not stop at sixty-two feet. The diver took more air and kept going as the needle climbed. It stopped at 103 feet. The diver came up and reported that the *Laurentic* had collapsed. The steel decks had fallen into each other, so that the passageway to the gold hoard was now about eighteen inches high and blocked with tangled girders and plate. The high rail of the ship was 103 feet down. Damant suited up and dived. He landed on the starboard rail, and started along it "like a cat on a ridge of a roof," he said. He clung to the rail when rollers surged at him and moved along the rail between them. The heavy blocks on the lifeboat falls, extended sixty feet when the boats left the ship, swung at his head in the dark water. He made his way into the cargo port and started crawling head down in the shrunken passageway. Soon he came to an impasse. He had to push himself backward out of the tunnel, minding his air pipe and life line. The tunnel was full of torn steel.

There seemed two alternatives: to enlarge the collapsed passage with a series of light guncotton explosions and shore it up with pit props; or to blast through the five steel decks on top of the gold room, lifting out tons of steel to reach the treasury. Both would be long, hard jobs. The ten-week loot took on the dimensions of months. Fortunately for their morale, no one could guess that it would take seven years.

Damant chose to tunnel. As the divers burrowed, their explosions killed fish in a thousand-foot sphere. The divers slipped and fell on dead fish. Damant noticed that one species, the dogfish shark, was not affected by the explosions. Sharks snatched fish near men trying to lay precise guncotton charges; and seized floating bodies before the foam of the explosion had subsided. There were other explosions, too. Mine-laying U-boats continued to seed mines in the water round, and British sweepers harvested them, sometimes detonating mines in their drag wires. The divers were shaken up and one stunned by an explosion two miles away. They continued foot by foot, week by week, sapping their way to the gold. Then a diver reached the gold room. It was 120 feet down, the depth of the floor itself. On the phone Damant heard an excited voice announce, "The gold's not here, sir! It's gone. The deck is full of holes." Damant thought, "Evidently the gold had slid away to port and downward, dropping through decks and bulkheads as they tore asunder during the collapse of the ship." He pondered this cruel defeat of all their grand exertions.

The gold bricks were scattered deep in the debris. "It was now clear that the entry port route was too dangerous and must be abandoned," Damant said. "There were five decks above the divers, supported by nothing in particular, and settlement was still going on, as was evidenced by loud noises and tremors which occasionally disturbed the men as, in darkness far inside the wreck, they struggled to squeeze themselves onward through narrow chinks."

He decided to blast down, deck by deck, to the gold, lifting out everything to make a wide shaft. They toppled the mainmast and cleared the tangled rigging and began. A diver slung a heavy wire cable over the loose corner of a plate and the ship's winch heaved it up so the man could crawl underneath and place and wire his charge. One afternoon diver Blachford was under a plate hauled in tension. He was phoning instructions, when a shackle on the hauling cable parted. The plate snapped down on his back pinioning him with a bag of guncotton in his hand.

On deck they saw the cable whip out of the water. Damant listened intently to the phone and heard a calm voice, "Give me all the air you can, sir." Blachford thought he could relieve the weight on his back by turning his suit into an air cushion. Damant opened the valve further. "That's right, give me more yet," said the diver, "and get another diver down here as soon as possible." Diver Clear, who was half-undressed, hastily got back in his suit. The tenders bolted his helmet and handed him the bight of a new cable. Damant saw on the pressure gauge that Blachford's dress was inflated past the bursting point. Damant figured that it might have already exploded, and the trapped man was trying to pile up pressure in his helmet to keep from drowning. It was "a dilemma, not to be solved by question and answer," said Damant. "The roar of the air already passing through his helmet all but drowned his voice on the telephone, and evidently he could hear nothing of ours." He throttled the air a bit to hear what Blachford was saying. The voice said slowly and deliberately, "Give me more air." Damant decided, "Balancing the risks, it seemed wiser not to do so."

Diver Clear was by now sinking rapidly with his hand around Blachford's air pipe as a guide. He landed and bent the cable around the plate. He phoned, "Heave away, three feet." The plate creaked and rose revealing Blachford swollen like the Michelin man. His suit had not exploded. He valved off air and crawled out. On the surface Damant said, "I was afraid your dress would burst." Blachford said, "You know, sir, I never thought of *that*. I was afraid I'd break my back."

After nine months' toil the team was called away for urgent work on sunken submarines. They had recovered £800,000 in gold by then. Damant tried to scrounge a better salvage vessel and came upon HMS *Racer*, a teak-built barque on which he had served as a cadet in 1895. She had been laid up in the knacker's yard, until Sir Frederick

Young, the bustling salvage chief, exhumed a half-dozen of her type, gutted them and installed beat-up destroyer engines. Damant was very wary about his choice of Young's salvage fleet, because some of them had port engines out of twin-screw torpedo gunboats, and these propellers turned the wrong way. (Later, another of Sir Frederick's conversions broke up on the rocks near the Lough Swilly. Damant's people boarded the sinking hulk and hove out her priceless pumps.)

Damant found the *Laurentic* little changed in 1919, but the gold mine soon petered out. Apparently the lode had burst out in two piles and the largest part was somewhere else. The shaft had been driven down through the well deck, or depressed main deck which was overhung by the public rooms of the liner. These had not collapsed, but as the excavation deepened the saloons threatened to fall in on the divers. "So long as gold was coming to hand I was very reluctant, however, to break off work for the purpose of dealing with these superstructures," said Damant. When they started to work the next spring, 1920, they found the top deck had been swept into the hole. The crater was sealed off with steel and plank decking, and underneath it was a compacted mass of rubbish, hundreds of smashed saloon chairs, mattresses, carpets, bedsprings, bathtubs, tiles and paneling. Waterlogged debris of furniture was washing to and fro, and it settled into a fresh excavation overnight. The mess was almost like cement, for now the sea was sweeping sand and pebbles into the shattered *Laurentic*.

They went to work to clear the crater. Damant tried a powerful twelve-inch suction pipe, but it clogged on mattresses and rugs. The only way left was the most primitive one of pulling the junk out by hand. The divers became ragpickers. They went down with rubbish sacks around their necks and fire hoses to loosen the mess. In the dark swirling water, they delved for gold with their bare hands. They could not feel a gold bar through gloves. They wore their fingernails to stumps and their finger-tips raw. The extra exertion brought queer cases of bends. A man who had screwed a series of shackle pins knew he would have bends in his forearm.

One day Miller was in the decompression chamber when Commander Damant began to see double, an hour after a dive. His sight grew worse and a severe headache came. He waited outside the chamber for Miller to finish decompression. The diver looked out the port and saw his chief in distress. Miller still had forty minutes to go on his cure, but he blew off his pressure, opened the door and admitted Damant. Compressed air whistled them into depth pressure and

Damant's eyes cleared. Miller's bends reappeared, owing to his gallant interruption. He was in pain in the chamber for six and a half hours, with Damant staying inside to aid him. At 1:30 A.M. with a new dawn of diving coming up, the chief diver begged Damant to blow off pressure so the master could get some sleep. Miller's seizure lasted far into the next day.

At the end of four years' work they had only a fraction of the gold. The war was long since over and England's life did not depend on blind men grinding their fingertips off in the black icy water. But they carried on.

The salvage began as duty. The man who brought up the largest single haul—$225,000—had been given fifty cigarettes. Damant accrued a morale problem with men risking their lives in years of painful work to bring up gold for somebody else. The government decided to give the divers one-eighth of a cent bonus on each dollar recovered. It produced lust for gold among the gropers. Treasure hunter Light was one day working head down between steeply slanted plates with his life line and air pipe tied off out of harm's way on a projection forty feet off. He saw a gold bar sticking out of the sand below him. He stretched far down to grab it. The air in his suit rushed to the legs and ballooned him. He soared out feet first and came to a stop forty feet up on the end of his tether, grotesquely inflated. His sleeves stood straight out from his shoulders so stiffly that he could not move his arms to valve air. This might have seemed slightly droll, since his relief man was almost due, except that water in his suit drained off into his helmet and rose over his scalp, promising to drown him. Light phoned Damant about the situation. Damant grabbed another phone and called Blachford, who was decompressing thirty feet down. Blachford slid down Light's lines to where they were tied off and severed them. Light rocketed feet first to the surface, was fished out and clamped into the recompression chamber. Blachford returned to thirty feet and resumed stage decompression.

The salvage of the *Laurentic* was completed in 1924 after five thousand dives in seven years. The ragpickers recovered all but 25 of the 3,211 gold bricks, at a salvage cost of less than 3 per cent. Their commander brought them through without the loss of a man or serious injury. The divers received decorations and Damant was made captain and retired for a second time.

I asked Captain Damant if he had taken any souvenirs from the *Laurentic*. He replied, "I found a groat of the time of Edward First.

Part of someone's private coin collection, I suppose. I was allowed to keep it." He remarked, "Today I would do this business of gold salvage differently. You should leave it down there as long as you can. It gets more valuable. Then get it up and send it to America." He grinned. "I'm not talking about ancient treasure wrecks. The only gold worth going after is in a newly sunk ship, when the government shows you the bill of lading and where the strong room is. Vigo, Navarino and what do they call that one in the west of Scotland, the Tobermory galleon? How does anyone know there is any treasure there?"

The man who brought up five million pounds in gold did not believe in treasure under the sea.

*

Underwater Demolition Team: Fifth Century B.C.

There was some skirmishing in the harbor around the palisades the Syracusans had planted in the sea so that their ships could not be reached by the enemy. The Athenians sent a 250-ton ship with wooden towers to pull up the palisades or they dived and sawed through them underwater, at length destroying most of the stakes. There were some stakes out of sight in the water, the most dangerous of all, and these were sawn off by hired divers.

Thucydides, SIEGE OF SYRACUSE

Several years ago the editors spent a month on Aldabra, a magical coral atoll in the Indian Ocean, studying the barrier reef, the channels into the great lagoon, and the extraordinary bird and reptile life of the island. In the mangrove jungles of the lagoon, sharks' fins protrude inches below perching frigate birds and false cuckoos, and on the singular upraised dead coral reefs there are possibly a half-million giant land tortoises, and thousands of feral goats. There are no seasons on balmy Aldabra, the island that time forgot, except for the nine islanders' expectation of the annual supply boat and the mating advent of the sea turtles. We were reminded of Aldabra by reading an account by an Australian, William Travis, of his expedition to the atoll to harvest the green sea snail, a valuable pearl shell.

Beyond the Reefs

BY WILLIAM TRAVIS

*E*very day we divers met more and more turtles underwater, for by now the breeding season was well advanced and fresh arrivals were constantly increasing the numbers that spent the daylight hours roaming the reefs in search of a mate. On seeing us the amorous and perhaps shortsighted creatures would hastily swim right up, hoping to find a new spouse, but in this they were disappointed and would content themselves with circling us wistfully at a few yards range.

If one let one's arms hang downward and outward limply in the water, kicking one's legs in parody of a turtle's movements, the lusty males would rush up with obvious intent, completely ignoring one's evident lack of turtle attributes, and press home their suit to the point where one was forced to flee to the sanctuary of the dinghy. Conrad, in particular, having a peculiarly graceless and froglike movement in the water, was always being chased and on one occasion we were all reduced to hysterics by his being "blockaded" in his boat by an enormous bull, who must have been very shortsighted since he continually tried to embrace the youth each time he entered the water! In deference to this gallantry we did not harpoon the old bachelor but left him to find a more suitable mate. The episode considerably shook Conrad, who, for a long time after, could be made to swim for his life without a backward glance by someone shouting, "Conrad! Conrad! *Tortue derrière où!*"

One thing that was very noticeable was the number of turtles of either sex who were missing flippers, usually one of the hind ones. These, from the scars remaining, had obviously been bitten off by sharks and many of them were freshly wounded. Once, I even saw a female who had lost both rear flippers and one of her front ones as well, but she got along remarkably fast, scooping at the water with her remaining flipper and craning her neck far to one side out of her shell to offset the uneven thrust. Of all meat, sharks prefer turtle and a hook baited with the flesh or offal of this reptile will succeed when all else has failed and the brutes ignore all other lures.

Toward the end of each day the turtles would hide themselves a way under ledges of coral or shelves of rock, within caves or crevices, in an effort to find safety from the night-prowling Tigers, Hammerheads and other such marauders. Only at full moon would the turtles continue with their love-making throughout the night and then only within the comparative safety of shallow water. Even this did not always provide the necessary security as we ourselves saw.

One evening Ravile and Ton Pierre, bored and wanting a change, borrowed my electric lantern and set off in a dinghy to scour the sea bed to see if they could find any turtles at rest in the shallow water that lay between the fringing reef and the shore. Paddling silently along, the beam of the torch sweeping the sand floor beneath the bows, they heard a violent commotion in the water not very far off. A turtle was thrashing wildly about, somewhere out there in the darkness. Perhaps a mating pair! Discarding all idea of stealth they rowed hard toward the noise, which was now close by the shore.

Running the boat up onto the sand, Ravile carrying the torch and Ton Pierre the harpoon, they ran along the beach toward the floundering. In the beam of light they saw a turtle half in and half out of the water, struggling desperately to free itself from something that had hold of it, something whose back was awash and whose large dorsal fin rose three or more feet into the air! Not knowing quite what to do, they stopped and at the same instant the turtle tore free and scrambled madly up the sandy ramp that led up the beach. It was almost clear when the Tiger Shark surged up after it, jaws champing futilely behind its fast escaping prey. Such was the fury of the brute that by lashing the shallows into foam with his powerful tail it succeeded in driving its heavy bulk right out of the water, up on the ridge of sand, where the weight of its body was supported by the two pectoral fins splayed out like stunted arms on either side of its gross torso.

In doing so it undermined the soft sand, causing the turtle to slide backward down the slope right into the horrible armed mouth. The shark lunged again and this time its teeth did not close on the empty air but on that mangled hind flipper, this time higher up. As the ugly monster squirmed obscenely in the sand in an effort to wriggle back into the water, Ravile and Ton Pierre closed in. Ravile dropped his torch on the sand so that its beam shone downward along the sloping ground directly at the turtle and into the cold gleaming eyes of the Tiger Shark beyond. He then grabbed the turtle by its two front flippers in an effort to pull the poor creature free. At the same time Ton Pierre reversed his harpoon and beat the Tiger on its upturned snout. Nothing coming of this, he proceeded to jab the butt into the beast's eye which continued to stare at him coldly and without any expression whatsoever until he had reduced it to a sightless white cavity. Only then did the shark let go and then only to turn and snap ineffectively at the harpoon haft. Finally, with a terrific muscular contraction, the brute succeeded in swinging round and half-slid, half-wallowed back into the sea, covering the two fishermen with sand and drenching them with water under the furious lashings of its tail. There was a swirl, a few wavelets lapped the edge of the sandbank and then it was gone into the night.

*

The Bait

When thou wilt swim in that live bath,
Each fish, which every channel hath,
Will amourously to thee swim,
Gladder to catch thee, than thou him.

John Donne

The first undersea-boat attack in the history of warfare came in August, 1776, in New York Harbor when a Yankee craft called the Turtle *assailed Admiral Lord Richard Howe's flagship, HMS Eagle. The one-man submarine was designed and built by David Bushnell, who conceived the idea while a student at Yale. After his* Turtle *was frustrated, Bushnell served in the Continental Army sappers until 1783, then went to France trying to get backing for a submarine. He failed and went back to Warrenton, Georgia, and practiced medicine under the name of Dr. Bush. The universally inquisitive Thomas Jefferson, then American minister in Paris, wanted to know all about the* Turtle, *and this is part of the inventor's reply.*

Mr. Jefferson Hears
About the First Submarine Attack

STAMFORD IN CONNECTICUT Oct. 13th 1787

Sir:

In the latter part of the year 1785, I received a Letter from Colonel David Humphreys, and soon after, another from Doctor Ezra Stiles, President of Yale College in Connecticut, informing me that Your Excellency desired an account of my submarine Vessel, and the Experiments which I had made.

Doctor Stiles, in his letter to me, transcribed from yours the following, "If he (Bushnell) thought proper to communicate it, I would engage never to disclose it, unless I could find an opportunity of doing it for the Benefit." In answer to this declaration, I shall submit the disclosure of it entirely to your Excellency, to do as you shall think proper; and beg leave to return you my sincere thanks for your generous intentions.

The external shape of the Submarine Vessel bore some resemblance to two upper tortoise shells of equal size, joined together; the place of entrance into the Vessel being represented by the opening, made by the swell of the shells at the head of the animal. The inside was

134

capable of containing the Operator, and air, sufficient to supply him thirty minutes without receiving fresh air. At the bottom, opposite to the entrance, was fixed a quantity of lead for ballast. At one edge, which was directly before the operator, who sat upright, was an oar, for rowing forward or backward. At the other edge was a rudder for steering. An aperture, at the bottom, with its valve, was designed to admit water, for the purpose of descending; and two brass forcing pumps served to eject the water within, when necessary for ascending. At the top, there was likewise an oar, for ascending or descending, or continuing at any particular depth. A Watergage or Barometer determined the depth of descent, a compass directed the course, and a ventilator within supplied the Vessel with fresh air, when on the surface.

In the forepart of the brim of the Crown of the Submarine Vessel, was a socket, and an iron tube passing through the socket; the tube stood upright, and could slide up and down in the socket six inches: at the top of the tube, was a woodscrew fixed by means of a rod, which passed through the tube, and screwed the Woodscrew fast upon the top of the tube: by pushing the Woodscrew up against the bottom of a Ship, and turning it at the same time, it would enter the planks; driving would answer the same purpose; when the Woodscrew was firmly fixed it could be cast off, by unscrewing the rod, which fastened it upon the top of the tube.

Behind the Submarine Vessel was a place, above the rudder, for carrying a large Powder Magazine; this was made of two pieces of oak timber, large enough, when hollowed out, to contain one hundred and fifty pounds of Powder, with the apparatus used in firing it, and was secured in its place by a screw, turned by the operator. A strong piece of rope extended from the magazine to the Woodscrew abovementioned, and was fastened to both. When the Woodscrew was fixed, and to be cast off from its tube, the Magazine was to be cast off likewise by unscrewing it, leaving it hanging to the Woodscrew: it was lighter than the water that it might rise up against the object to which the Woodscrew and itself were fastened.

Within the Magazine, was an apparatus, constructed to run any proposed length of time under twelve hours; when it had run out its time, it unpinioned a strong lock resembling a gun lock, which gave fire to the powder. This apparatus was to be pinioned, that it could not possibly move until, by casting off the Magazine from the Vessel, it was set in motion.

The skilful operator could swim so low on the surface of the water, as to approach very near a Ship, in the Night, without fear of being discovered, and might, if he chose, approach the stem or stern, above water, with very little danger. He could sink very quick, keep at any depth he pleased, and row a great distance, in any direction he desired without coming to the surface; and when he rose to the surface, he could soon obtain a fresh supply of air, when, if necessary, he might descend again and pursue his course.

The above Vessel, Magazine, etc. were projected in the year of 1771 but not completed until 1776. In the first essays with the Submarine Vessel, I took care to prove its strength to sustain the great pressure of the incumbent water when sunk deep, before I trusted any person to go under water without having a strong piece of rigging made fast to it, until I found him well acquainted with the operation necessary for his safety. After that, I made him descend and continue at particular depths, without rising or sinking, now by the compass, approach a vessel, go under her and fix the Woodscrew into her bottom, etc., until I thought him sufficiently expert to put my design into execution.

I found agreeably to my expectations that it required many trials to make a person of common ingenuity, a skilful operator. The first I employed was very ingenious and made himself master of the business [the inventor's brother, Ezra—Ed.], but was taken sick in the campaign of 1776, at New York, before he had an opportunity to make use of his skill, and never recovered his health sufficiently afterwards.

After various attempts to find an operator to my wish, I sent one [Sergeant Ezra Lee—Ed.] who appeared more expert than the rest, from New York to a fifty gun ship lying not far from Governor's Island. He went under the ship and attempted to fix the Woodscrew into her bottom, but struck, as he supposes, a bar of iron, which passes from the rudder hinge and is under the ship's quarter. Had he moved a few inches, which he might have done without rowing, I have no doubt, but he would have found wood, where he might have fixed the Screw; or if the ship were sheathed with copper, he might easily have pierced it: but not being skilled in the management of the Vessel, in attempting to move to another place, he lost the Ship. After seeking her in vain, for some time, he rowed some distance, and rose to the surface of the water, but found daylight had advanced so far, that he durst not renew the attempt.

He says that he could easily have fastened the Magazine under the stern of the ship, above water, as he rowed up to the stern, and touched it, before he descended. Had he fastened it there, the explosion of one hundred and fifty pounds of powder, must have been fatal to the ship. In his return from the Ship to N. York, he passed near Governor's Island, and thought he was discovered by the enemy, on the Island; being in haste to avoid the danger he feared, he cast off the magazine, as he imagined it retarded him, in the swell, which was very considerable. After the magazine had been cast off, one hour, the time the internal apparatus was set to run, it blew up with great violence.

Afterwards there were two attempts made in Hudson's River above the City, but they effected nothing. One of them was by the aforementioned person. In going towards the Ship, he lost sight of her, and went a great distance beyond her, before he found her; when he arrived, the tide ran so strong, that as he descended under water, for the ship's bottom, it swept him away. Soon after this, the Enemy went up the river, and pursued the boat which had the Submarine Vessel on board, and sunk it with their shot. After I recovered the Vessel, I found it impossible, at that time, to prosecute the design any farther. I had been in a bad state of health from the beginning of my undertaking, and was now very unwell; the situation of public affairs was such that I despaired of obtaining the public attention, and the assistance necessary. I was unable to support myself, and the persons I must have employed, had I proceeded. Besides I found it absolutely necessary that the operator should acquire more skill in the management of the Vessel, before I could expect success; which would have taken up some time, and made no small additional expense. I therefore gave over the pursuit, for that time, and waited for more favorable opportunity which never arrived.

With the most respectful sentiments I am your Excellency's most obedient and most humble servant,

David Bushnell

Both German and Japanese submariners suffered from poor high command decisions in the Second World War. Hitler was at one time so frightened of Allied landings in Norway that he stopped the successful U-boat campaign in the Atlantic and sent the boats to guard Norway. This is an example of what Japanese undersea warriors had to put up with from Tokyo. Commander Hashimoto is guilty of literary sin almost as heinous: what in the devil happened to the gallant officer he leaves hanging one-handed from the rail of the American boat, waving his sword?

Supplying Guadalcanal

BY MOCHITSURA HASHIMOTO

In July, 1942, I was given command of the submarine *RO.31* attached to the Yokosuka Command. We were busily engaged in training and in urgent trials and research, from which there was no respite. One day a military truck loaded with bags of rice suddenly appeared at the wharf near the Naval Port, bringing a number of naval and military officials who requested us to try out firing bags of rice from the torpedo tubes! The situation at Guadalcanal Island made it dangerous for our submarines to hand over supplies when surfaced, so the idea was to eject them from the tubes when submerged.

We tried all sorts of schemes. Biscuit boxes were fired, but about a third of them were broken by the projections inside the torpedo tube and the all-too-precious rice was being scattered all over Tokyo Bay. Then we had the idea of stacking rice in rubber containers on deck and fitting a device to release them from inside the boat while submerged. Finally we tried firing the rice in a wooden container shaped like a torpedo, but the container broke up and likewise the bags of rice.

At the end of the trials the naval C.-in-C. at Yokosuka was obviously very moved when he spoke to us about the sorry plight of the garrison at Guadalcanal and the necessity for attempting such fantastic measures.

After the American attack on Guadalcanal on August 7, 1942, supplies had to be brought in by destroyers and submarines owing to the

138

continued heavy losses in other surface vessels occasioned by the
enemy's air superiority and our lack of airfields. In fact, after our
defeat in the third general attack, there was no hope of recovering
the aerodrome, and the garrison had to rely on submarines for supplies.
A conference was held at Truk on board the submarine fleet flagship
to discuss matters. All the senior officers of units and commanding
officers of submarines were opposed to a plan which would virtually send the boats to their death merely for the sake of supply-
landing, a purpose divorced from the normal functions of a submarine. However, the admiral commanding the submarine fleet announced that it was the Imperial command that the troops on Guadalcanal Island were to be supplied at all costs. No further dissenting
voices were heard. Thus our submarines became carriers, and the
great majority, at that time dispersed patrolling the high seas, the
Pacific, the Indian Ocean and the Australian waters, in search of
targets in the shape of warships and merchant vessels, were recalled
to the confined waters around Guadalcanal Island and were relegated
to lying in wait, submerged, for enemy patrol craft and submarines.
Each submarine had one gun removed and was left with only two
torpedo tubes, a modification which, while giving them more space
for carrying provisions, greatly reduced their offensive power.

Supplies were to be taken on at the port of Buin on Bougainville
Island and landed at Kaminpo on Guadalcanal Island, one submarine
making this trip each day. Supplies were to be unloaded mainly
in the dark hours after sunset.

From November, 1942, to early February, 1943, when Guadalcanal Island was finally evacuated, this transport scheme was carried
out in the face of heavy losses. By January, 1943, there were about
twenty submarines engaged on supply duties, including most of the
latest types.

As time passed, progress was made in the method of transport.
At first the packages were passed by hand from the inside of the
submarine and transferred to motorboats. Then the rice was packed
in rubber bags secured to the upper deck, but they got soaked with
water, so drums were used instead.

If it was difficult to surface at the appointed landing point, the
drums were released and rose to the surface while the submarine
remained submerged. Freight "tubes" were adopted. They resembled a motor landing craft fitted with a deck; two torpedoes were used
for motive power, producing a speed of three knots. Its radius of
action was about four thousand yards and it could carry about two
tons of supplies. It was piloted by one man who embarked prior to

launching, and could be released from a submerged submarine.

There was one other method used in supplying Guadalcanal. This was a tanker-like submarine which was towed and which submerged with the towing submarine. This craft could carry fifty tons of goods but in practice it was very little used. As enemy strength gradually improved our successes correspondingly diminished. However, there was no alternative and these methods of supply continued until the end.

Submarine *I.1*, under a new captain, Lieutenant Commander Sakamoto, left Rabaul on January 26 in preparation for a night supply run to Guadalcanal three days later. At this period supplies were being delivered every two days: one submarine was able to provide the land force of thirty thousand men with two days' supplies. The round trip took four days. From Bougainville onward, the voyage was made submerged both by day and by night, only surfacing for about four hours to charge the batteries. The landing point was Kaminpo.

The normal practice was for the submarine to enter the anchorage at dusk with conning tower awash and only proceed inside the reef after a careful inspection. On this occasion, *I.1* was proceeding as usual and had just raised her periscope at the entrance when she was attacked from astern by an American torpedo boat firing machine guns and torpedoes from a range of about two thousand yards.

Sakamoto at once abandoned the idea of entering the reef, and without waiting to lower the periscope, altered course and gave the order "Ninety feet," in a desperate effort to escape. He was too late, and depth charges exploded almost immediately overhead. The inside of the boat was suddenly pitch-dark and the concussion was terrific. The main switch on the switchboard went flying and all the motors stopped. Neither the rudders nor pumps would work. The high-pressure air pipes were broken, the batteries were out of action and confusion reigned in the control room. The boat, with a bow-down angle of forty-five degrees was plunging to the bottom out of control. Every loose piece of equipment and cargo went tumbling forward as the downward plunge continued. Sakamoto ordered "full astern" on the main motors and the main ballast tanks to be blown. The safe diving depth for *I.1* was 190 feet, but the depth gauge was hopelessly inaccurate after the depth-charging and was registering 450 feet. Suddenly, the man at the after hydroplanes, who was bracing himself for the moment when the boat would cave in owing to water pressure, reported that the needle of the depth gauge was stationary. Then the boat began to rise. Almost simultaneously came the report "Water coming into the torpedo compartment." All the provisions had slid to the forward part of the submarine which was becoming increasingly heavy. Then she broke surface. She went down again but was so heavy forward that it was impossible to proceed submerged. Then the boat appeared to come to rest on the bottom with her bow down at a very steep angle.

The time had come to take the final step. With a struggle the boat was brought to the surface and fire opened on the destroyers and torpedo boats. After only four or five rounds had been fired enemy machine-gun fire swept the submarine's bridge and wiped out everyone except the navigator, who came rushing down the ladder into the control room shouting "Swords—swords!" This was the first news of the situation on deck. The first lieutenant dashed up to the bridge, sword in hand, and found the gun crew all killed and no trace of the captain. He immediately summoned the reserve gun crew and, peering through the gathering darkness, discerned an enemy torpedo boat almost alongside—aft on the port side—why wasn't she firing?

The submarine had left Rabaul with a defective port engine and could only make twelve knots using the starboard engine alone. Consequently the steering was difficult and at this juncture, she suddenly swung around to port, close to the enemy boat. The navigator, who was an expert in swordsmanship, tried to leap aboard the enemy torpedo boat, sword in hand, but the rail being high, he was left hanging on the rail in mid-air by one hand and was unable to pull himself aboard. Then the craft swung apart again.

Once more the enemy opened fire. There seemed to be three or four enemy ships. Soon the petrol in the motor landing craft, which was carried on the after part of the submarine, caught alight. In this glare, as if from a gigantic torch, the attacking ships could probably see the submarine quite plainly, but she could see nothing of them. Meanwhile the enemy switched on his searchlights and two of the submarine chasers opened fire with their 5-cm. guns. The boat was also being fired on by what seemed to be 20-mm. machine guns. There seemed to be two torpedo boats but it was difficult to see clearly. *I.1* was still firing but the enemy came round astern and the submarine's gun could not train in that direction. She had removed one gun in order to carry the motor landing craft, so she was at a serious disadvantage. The submarine was firing at the torpedo boat astern with tracer machine gun and rifle, but not getting many hits. On the other hand the submarine, which was well lit up, was being repeatedly hit, particularly in the conning tower, which was holed again and again by the enemy's 5-cm. guns. The steering gear broke down so that hand steering was necessary: the boat was completely out of control.

The torpedo boat fired three torpedoes; fortunately all three missed. While the absorbed first lieutenant was roaring out orders, the submarine's 14-cm. gun scored a hit on the enemy submarine chaser and sank her amid cries of exultation from the submarine's crew. Now one of the enemy torpedo boats launched a sudden attack from the starboard side and the submarine countered with rifle fire. The enemy's fire seemed to weaken—perhaps she had exhausted her ammunition. She came on, and with a crash rammed with the submarine, got free and made off.

I.1 was on the point of sinking, having fought under extreme difficulty an hour and a half. Her tanks were badly holed. The first lieutenant decided to run her aground and accordingly turned her head toward the shore. At the very instant the boat grounded, the stern sank, leaving the bow sticking up out of the water, and she settled on the bottom with a big list to port. The survivors immediately abandoned ship and landed, but those inside the boat failed to escape owing to the sudden inrush of water; over thirty dead were left behind. The remaining fifty assembled on shore, their only weapons two swords and three rifles.

The fact that submarine *I.1* kept afloat for so long after being badly holed was remarkable. It was due to the continued operation of the low-pressure discharge pump, a pump which in the ordinary course of events was only used for periods of fifteen minutes, otherwise it would soon run "hot."

When the sinking of the submarine appeared imminent, preparations were made to destroy secret books, but only a few were actually destroyed. If they had been burnt ashore, the rising smoke would have attracted enemy aircraft, so they were torn into shreds and buried in the sand. However, there was a grave risk that the remainder, left in the submarine, might fall into the hands of the enemy and orders were issued to secure their effective destruction. Eventually three men, under an officer, waded into the sea under cover of darkness and sank the protruding parts of the submarine by explosive charges and were afterward withdrawn by destroyer. Nevertheless another submarine was ordered to complete the destruction of *I.1* to ensure that the secret papers should not be recovered by the enemy. Our own aircraft too were ordered to complete the destruction of the boat, but they were unable to detect the submerged remains.

In 1955 a young American, John Potter, Jr., and a group of French, English, Belgian and American youths, sought the famous sunken galleons in Vigo Bay, sunk in 1702 in a savage raid for gold by an Anglo-Dutch fleet. Undeterred by the fact that seventy-odd salvage expeditions had worked there before them, Potter's lighthearted lads proceeded to learn the lessons of underwater archaeology the hard way, by trial and error. In the course of their education, they became adept at documentary research and learned a good deal about the Celtic people of Galicia. All of this is set forth in Potter's high-spirited book, Treasure Divers of Vigo Bay. *If they never find their treasure, the gallant divers have accomplished two more important things—they have become experienced underwater technicians and they have related free diving to the community in which they found themselves. One of their voluntary services was to clear river-bed snags which had been stealing fishermen's nets for fifty years and another was the deed described next.*

Cadavers

BY JOHN S. POTTER, JR.

On the stormy morning of November 10, 1957, at low tide, the drowned and battered bodies of two seamen were found at the seaward entrance of the passage between the Cies Islands, where they had been thrown up by waves onto the rocks. Simultaneously a chilling report spread among the closely related families of Moana, on the north shore of Vigo Bay. One of their fishing ships was missing at sea. Aboard were twenty-five men and boys—fathers and sons from nearly every home in the little community.

Newspaper headlines of the next day confirmed the terrible news: "Consternation Throughout the Bay over the Catastrophe of the *Ave del Mar*—1,000 people affected by the great tragedy." Sometime during the night of the ninth, the twenty-ton fishing ship, groping her way back to port through fog and rain, had struck the reefs off Point Galera and been dashed to pieces by heavy seas. Aside from some wood splinters and the two bodies there was no trace of her nor her crew. The annual fiesta of Moana had just begun. Sounds

143

of laughter and fireworks abruptly changed into hysterical weeping of widows as a tide of grief rolled over the stunned, bereaved pueblo.

Two helmet divers were sent out to look for the bodies of the victims. They dropped below the surface from their lines and air hoses, landing on a sea bed of jagged rock peaks and twisting ravines, hidden under a submarine jungle of seaweed, undulating in the strong swells. Limited in mobility over the terrain by their cumbersome equipment, they could only rise from the weeds and drop into new spots, again and again, through manipulation of the air volume within their suits. After two days of futile searching they gave up without having found a piece of wreckage.

On the thirteenth a black-bordered death notice appeared in the morning paper, listing the names of the twenty-five victims and requesting friends and associates to pray for their souls. On the following day a photograph of the *Dios te Guarde,* identified as the barge of the *hombres-ranas* (frogmen), was displayed alongside the headline "200,000 Soviet Troops Enter Hungary." Underneath was the caption, *"Frogmen Will Search for the Bodies."*

Our free divers were working a little to the south of Carrumeiro when an unfamiliar fishing launch approached, flag at half-mast. On the stern were two wooden coffins. A rope was thrown to the *Dios te Guarde.* From the launch stepped a short, pale-faced man, dressed entirely in black. He introduced himself: "I am the owner of the *Ave del Mar,* and the father of her captain." In a trembling, exhausted voice, repeating himself frequently, he told our team that he had been in the Cies Islands for three days and nights without sleep, waiting for the ocean to return the body of his son and the other crew members, nearly all of whom were his cousins or nephews. Offering two thousand pesetas for each body that we could recover, he begged, "Won't you help me find my son?"

Robert Stenuit, Florent Ramaugé and John Nathan were moved by the pathetic plea. Turning down the remunerative offer, they agreed immediately. Within an hour the *Dios te Guarde* was going out through the Freo de la Porta—the passage between the two principal Cies Islands. On the ocean end a strange and mildly disagreeable odor was noticed in the air. It grew stronger as the estimated site of the shipwreck was reached. Rough waves were breaking against the nearby rocks, and a slight brownish tinge was visible in the spume. Our local companion, Faustino Otero Lino, stared at the spray for a few moments, then shuddered. "Corpse soup," he muttered.

Robert made the first dive, reaching bottom at fifty feet. The visibility was surprisingly good, but the familiar thick blanket of seaweed lay over the rocks, covering all but a few bare pinnacles. Robert spotted a shredded fishing net tangled on one of these. Then he encountered a splintered wood board. There was no other sign of the boat. Florent and Johnny dived after him and found scattered pieces of wreckage. When they had completed their searches neither wreck nor bodies had been located.

For the following two days stormy weather prevented the *Dios te Guarde* from reaching this dangerous site. Then the wind and waves subsided, and a search pattern was set up off the reefs, with the divers combing the bottom at forty-foot intervals. Florent had made six parallel runs when he came across a fuel tank. On the succeeding dive Robert discovered a water tank jammed into a ravine and nearby a broken section of the propeller shaft. A submarine cliff jutted up on the shoreward side. Reasoning that this would halt the drift of ocean-impelled wreckage, he followed its base to a sunken, sand-floored arena. It was strewn with broken remnants of the *Ave del Mar*—the rudder, twisted iron fragments, wood splinters, and several fishing boots.

A pale apparition caught his eye. Swimming closer, Robert found himself hovering over an alabaster-white cadaver, stripped of clothing, moving gently with the wave motions on the sand. His arms were outstretched limply from a grotesquely swollen trunk, and a faceless ivory skull, with shreds of cheek skin waving gently around hollow eye sockets, grinned up at him. Two more cadavers lay on the sand. Swimming farther, Robert came across another body that looked tiny even in the magnified submarine world. It was that of the ship's boy, only fourteen. He was lying on his back, partly cloaked in sea-weed, little arms placed in a cross over his chest. On his sea-floor bed, the child seemed resting in peaceful slumber. When he had finished his tour, Robert had counted eleven bodies. Naked, or clothed in blue trousers and here and there a plaid shirt, the crew had obviously been asleep at the moment of the shipwreck. He had still not found the *Ave del Mar* and wondered why the corpses had assembled in this place. Then he realized that it was the center of an eddy. The currents were assembling here material and bodies which had been swept from the shattered wreck. Robert let himself rise a few yards over the sand and gazed down through the unusually clear water, contemplating the gruesome task at hand. Then he returned to the surface. On the *Dios te Guarde* he told the others, "I have counted eleven."

"Eleven what?"

"Bodies."

"What do they look like?"

"White like marble," replied Robert. "Like statues, only they move sometimes, very small, like children asleep. Some are not entire—the sea has not been gentle with them." Shouts crossed the water to the nearby fishing launch from Moana, crowded with close relatives of the victims. They seemed relieved to hear the news but gave no other sign of emotion.

Robert returned to the submarine graveyard with Florent and Johnny, carrying two lengths of rope. While Johnny searched for the missing ship Robert and Florent gingerly approached the cadavers, then separated, each selecting a group to string together on his rope. The flesh felt soft, and involuntary shudders ran through the divers as they lifted weightless bodies, passing the rope under their arms and knotting it in front.

After attaching four corpses Robert found that the rope would not reach the others, which were some distance away. He tugged at the ones which he had tied. They jumped up from the sand. Swimming hard, Robert pulled his ghastly train across the bottom, watching the cadavers rise to their feet and follow him, arms and legs waving in a macabre dance. He stopped at the next group and bent over the closest body. A footless leg brushed against his cheek. Turning, he saw the first four corpses, still advancing under their momentum, prancing overhead. As quickly as he could he completed the job, trying to avoid looking more than necessary at his cargo. When he swam back to the surface he trailed behind him the remains of eight lifeless fishermen from the *Ave del Mar*.

Florent was on the barge, and his salvage of three corpses floated in the water near the diving ladder. Johnny had found the sunken ship, which had been battered into kindling wood, and attached a sling to the motor, with which to raise it later. A Spanish naval launch from Vigo had arrived on the scene. Faustino, King-of-the-Grapes, and the divers climbed aboard to help load the corpses. There was muttering among the navy crew, then the petty officer told King-of-the-Grapes that the bodies would have to be loaded on the *Dios te Guarde*—that our boat should return them to Moana. They didn't want the navy craft smelling from the bodies. Johnny exploded, "For Christ's sake, what about *our* boat? We brought them up. The least they can do . . ." Turning to Faustino he said angrily, "Tell them that if they want the bodies they'll have to take them back themselves. We'll help with the loading."

The navy crew withdrew into a huddle at the bow of their launch while Faustino, Juan, and King-of-the-Grapes lifted the corpses, smelling of death, from the water and stacked them on the poop. Now they were inert, no longer possessed of their leisurely, wave-given movements. As the last of the bodies were piled on the deck the sound of vomiting was heard from the bow.

On the following day, which was Sunday, a solemn mass interment took place in the Moana cemetery. The entire community, wearing black, had assembled, as well as government and naval officials from Vigo and Pontevedra. Beneath the visible manifestation of heartache in the quietly sobbing women and grim-faced men ran an undercurrent of gratitude to the *hombres-ranas* for the return of the eleven bodies being laid to rest. These deeply religious people attached a profound importance to burial of their dead under the sacred soil of a cemetery blessed by the representative of God. Here, through the ages, their departed kinsmen would receive the benefit of future special orations. And on the resurrection before the final judgment they could rise in their entirety to face their Maker. Souls lost at sea seemed deprived, in some intangible respect, of the full benedictions of those over whose mortal remains the parochial priest could intone the reverential *"Pro Fidelibus Defunctis."*

During succeeding weeks a subtle change was noted in the attitude of people who addressed the members of our team. Beneath the joking "And the water? Isn't it cold?" ran a thread of new intimacy and respect. But the work was not over. There were still twelve unrecovered bodies. The weather prevented resumption of the human salvage for four days, while sheets of spray exploded upward from the rocks adjacent to the wreck site. Then, on Friday, the *Dios te Guarde* was carefully steered out through the passage and anchored a hundred yards from shore with her bow facing the incoming waves which lifted and dropped her in monotonous regularity. During the preceding days the sea had begun in earnest its work of decomposition on the remaining bodies. The sickening sweet smell was noticeable downward for half a mile and over the work site it was nearly overpowering. The ocean reeked with death.

A little pale, Robert lowered himself into the noxious water and hung from the back of the rowboat as Faustino rowed him as close to the sand pocket as he could. Then Robert dived into a maelstrom of opposing currents. Swept to and fro like a leaf in the wind, he fought his way to the graveyard, where he reasoned other bodies would be assembling. He was correct. Five cadavers awaited him, horribly mutilated, rolling and somersaulting across the sand in the wave motions. The water was no longer clear but clouded with thousands of white specks. Biting firmly on his mouthpiece to prevent water seeping in, he swam into the soup of human flesh particles and began chasing the cavorting bodies. With all five tied firmly to his rope, Robert thought he had seen a glimpse of still another chalky cadaver at the limit of his visibility and rose to study the terrain. His eyes were drawn in macabre fascination to the animated forms on his line. He grew philosophical, down there on the ocean bottom, cold and alone in this world of the dead. How sudden, he thought, can be the transition from life.

Something tapped him lightly on the elbow.

His heart stopped. A violent shiver ran down his body as he spun around in a lightning-flash reaction. Then he closed his eyes and drew a deep breath. A piece of broken wood had drifted against him. The five cadavers were delivered to the navy launch, and Robert told the others his unnerving experience. "I turned my head so fast that the mask slipped sideways," he said with a reflective shudder.

Day after day Robert, Florent, Johnny and Owen Lee—who had just returned from a vacation—dived on the underwater assembly point and surfaced with corpses. Finally, when they terminated their efforts, twenty-three of the *Ave del Mar*'s complement had been returned to Moana and buried. Only two were still lost at sea, voyaging silently through the submarine depths to inknown destinations.

Several days and many hot scrubs after the last dive into the "corpse soup" the clinging sweetish odor was finally washed from the divers' bodies. Often aftereffects lingered on. Nightmares of approaching hordes of cadavers continued for weeks, and so did a weird daytime visual phenomenon. Frequently when interviewing Galician fishermen, Robert or Florent or Johnny had the illusion that the face of the man with whom he was talking had turned into a grinning ivory skull.

On my return to Vigo I realized how deeply the team's deed had been appreciated when a friend handed me an editorial by our newspaper chronicler, Bene. Captioned "Praise for the Amphibious Men," it lauded their work over the *Ave del Mar* and concluded with:

> In this permanent battlefield of the sea, with its evident risks, we have seen how the amphibious men threw themselves forward, not in their accustomed search for treasure, but in the search of their dead brothers of the sea. We saw them go, without awaiting the calm summer days—which

for this mission of the deepest human sentiment would be too late—into this difficult and dangerous work, time and again, in search of those lost bodies, abandoned to the whim of the waves and the greed of the fish. These they tenderly raised to the surface to be given Christian burial in their parochial cemeteries. This deed deserves full praise and public gratitude, for it was carried out in the spirit of civic feeling and human solidarity.

*

Ancient Diving Masks

The people of Siraf are Persians of noble stock, and amongst them there is a tribe of Arabs who dive for pearls. The pearl fisheries are situated between Siraf and Bahrein in a calm bay like a wide river. Before diving the diver puts on his face a sort of tortoise shell mask and a tortoise shell clip on his nose, then ties a rope around his waist and dives. When he reaches the bottom of the sea he finds the shells there stuck in the sand, and he pulls them out by hand or cuts them loose with a knife, and puts them in a leather bag slung around his neck.

Ibn Battuta, TRAVELS IN ASIA AND AFRICA, 1331

Sharks of Raraka

BY WILMON MENARD

"*R*araka is the atoll where all the sharks of the world were born." This is what Roo, my Tahitian shark-fisherman friend, told me when we set sail one morning aboard a copra schooner for the Dangerous Isles, northeast of Tahiti. That the lagoon of Raraka was the womb for all the killer sharks of the seven seas I doubted, but there were specific aspects of Raraka Atoll that gave heartening promise of many man-eaters in its waters.

First, it was almost a circular atoll, fourteen miles long and eleven wide, enclosing a huge, deep lagoon. There was a reef passage, giving entrance to the lagoon, on the northwestern side through which trading schooners of some size could easily pass. Sharks favor the quiet lagoon water for spawning and foraging, and will never enter a lagoon's entrance unless it is very wide, which assures a quick escape should they be attacked by schools of barracuda, their eternal enemies.

We made ourselves comfortable in the small village of Matahai, situated on the eastern side of the pass, and two days later we were ready to kill sharks. My interest in spearing and hooking sharks was not purely sportive dislike. I had a market in Papeete for the hides of the monster. This agency, in turn, had markets for the shagreen in Australia, America and England.

Early one morning Roo and I paddled in an outrigger canoe to the deepest part of the lagoon of Raraka. The surface of the lagoon was unruffled, and the marine garden which spread out below us could be seen as clearly as if viewed under an immense magnifying glass, making shapes and sizes of marine life and plants appear gigantic and grotesque. No soil nor mud fouled the crystal-clear depth, nor was there any floating debris, as the coral was hard and brittle and shed no particles to cloud the clarity of the water.

The shifting sunlight wavered in wide ribbons of light through the water and was reflected from the coarse, sandy bottom and stark-white coral ledges. Diffused rays shot through the green translucence again and again, creating halations around coral grottoes and spires and casting deep shadows in coral caverns where lagoon monsters were possibly lurking. Filtered through the rough, uneven windows of great pagodas and minarets, the sun's rays poured in subdued patters through interminable forests of coral trees in which blue butterfly fish flitted. Now a shaft of light would transfix the sliding silhouette of a shark or the slimy green of a twisting, convulsing conger eel. It was like an amazing kaleidoscopic performance.

When I turned to speak with Roo, who was in the stern, I saw him unwrapping his long shark knife. "I will go below and tickle their stomachs with this," he said in Tahitian. I had never seen Roo fight sharks underwater, although I had heard many accounts of his encounters with tiger sharks, and the prospect at hand excited me. He inspected the lagoon's depth through a glass-paned water box, and in the blue murk, shadowed by the overhanging coral ledges, he saw the long gray shapes of killers. He pointed out a huge brute that was cruising slowly among the smaller sharks. "He will catch hell first," he announced with vigor.

The canoe rocked suddenly and Roo was over the side, with hardly a ripple to mark his descent. Through the water box I watched him descend feet first, the knife flashing brightly in the clear water. Then, at a depth of about ten feet, he turned and shot like a rocket, head first, for the bottom. The smaller sharks took instant flight at his intrusion, but the large tiger shark circled him warily at a distance.

Roo swam boldly toward the sharks, the knife extended in his left hand. The monster went deep, but Roo followed him, until I could only see a shadowy outline of shark and man. A few seconds later they rose higher, and I saw Roo make a sudden, quick lunge. His knife made lightning and a small jet of gray smoke squirted from the belly of the shark (in sea water at this depth blood becomes gray in color).

Goaded to wild rage, the shark circled quickly and charged Roo, who nimbly somersaulted, swimming deeper, and then came under the brute for another hard knife thrust. Roo was tormenting the shark in the manner in which a picador infuriates a bull. Now I saw that the shark was leaking puffs of gray smoke in two places. Again Roo swam nimbly around a coral fan and pricked hard the thrashing, enraged shark.

A small though dangerous-sized shark came into the scene, attracted by the blood of the punctured monster. It saw Roo first and moved to attack, but Roo was not to be caught napping. When the small shark swam past, flashing open its jaws wide for a bite, he sank the knife deeply into its body just back of the gills. The young shark was moving away from him at the time, and by its own momentum drew the knife along most of its length, opening wide its stomach. It floundered weakly off, vomiting blood from its gulping mouth and spewing forth entrails from the long and nasty incision.

But the large shark was still to be reckoned with. It rushed in for a swift attack on Roo, who darted aside just in the nick of time to escape a cruel bite. Now Roo realized he was exposing himself needlessly to danger with so much blood in the water; so he quickly reached out and grabbed the fluke of the brute, twisting his body under its stomach and at the same time sinking his knife deeply into its belly. Then he released his hold on its fluke, allowing the force of the shark's motion through the water to rip open its stomach. Blood and viscera poured out of the shark's sliced belly. The monster swam several yards in a wobbly fashion, finally giving a convulsive tremble and sinking slowly toward the bottom of the lagoon.

Roo came to the surface, blowing his nose lustily, and began to give the whistling gasps through clenched teeth in that peculiar fashion of divers of the Dangerous Isles, to relieve his strained lungs and to accustom his chest muscles to normal action. Then he climbed unaided into the canoe and wrapped his shark knife in the fish-oil-saturated rag. "Someday I will show you how to do that, Willie," he said.

Aside from rare specialists like Roo, the barracuda is perhaps the only real menace the shark has in the South Pacific. A large barracuda can give a shark a handicap of about one hundred yards and still overhaul him in short order, pulling him down as a wolf does a stag and killing him within fifty feet of the spot where he first caught up with him. Personally, I never molest six- or eight-foot South Pacific barracuda. They are mean customers. They have fittingly been called the "wolves of the sea."

Another insidious enemy of the shark is the *Diodon antennatus*, which has a diabolical method in killing sharks. In size and mien the Diodon is a pleasant enough fellow, but if a larger fish, such as the shark, has the audacity to gobble him up there's the very devil to pay. Surprised or angered, the Diodon can blow itself up by taking in air and water, erect the long thorny spines on its body, and then can look and act like a vertible gorgon of marine life. It can wheeze and snort like an irate, asthmatic old man; it grinds its teeth savagely and can squirt a caustic fluid out of its mouth, blinding its enemies at a distance of eighteen inches.

What if a shark swallows Diodon by mistake while it is normally deflated? Well, sir, Diodon inflates itself in the shark's stomach, spews out a carmine fluid which gives the shark acute belly cramps, and then gnaws its way through the stomach lining and hide and swims indignantly off. Which, of course, leaves the shark with a gaping hole in its side, drowned and quite scuttled.

*

The Great Armada

But far beneath this wondrous world upon the surface, another and still stranger world met our eyes as we gazed over the side. For, suspended in these watery vaults, floated the forms of nursing mothers of the whales, and those that by their enormous girth seemed shortly to become mothers. The lake, as I have hinted, was to a considerable depth exceedingly transparent; and as human infants while suckling will calmly and fixedly gaze away from the breast, as if leading two different lives at the same time; and yet while drawing mortal nourishment, be still spiritually feasting upon some unearthly reminiscence; even so did the young of these whales seem looking up toward us, but not at us, as if we were a bit of gulfweed in their new-born sight. Floating on their sides, the mothers also seemed quietly eyeing us.

Herman Melville, MOBY DICK, LXXXVII

The original nuclear-powered vessel, the Nautilus, *first-born of thirty-three atom subs ordered by the U.S. Navy, thrilled the world with a high-speed passage under the Arctic ice cap, splitting the North Pole and cutting five thousand miles off the sea route from England to Japan. Lieutenant Lalor is one of the new breed of sailor-atomic technologists in the nuclear submarine division. Here is his story of the transpolar dash, from the* National Geographic Magazine.

Submarine Through the North Pole

BY WILLIAM G. LALOR, JR.

*F*rom the slender antenna of *Nautilus*, in staccato *dit's* and *dah's*, a brief, triumphant message flashed across oceans and continents: "*Nautilus* Ninety North."

Our radioman took his hand from the sending key. Beside him, waiting, stood the captain, Commander William R. Anderson. In less than a minute high-pitched signals of acknowledgment came winging back from United States Navy radio operators in Japan, Hawaii, and England.

"Send the other one now, Thomas."

Out into the Arctic air crackled a second message, again for relay to Admiral Arleigh A. Burke, Chief of Naval Operations:

"Ninety-six hours, Point Barrow to the Greenland Sea."

Two terse reports . . . a scant dozen words. Yet, in essence, they told a complete and dramatic story. *Nautilus* had safely concluded a voyage without precedent, one that, within hours, would be headlined around the world.

It was the morning of August 5, 1958. On the surface and basking in unaccustomed sunlight, we cruised south in calm water between Greenland and Spitsbergen. To north and west we could see the stark outlines of our conquered adversary, the ice pack of the Arctic.

Our nuclear-powered submarine had sped 1,839 nautical miles beneath that treacherous mass, completing in four days the first submerged voyage across the Arctic Ocean. En route she had become the first ship in history to reach 90° north latitude—the North Pole.

A holiday mood prevailed throughout the ship. The jukebox blared its usual fare of everything from "Purple People Eater" to Hawaiian melodies. But, despite joking remarks and the noise of our record player, I suspected that many men, like myself, were offering silent prayers of thanksgiving for our swift and trouble-free journey.

Nautilus, while pioneering a new Northwest Passage, had carried 116 men in comfort that would have astounded the oak-tough individualists of past Arctic exploration. Yet the trip had not been without frustration and drama. Indeed, we had started our cruise feeling like conspirators in a mystery novel.

I began a personal log when we backed away from the pier at Pearl Harbor in the Hawaiian Islands. The first entry reads:

> July 22—8 P.M. In spite of the hour, about 200 people are on the dock to see us off. Among them is Rear Admiral Grenfell, Commander Submarine Force, Pacific Fleet, one of the few here who know we are bound north. The last few days have been very frustrating. An elusive fault in our all-important master gyrocompass has kept us at the dock since Sunday on a two-hour readiness. It's pretty hard to enjoy Hawaii this way, and we are anxious to be off.
>
> Reports from planes scouting ice above Bering Strait are encouraging. Looks like the ice is moving farther north each day.

Nautilus sped out the channel and turned to round Oahu Island. On deck seamen painted out the telltale white number, 571, on our sides. Our orders: remain undetected and conceal your identity until the trip is completed and an announcement made.

As far as the world and our families knew, we were making a long underwater endurance cruise to Panama. My wife Sally had listed shopping items for me to pick up in Colon, and the captain and executive officer, Lieutenant Commander Frank M. Adams, had accepted dinner dates with friends in the Canal Zone.

The reason for veiling our true mission was simple. The Navy had taken on a unique, exacting job; we must show we could do it before we talked about it. Moreover, our crew knew from rueful experience that bad luck might turn us back.

From the deepwater Atlantic side, we had made three probes beneath the Arctic ice in August, 1957. On one of them we reached within 180 miles of the Pole, only to beat a reluctant retreat when an electric power failure shut down our master gyrocompass.

In June, 1958, we explored from the Pacific side, a far more difficult point of access. Layers of thick ice jam up in the narrow bottle-neck between Siberia and Alaska. Running beneath that solid shroud is tricky, for water depths in the Chukchi Sea, lying between Bering Strait and the deep Arctic Ocean, average only 120 feet.

Nautilus, in June, had turned back after almost smashing into a deep floe—but more about that later.

Now we hopefully faced a new assault on the Arctic. The diving alarm sounded twice. With a rush of air escaping from ballast tanks, the ship tilted gently down. We were clear of Pearl Harbor and its shipping as we glided into the depths and checked for possible leaks in the thousands of valves and fittings crammed into the twenty-seven-foot-diameter hull of *Nautilus*.

We were in our natural element. Down below, the water is always calm. Storms, seasickness, or fog never interfere. There was practically no vibration to disturb my pen, though we moved at more than twenty knots.

Temperature aboard *Nautilus* is 72°, winter and summer, Arctic Ocean or the Caribbean. She carries tons of air conditioning. The humidity remains always below 50 per cent.

Now, as we cruised northward, automatic devices kept our blunt bow on course and our hull at exactly three hundred feet. Teams began a careful final inspection of the ship for fire hazards—serious on any submarine, of course, but doubly so under ice, where finding a hole big enough in which to surface or raise our air-intake snorkel to clear smoke might be hard.

We traveled deep most of the next day, July 23, before coming up near the surface to copy radio traffic. Low-frequency waves from powerful Navy shore stations penetrate water, but not down to three hundred feet. We received another message about ice conditions.

Early in July Lieutenant Shepherd M. Jenks, our navigator, had flown to Alaska to set up ice reconnaissance flights to Point Barrow and west along the pack boundary. Our naval aviator friends didn't know whom they were helping. Their latest relayed report said the ice still receded, although the Alaskan shore just west of Point Barrow was cluttered.

The next night our daily paper, whimsically named the *Panama-Arctic-Pearl-Arctic Shuttle Boat News*, featured Engineerman 1/c Harry D. Hedin's eight-pound baby girl—number three. The radio had told Hedin of her birth.

In the crew's mess I watched *The Lieutenant Wore Skirts*. Friends at the movie exchange in Pearl had been kind to us—thirty-eight movies on board. Fifty men lounged in our spacious—by submarine standards—recreation center, with its hi-fi, tape recorder, library, and magazine racks.

> July 25—We are moving along at a very fast clip for the Aleutians, now only 400 miles away. Everything is working smoothly. Even our balky master compass performs perfectly, and the propulsion plant purrs like a fine watch.

I had turned over the job of navigator to Shep Jenks in January; since then I had been in charge of propulsion-plant machinery; turbines, condensers, pumps, piping, valves, steam system, and the mechanical components of the reactor plant. After three and a half years of operation, our nuclear power plant still seemed a marvel. It had propelled *Nautilus* more than 120,000 miles.

In the reactor compartment upper level, shielded from the lower level by a deck covered with lead and polyethylene, we cannot even hear the sealed pumps. They move primary water in a closed loop through the reactor and two heat exchangers. The primary water picks up the heat of controlled nuclear fission and transfers it to unpressurized secondary water, which boils into steam. Pipes carry the steam to two turbines driving nine-foot propellers and to four turbogenerators. These generators furnish electricity for lights, motors, cooking—everything, in fact.

A four-hourly report comes to the conning officer and the engineer officer from our ship's doctor, Commander Richard F. Dobbins: "Oxygen 20.3 per cent, carbon dioxide 1 per cent, carbon monoxide 10–20 parts per million."

This tells us that our sealed atmosphere is healthful—almost as good as the air outside. Oxygen is kept at a uniform level by "bleeding" it into the ship from bottled stowage in tanks around the hull. Machines called burners and scrubbers hold carbon monoxide and carbon dioxide at very low levels.

To keep any possible radioactivity in the ship at a minimum, Dr. Dobbins has stored all radium-dialed wrist watches in a sealed can. Each day a voice solemnly intones over the speaker, "Now, Dr. Dobbins, wind all watches in your care."

> July 26—We are approaching the Aleutian island chain. At 3 P.M. we crossed the Aleutian Trench, a 40-mile-wide 25,000-foot foredeep running east and west parallel to the Aleutians for almost 1,000 miles. We're able to check our latitude very closely by Fathometer.

The Fathometer, a sonar device, measures distance to the bottom by computing the time required for a sound signal, moving at 4,800 feet per second, to travel from ship to ocean floor and back. Since the trench had been accurately charted, its recognition on the Fathometer confirmed our position.

Nautilus also now carried half a dozen echo sounders topside. They would show distance to the ice above by sending signals straight up. In addition, a television camera would eye the ice and relay to our monitor screens pictures of ice formations scudding by like clouds. This battery of vital gear was the special charge of Dr. Waldo K. Lyon, distinguished Navy scientist, ice expert, and veteran of thirteen Arctic expeditions.

By 9 P.M. on the twenty-sixth we were between Herbert and Yunaska islands in a pass little used by other ships. The periscope confirmed our position; we slipped through into the Bering Sea and returned to high speed.

In the wardroom a group of officers prepared to give promotion examinations to some of the enlisted men. They would do well, as always. We have had fifty-five men advanced to officer status in three and a half years.

> July 27—Still in deep water just north of the Aleutians. The Pribilof Islands, with their huge seal fisheries, lie well to the east. Finally at 4 P.M. we are forced to slow down . . . came up from 300 feet to 150 feet. Soundings continuously now instead of every 15 minutes. We've crossed the 100-fathom mark and the deepwater honeymoon is over.

Our North Pole celebration committee, headed by Captain Jack L. Kinsey, a medical observer from the Navy's Polaris submarine missile program, met behind closed doors. Meanwhile, many men spent their spare time working on two contests, one for design of a ship's flag to commemorate the crossing, and another for an appropriate name to give those who made the transpolar voyage. Some of the interest in these contests may not have been entirely due to the celebration; the prizes were three days of liberty in Europe.

At 11:30 P.M. on the twenty-seventh, the quartermaster awakened me and handed me a pair of red goggles. Time for my watch again. As conning officer, I had to wear the goggles until I had a cup of coffee and went back to the darkened attack center. We keep the center lighted only by red lights between sunset and sunrise, so that our eyes are always adapted for night vision should we have to come up during darkness and use the periscope.

Down the ladder in control, the diving officer reported to me that depth and course held well, the compasses checked with each other, and the sounding showed three hundred feet. I relieved the watch and made another careful check of positions plotted on the chart.

While doing so, I reflected on the navigational complications we would face when we were under the ice pack. Beneath that massive canopy we could not confirm our position by observational fixes or by radar. Success or failure would hinge upon how well we used five sensitive navigational aids.

Nautilus carried two magnetic compasses. Errors would creep into their reading, of course, for this type of compass is not wholly reliable so near the North Magnetic Pole. It tends to wander and finally, at the Magnetic Pole itself, to spin erratically.

We also had on board two fine gyrocompasses, one of them the master. You can point a gyrocompass at north and it will cling there, provided you compensate periodically for changes in the speed of the earth's rotation. This speed lessens as you journey north.

Our ace in the hole, however, was an amazing instrument called an inertial navigator, an aid we had lacked in 1957. Its stable platform points always at earth's center. Two instruments on the platform sense changes in acceleration, and hence changes in direction and speed, somewhat as a blindfolded person in a car can interpret movements by sensing how his body reacts against the seat as the car speeds up, brakes, or turns.

A computer records the machine's signals and disgorges information for us. In effect, this brainy navigator shows where it is by remembering where it has been.

3:20 A.M. Sounding 130 feet.

I had slowed *Nautilus* to ten knots. She measures fifty feet from keel to the top of her "sail," the streamlined tower housing periscopes and antennas. Therefore, at this shallow depth, we had only eighty feet of water for maneuvering.

Later, just before turning in, I commented to Doc Lyon how quiet the ship had become at ten knots. He had noticed it, too. There was absolutely no vibration or sense of motion, no sound of water rushing by along the hull. I felt suspended, as one might in space.

July 29—By 1 A.M. we were well into Bering Strait. Visibility was very poor, but we got a quick radar position from the Diomedes and Fairway.

Our radar fix also had given us a good check on the inertial navigator. It was performing like a champion—testimony to the hard work of Tom Curtis and George Bristow. These two gifted engineers had been assigned to us by North American Aviation, Inc., builders of the inertial system. Its mechanism was designed to guide the Navaho missile on a three-hour, fifteen-hundred-knot flight, but we had had it working now for weeks in a submarine.

At 6:25 A.M. on the twenty-ninth, everyone on board became Bluenoses again as we crossed latitude 66° 33′ N.—the Arctic Circle. We were making good progress. Our spirits rose when, later that day in the Chukchi Sea, we safely passed the point of our near disaster of the previous June.

With the exception of the captain himself, perhaps I had more reason than the others to recall vividly that harrowing ordeal. I had been the conning officer, responsible for the safe maneuvering of the ship. At that time the Chukchi ice stretched farther south, and *Nautilus* had ducked beneath the pack.

The Fathometer showed only 160 feet of water. Yet it seemed unlikely that the congealed mass overhead would reach down to us. Instruments tracing the ice contour revealed underwater ridges averaging only ten feet deep.

But sonar soon picked up deep ice ahead. With much inner apprehension, I watched the ink recorder draw the profile of a jagged tongue sixty-two feet down, a depth we had never before experienced. It cleared our sail by eight feet. Quickly I slowed the ship and called Commander Anderson.

Without hesitation, he ordered me to turn around and ease down to 140 feet, only twenty feet off the bottom. *Nautilus* was still in her turn when sonar reported a massive ice ridge stretching more than two miles across our path. It could not be dodged. Instinctively, while staring hypnotically at the swooping pen of the recorder, we ducked our heads.

The ridge cleared us by a mere five feet; its depth: an incredible eighty-five feet. As Commander Anderson remarked to me later, "God's hand was on my shoulder when I said make your depth 140 feet instead of 130 feet." Ice has the consistency of a poor grade of concrete, and the ridge would have damaged our sail severely. There had been no sense in continuing, for three hundred miles of shallow water lay ahead. We had set course for Hawaii.

But now, late in July, that incident was only a haunting memory. Again we dared the Arctic, and we sailed a lucky ship.

> July 30—1 A.M. At periscope depth, 15 knots, visibility poor to fair.

When I took over the watch from Paul Early, he pointed out our first ice of the trip through the periscope. It was a lone floe, about one hundred yards long, which we easily dodged. It looked like a beautiful sailing ship moving majestically by, reflecting a rainbow of colors.

An hour later I sighted a two-foot transparent chunk of ice ahead. In a few minutes, scores of these pesky blocks surrounded us, and the captain reluctantly decided to surface and get a better look at the situation.

> Pack in sight to the west. One ice cube on deck recovered and preserved in the freezebox.

Nearly a month later, in New York, we presented that chunk as a souvenir to Rear Admiral (now Vice Admiral) Hyman G. Rickover, whose ingenuity and tireless drive had been so largely responsible for construction of *Nautilus*, world's first atomic submarine.

Cruising slowly south, we began a disheartening routine that held for the next twenty-four hours. Since ice loomed to the west and the sea that way was shallow, we turned east and then north again, hoping that the pack boundary would be closer to deep water along the new approach. Our object was to reach at least three hundred feet of ice-free water before diving.

My log shows the way it went:

> July 30—3 A.M. Clear of ice . . . 4 A.M. Turned north after running east 15 miles. Visibility changing from 10 miles to 300 yards. Complete overcast . . . 1:20 P.M. Pack edge at 72° 24' N. Close but no cigar . . . 6 P.M. Five miles farther east. Pack edge at 72° 15' . . . 12 P.M. Fifteen miles more to the east. Pack in sight all along to the west . . .

> July 31—1 A.M. Turned on our radar and picked up ice ahead at about 30 miles. We may make it. Visibility and speed variable. Captain up almost continuously now. Going to catch cold on the bridge. It's between 35° and 45° but raw. Sea is flat calm. Many walruses in sight.

2 A.M. 72° 45' N. 165° W. End of the line. Solid ice to west and north, also 15 miles to the east. Moved into pack but deepest water only 180 feet. We couldn't make it this way. At 4 A.M. the captain ordered course set for Point Barrow.

Now we would try to find a deepwater lead by moving in toward the Alaskan shore.

Quartermaster Richard Williamson came up on the bridge and took a long look at the dirty, heavily ridged ice.

"Do you mean to say that men ever ran dog sleds over that? Some of those ridges are thirty feet high," he said.

I, too, wondered how they did it. We owed a great deal to those men—Peary, Nansen, Sverdrup, and many others. Without the information they obtained so heroically, *Nautilus* would not be venturing into the Arctic.

At 4:37 A.M. on August 1, we cruised north of Point Barrow, invisible just over the horizon. The Fathometer, whose moving arm had been monotonously showing 160 to 180 feet of water, now suddenly indicated 420 feet. There was jubilation in the voice of Chief of the Watch John J. Krawczyk as he called the bridge on the intercom. We were there—in a tongue of the deep Barrow Submarine Canyon, which should lead us north to the even deeper Arctic Ocean. This tongue had been discovered previously by icebreakers.

The captain, in the attack center, spoke to Lieutenant Robert Kassel on the bridge. "When you are ready, clear the bridge and submerge."

The diving alarm honked twice; in a minute *Nautilus* slipped beneath the sea. The ship eased down to two hundred feet, three hundred, then deeper, as we followed the ever-deepening bottom. Hereafter we would be measuring depth of water in hundreds of fathoms rather than feet.

The captain, exec, navigator, and others plot our position with extreme care. Compasses are watched constantly, checked one against the other. The inertial navigator, with sleepless Tom Curtis watching it like a worried mother, clicks cheerfully. Our major problem now: navigation.

Men on watch—those by the shiny stainless-steel reactor cylinder, those carefully checking temperatures near the humming turbines, and the men in the control center—do exactly what they do any time at sea. Their job is the same, surfaced, submerged, under ice, or in clear water: answer the bell. Telegraphs read "Ahead Full" now, and they won't change for four days.

Our undersea "ears," the echo sounders, give out a cacophony of sounds. From the control room I can hear one instrument bouncing signals off ice or open water above us. It chirps when an echo returns from open water but sounds a dull thud when the echo returns from ice. I can also hear a Fathometer sounding the bottom, and the bow-mounted sonar probing ahead for submerged mountain peaks or ice in our path.

By 4:30 P.M. we had reached 74° N. with things looking good. Went up slightly to blow sanitary tanks and eject garbage. When we eased back down the captain watched the ice again for a while. We went to 20 knots, one degree of latitude every three hours.

The ice seemed meaner to us than it did in 1957, much more rough and jagged. Dr. Lyon thought it was because his equipment was better, more sensitive than before.

Watching the ice trace coming from our sonic recorder, I felt glad for Sir Hubert Wilkin's sake that his old submarine, also named the *Nautilus*, did not get under the ice pack in 1931. A stern-plane failure balked the attempt. He was certainly ahead in his idea of using a sub under the Arctic ice, but the runners he was going to use to slide along under the floes would just not have worked. Too many ridges! Moreover, only an atomic sub, its propulsion plant independent of the atmosphere, could traverse the Pole safely.

August 2—At latitude 76° 22', soundings went from about 2,000 fathoms to 500 fathoms very abruptly. We were crossing a 9,000 foot submerged mountain range, uncharted and unknown. This feature continued for 70 miles, when the soundings just as abruptly smoothed out again, about 2,000 fathoms. . . .

80° N.—600 miles from the Pole, and 1,200 miles from the ice edge in the Atlantic. Just past noon we shifted our master compass to a high latitude mode. Everything checks perfectly. . . .

Big news! Lieutenant Wes Harvey announced the winners of the flag-design contest, Electronics Technician 1/c James P. Knotts, Chief John Krawczyk, and Electrician's Mate 2/c James A. Morley.

Chief Sonarman James R. Norris was declared winner of the second contest. His name for transpolar veterans: PANOPO (Pacific to Atlantic via the North Pole).

A paper blizzard engulfed the wardroom. Letters were being prepared, for signature at the Pole, to families, friends, and others most closely connected with *Nautilus* and this voyage. Yeoman 1/c Charles A. Payne groaned when he saw the work piling up.

These letters would go out later with our North Pole cachet and postmark. Engineman 1/c Ernest F. Holland carved the postmark from a sheet of rubber. A commercial firm in Hawaii made the cachet for us with the words "Pearl Harbor" in the center. We substituted "North Pole," and Oahu Island became the ice pack.

> Passing through fairly light ice now—six-tenths coverage with many large water openings suitable for surfacing as we near the Pole of Inaccessibility.

This imaginary area is supposed to be the hardest to reach in the Arctic, almost the geographic center of the ice pack. It was located by taking all the points reached in the Far North by ship or sledge and then marking the center of the unexplored region. I found it hard to imagine the grinding floes and bitter cold overhead as I sat in my shirt sleeves, smoking my pipe and writing to my wife and my small sons Billy and Michael.

> August 3—10 A.M. Latitude 87° N. Passing history's and our, farthest point north by ship.

Soon the bottom rose up again as we crossed the Lomonosov Ridge. This nine-thousand-foot mountain range is named for the Russian scientist who first predicted its existence from geophysical studies of the earth's crust.

I had hoped we would reach the Pole on my watch, but it was not to be. Close, but still some seventy-five miles to go when I went off duty.

Dinner was delayed to allow party preparations to go on in the crew's mess. Leading cook Jack L. Baird put the finishing touches on his North Pole cake, with the replica of our polar flag as icing. Ship's cameramen set up floodlights; another group prepared a tape recorder.

I sat with the captain in the wardroom as he signed letters and put the finishing touches on those to the President and to the ship's sponsor, Mrs. Eisenhower. Frank Adams came in.

"Two miles to go, Captain." The jukebox was turned off, and the captain spoke briefly and movingly over the intercom:

"With continued good fortune, *Nautilus* will soon accomplish two goals long sought by those who sail the seas.

"First, the opening of a route for rapid voyages between the great Pacific and Atlantic oceans.

"Second, the attainment of the North Pole by ship.

"Thus our remarkable ship has been blessed with her greatest opportunity—the discovery of the only truly practicable Northwest Passage. On this historic Sunday, August 3, 1958, let us offer our thanks to Him who has blessed us with this opportunity and who has guided us so truly. . . ."

We observed a moment of silent prayer. As *Nautilus* approached the Pole, the captain began a countdown: "8. . . . .4. . . .2 . . 1. . .Mark! August 3, 1958. Time, 2315 [11:15 P.M.] Eastern Daylight Saving Time. For the United States and the United States Navy, the North Pole."

A dream had become reality. We had arrived. Sounding, 13,410 feet, a lot of water.

As we watched in awe, our gyrocompasses swung, finally to point back to where we had been. Tom Curtis was manipulating his slide rule beside the inertial navigator. I asked how close we had come to the exact Pole.

"We pierced it, Bill."

In the crew's mess, Electrician's Mate 1/c James R. Sordelet came forward, and the captain swore him in for another six years in the Navy, the first man to re-enlist at the Pole. Eleven others received the captain's congratulations for completing their qualification in nuclear submarines. Behind them was up to a year of making drawings, checking pipes, switches, valves—everything in our 320-foot-long ship.

"What are you doing dropping garbage all over my front lawn? Merry Christmas!"

Engineman 2/c William J. McNally, Jr., as Santa Claus, appeared in a costume the quartermasters made from some red flag material and cotton. He had "a message for the children," and then it was time for our steak dinner and North Pole cake.

Now that the Pole lay behind us, however, we had another goal and job to do. We had to reach the Atlantic, completing our transit of the Arctic Ocean safely.

Actually, all of us knew that we were now playing a game of longitude roulette for very high stakes. At the North Pole all directions are south, and an error in navigation could head us for the U.S.S.R., Alaska, or Canada instead of for our planned exit into the Greenland Sea. Concentration on our instruments never flagged for a moment.

We steered for our old stamping grounds, a deepwater opening between Greenland and Spitsbergen. There an arm of the Gulf Stream curved north, and we hoped to reach open water little more than six hundred miles from the Pole.

I was sleeping when it happened, but at almost the same spot as in 1957, we lost the power supply to the master compass. Experience pays off, though. We had installed an emergency supply, and it took over without skipping a beat.

By noon of August 4, when my watch began, we were feeling so good that we decided to divert ourselves with television—"Polar TV network, Channel 571," we dubbed our underwater ice observation hookup. It had been installed primarily for finding small ice in otherwise open pools. In 1957 one bent and one ruined periscope had taught us the danger of being in a hurry when surfacing in ice, and the limitations of our sonar.

The television received enough light to outline clearly the edges of floes; we watched the screen avidly.

> August 5—In the hours past midnight, almost everyone is up waiting for us to clear the ice. The inertial system and our navigator's best plotted position from compasses and distance indicator are only 15 miles apart. Sea-water temperature is up to 38°, indicating we are in the right slot and running into the Gulf Stream branch. Soundings decreasing gradually, up to 700 fathoms, indicating we are passing over Nansens Rise between Greenland and Spitsbergen. Even the ice says we are approaching the edge. Many 400-yard holes, and a lot of 1- and 2-foot new ice. By 2:30 A.M. soundings read 1,000 fathoms. Our position: 80° N., 2° E. We still had about 60 miles to go.

At 3 A.M. the bottom dropped suddenly to 2,500 fathoms. There was nothing like that on the chart, and we were in a fairly well-known area. In fact, we had explored this area ourselves in 1957 and had observed nothing over 1,500 fathoms. To add to the confusion we found ourselves under a giant floe that seemed never to end, more than ten miles long, twelve feet thick on the average, and with many fifty-foot ridges.

All our confidence suddenly evaporated. Were we really in the right ocean? Nothing to do but go on; but about 4 A.M. we had the expected signs again—water temperature up, one thousand fathoms, thin ice.

At 5:12 A.M., quite suddenly, we ran into open water. All sonars and the television gave negative ice reports. We slowed and eased upward to check.

Nautilus stopped dead and got a perfect neutral trim. Commander Anderson ordered the diving officer, "Bring me up. Make it about ten feet a minute."

5:39 A.M. Hooray! Open water all around, ice visible to the north and west, but two-foot waves say this is the Greenland Sea.

In a short while our messages went out. Washington, New London, and Pearl Harbor could relax. And so could we, as *Nautilus* submerged again and barreled south toward Iceland. I turned in.

The next two and a half days seemed one continuous, frenetic scramble as the crew prepared for the captain's departure. A helicopter was to pick him up off Iceland for a flying trip to Washington. We began to doubt that a helicopter would hold him and his luggage. He would carry some fifteen hundred letters from the Pole, reams of technical data, still and motion pictures, a chart and clock for Mrs. Eisenhower. The paper flew as we passed lonely, volcanic Jan Mayen Island.

But very early on the eighth we were ready. Two seabags, two suitcases, a briefcase and chart had been stacked in the wardroom. *Nautilus* lurked submerged ten miles off the coast of Iceland; meanwhile, the captain took a nap, his last sleep for quite a while.

Right on schedule the helicopter appeared, we surfaced, and crewmen boosted the skipper into the hovering 'copter. *Nautilus* submerged again and loafed along toward Europe.

In the next few weeks and months we would receive overwhelming receptions in England, New York, and Groton; honors, luncheons, speeches, letters, telegrams—enough to amaze us all. The first and most meaningful message, though, came that early morning off Iceland in a plain white envelope handed down from the helicopter. It was addressed to the "Acting Commanding Officer." Inside we found a letter that said:

> To the officers and men of the *Nautilus*. Congratulations on a magnificent achievement. Well done.
>
> *Dwight D. Eisenhower*

In the Malay States small-boat fishermen are led by divers who have the uncanny art of listening underwater with the unaided ear for particular species of fish suited to the four types of nets deployed from the boats. This account of their techniques was written by Professor Raymond Firth, an anthropologist from the University of London, from observations before and after World War II.

Listening for Fish

BY RAYMOND FIRTH

The term *juru selam* is a generic one applied to all experts in locating fish by diving; there are *juru selam takur, juru selam pukat tarek* and *juru selam payang*, each particularly adept in dealing with the requirements of the type of net in which he specializes. But their training is broadly the same; it consists essentially in going out as pupil to an expert, who acts as teacher, and learning the craft by imitation and practice. One of the most important elements of the craft is the technique of submerging oneself in the water and listening for fish. The expert holds on to the boat with one hand and keeps his head and body below the surface, listening for the noises which the fish make. His first task is to locate the fish in the vicinity, identify what kind they are, and form an opinion as to their quantity. All these facts are important, because his net is adapted to take only certain kinds of fish, and if these are not plentiful his crew will waste time and labor in casting the net. No large net is ever cast at random; the expert always explores the prospects beforehand. Hence his ability to interpret the sounds made by the fish is one of his essential functions. These sounds are said to be due to pelagic fish swimming through the water in shoals or to demersal fish feeding at the bottom; some are due to fin and tail movements of large fish. Experts, when asked to describe them, used various noises and similes. The commonest fish taken in the lift-net, *selar kuning* (a small horse mackerel with a yellow stripe along its body), was said to make a sound "like the wind," "O. . .o. . .o. . .o," or "*ro-o, ro-o.*" *Lechen*, another small horse mackerel taken in the same net, was said to make a noise "like parched rice," "*to ta to ta to ta,*" while the shark which comes

after the fish and is a pest to the fishermen was said to make a
noise with its tail, heard as *"peyup, peyup; siu-up."* The scabbard
fish (*layur*), taken by the seine, was said to have a "good voice—
like a crow," making the sounds *"ok, ak; ok, ok o'."* The experts
are apt to describe these sounds in different ways, partly because
each man has his own mental associations for them, but partly because,
being usually a specialist on one type of net, he is most familiar
with the kinds of fish which that net is best adapted to take.

The training of an expert takes time, and involves him in some
cost. One of the acknowledged older experts of the Perupok area
took a year to learn, when he was a young man. At the end of the
time he gave his teacher the customary present of a jacket, with a
cloth and five dollars; he also made a practice of inviting him to any
feast which he gave. The convention that a gift is the proper return
for expert knowledge is common to all forms of transmission of the
arts—including those of the manipulation of shadow-play puppets,
and of magic and the art of healing. In Malay ideas it is a breach
of the ritual code for a teacher to sell his knowledge in a direct
commercial way. It may be asked how the ritual element enters into
what is a technical process. The answer is that in theory at least
the expert relies not simply on his own ability but also upon
the bounty of God (and, less explicitly, upon the assistance of
spirits) to obtain his results. The old expert just mentioned said that
his teacher taught him to ask for fish from Tuhan Allah before diving
and also to make appeal to Nabi Kidir. Before descending into the
water the expert should wash his face over and "remember" God in
some such words as:

> "Peace be on you!
> I ask the favor of Allah,"
> The bounty of Allah."

And as he goes down he should touch the water first with his foot,
saying the creed: "There is but one God. . ." The old man added:
"He thinks of Tuhan Allah; if he does not so remember, he can't do
anything."

Another younger expert, who had learned net-dyeing and technical
and ritual matters of boat-handling from this old expert who has just
been quoted, had been instructed in fish noises and other fish-craft
by his own father. He was a pupil for two years in all, and it
took him over three months to "hear" the fish noises and to separate
them. At first he could not distinguish them from those of the sea

and the waves. "About other people I don't know; I myself took three months." Incidentally, I remarked to him that Europeans were ignorant of these fish noises. He replied in surprise: "How can they know, when they don't go to sea!" This attitude was part of a general Malay belief that no European knew anything about the sea or fishing—a reasonable inference when one considers the life of white people as seen by the peasants of Malaya. These people were only half-convinced that Europeans handled sailing craft and nets by being shown photographs by us. A common form of expression was, "Do people really go to sea in your country? Then, of course, they must be Malays!"

*

Cortège (a passage)

Giants covered with seaweed passed through cities
Under the sea, whose towers arose as islands,
And that sea, with its pellucid depths flowing
Like the blood in my veins, it is my heartbeat.

Guillaume Apollinaire

Louis Boutan, himself a marine biologist like Rachel Carson, said, "Science is the quest for beauty," an epigram which can be understood by anyone who has read The Sea Around Us *or* The Edge of the Sea, *Miss Carson's gleaming books. Millions have been drawn to the mystery and beauty of the sea through her works. She originally wanted to be a writer, forsook the craft for biology, and later joined the two in volumes that are read in many tongues. Miss Carson left the United States Fish and Wildlife Service in 1952, to pursue independent investigations and writing in her field.*

The Coral Coast

BY RACHEL CARSON

I doubt that anyone can travel the length of the Florida Keys without having communicated to his mind a sense of the uniqueness of this land of sky and water and scattering mangrove-covered islands. The atmosphere of the Keys is strongly and peculiarly their own. It may be that here, more than in most places, remembrance of the past and intimations of the future are linked with present reality. In bare and jaggedly corroded rock, sculptured with the patterns of the corals, there is the desolation of a dead past. In the multicolored sea gardens seen from a boat as one drifts above them, there is a tropical lushness and mystery, a throbbing sense of the pressure of life; in coral reef and mangrove swamp there are the dimly seen foreshadowings of the future.

This world of the Keys has no counterpart elsewhere in the United States, and indeed few coasts of the earth are like it. Offshore, living coral reefs fringe the island chain, while some of the Keys themselves are the dead remnants of an old reef whose builders lived and flourished in a warm sea perhaps a thousand years ago. This is a coast not formed of lifeless rock or sand, but created by the activities of living things which, though having bodies formed of protoplasm even as our own, are able to turn the substance of the sea into rock.

The living coral coasts of the world are confined to waters in which the temperature seldom falls below 70° F. (and never for prolonged periods), for the massive structures of the reefs can be built only

171

where the coral animals are bathed by waters warm enough to favor
the secretion of their calcareous skeletons. Reefs and all the associated
structures of a coral coast are therefore restricted to the area bounded
by the Tropics of Cancer and Capricorn. Moreover, they occur only
on the eastern shores of continents, where currents of tropical water
are carried toward the poles in a pattern determined by the earth's
rotation and the direction of the winds. Western shores are inhospi-
table to coral because they are the site of upwellings of deep, cold
water, with cold coastwise currents running toward the Equator.

In North America, therefore, California and the Pacific coast
of Mexico lack corals, while the West Indian region supports them
in profusion. So do the coast of Brazil in South America, the
tropical east African coast, and the northeastern shores of Australia,
where the Great Barrier Reef creates a living wall for more than a
thousand miles.

Within the United States the only coral coast is that of the Florida
Keys. For nearly two hundred miles these islands reach southwest-
ward into tropical waters. They begin a little south of Miami
where Sands, Elliott, and Old Rhodes Keys mark the entrance to
Biscayne Bay; then other islands continue to the southwest, skirting
the tip of the Florida mainland, from which they are separated by
Florida Bay, and finally swinging out from the land to form a
slender dividing line between the Gulf of Mexico and the Straits of
Florida, through which the Gulf Stream pours its indigo flood.

To seaward of the Keys there is a shallow area three to seven
miles wide where the sea bottom forms a gently sloping platform
under depths generally less than five fathoms. An irregular channel
(Hawk Channel) with depths to ten fathoms traverses these shallows
and is navigable by small boats. A wall of living coral reefs forms
the seaward boundary of the reef platform, standing on the edge of
the deeper sea.

The Keys are divided into two groups that have a dual nature
and origin. The eastern islands, swinging in their smooth arc 110
miles from Sands to Loggerhead Key, are the exposed remnants of the
Pleistocene coral reef. Its builders lived and flourished in a warm sea
just before the last of the glacial periods, but today the corals, or all
that remains of them, are dry land. These eastern Keys are long,
narrow islands covered with low trees and shrubs, bordered with
coral limestone where they are exposed to the open sea, passing into
the shallow waters of Florida Bay through a maze of mangrove
swamps on the sheltered side. The western group, known as the

Pine Islands, are a different kind of land, formed of limestone rock that had its origin on the bottom of a shallow interglacial sea, and is now raised only slightly above the surface of the water. But in all the Keys, whether built by the coral animals or formed of the solidifying sea drift, the shaping hand is the hand of the sea.

In its being and its meaning, this coast represents not merely an uneasy equilibrium of land and water masses; it is eloquent of a continuing change now actually in progress, a change being brought about by the life processes of living things. Perhaps the sense of this comes most clearly to one standing on a bridge between the Keys, looking out over miles of water, dotted with mangrove-covered islands to the horizon. This may seem a dreamy land, steeped in its past. But under the bridge a green mangrove seedling floats, long and slender, one end already beginning to show the development of roots, beginning to reach down through the water, ready to grasp and to root firmly in any muddy shoal that may lie across its path. Over the years the mangroves bridge the water gaps between the islands; they extend the mainland; they create new islands. And the currents that stream under the bridge, carrying the mangrove seedling, are one with the currents that carry plankton to the coral animals building the offshore reef, creating a wall of rocklike solidity, a wall that one day may be added to the mainland. So this coast is built.

A few miles outside the chain of the present Keys is the reef of living coral, forming the seaward rim of the shallows, and overlooking a steep descent into the trough of the Florida Straits. The reefs extend from Fowey Rocks, south of Miami, to the Marquesas and Tortugas and in general they mark the ten-fathom depth contour. But often they rise to lesser depths and here and there they break the surface as tiny offshore islands, many of them marked by light-houses.

Drifting over the reef in a small boat and peering down through a glass-bottomed bucket, one finds it hard to visualize the whole terrain for so little of it can be seen at a time. Even a diver exploring more intimately finds it difficult to realize he is on the crest of a high hill, swept by currents instead of winds, where gorgonians are the shrubbery and stands of elkhorn coral are trees of stone. Toward the land, the sea floor slopes gently down from this hilltop into the wide water-filled valley of Hawk Channel; then it rises again and breaks water, as a chain of low-lying islands—the Keys. But on the seaward side of the reef the bottom descends quickly into blue depths. Live corals grow down to a depth of about ten fathoms. Below that it is too dark, perhaps, or there is too much sediment, and instead of living coral there is a foundation of dead reef formed at some time when the sea level was lower than it is today. Out where the water is about one hundred fathoms deep there is a clean rock bottom, the Pourtalès Plateau; its fauna is rich, but the corals that live here are not reef builders. Between three hundred and five hundred fathoms sediments have again accumulated on a slope that descends to the trough of the Florida Straits—the channel of the Gulf Stream.

As for the reef itself, many thousand thousand beings—plant and animal, living and dead—have entered into its composition. Corals of many species, building their little cups of lime and with them fashioning many strange and beautiful forms, are the foundation of the reef. But besides the corals there are other builders and all the interstices of the reef are filled with their shells or their limy tubes, or with coral rock cemented together with building stones of the most diverse origin. There are colonies of tube-building worms and there are mollusks of the snail tribe whose contorted, tubular shells may be intertwined into massive structures. Calcareous algae, which have the property of depositing lime in their living tissues, form part of the reef itself or, growing abundantly over the shallows on the landward side, add their substance at death to the coral sand of which limestone rock is later formed. The horny corals or gorgonians, known as sea fans and sea whips, all contain limestone spicules in their soft tissues. These, along with lime from starfish and sea urchins and sponges and an immense number of smaller creatures, will eventually, with the passage of time and through the chemistry of the sea, come to form part of the reef.

The basis of this whole complex association is a minute creature of deceptively simple appearance, the coral polyp. The coral animal is formed on the same general lines as the sea anemone. It is a double-walled tube of cylindrical shape, closed at the base and open at the free end where a crown of tentacles surrounds the mouth. The important difference—the fact on which the existence of coral reefs depends—is this: the coral polyp has the ability to secrete lime, forming a hard cup about itself. This is done by cells of the outer layer, much as the shell of a mollusk is secreted by an outer layer of soft tissue—the mantle. So the anemone-like coral polyp comes to sit in a compartment formed of a substance as hard as rock. Because the "skin" of the polyp is turned inward at intervals in a series of vertical folds, and because all of this skin is actively secreting lime, the cup does not have a smooth circumference, but is marked by partitions projecting inward, forming the starlike or flower-like pattern familiar to anyone who has examined a coral skeleton.

Most corals build colonies of many individuals. All the individuals of any one colony, however, are derived from a single fertilized ovum that matured and then began to form new polyps by budding. The colony has a shape characteristic of the species—branched, boulder-like, flatly encrusting, or cup-shaped. Its core is solid, for only the surface is occupied by living polyps, which may be widely separated in some species or closely crowded in others. It is often true that the larger and more massive the colony, the smaller the individuals that compose it; the polyps of a branching coral taller than a man may themselves be only an eighth of an inch high.

The hard substance of the coral colony is usually white, but may take on the colors of minute plant cells that live within the soft tissues in a relation of mutual benefit. There is the exchange usual in such relations, the plants getting carbon dioxide and the animals making use of the oxygen given off by the plants. This particular association may have a deeper significance, however. The yellow, green, or brown pigments of the algae belong to the group of chemical substances known as carotinoids. Recent studies suggest that these pigments in the imprisoned algae may act on the corals, serving as "internal correlators" to influence the processes of reproduction. Under normal conditions, the presence of the algae seems to benefit the coral, but in dim light the coral animals rid themselves of the algae by excreting them. Perhaps this means that in weak light or in darkness the whole physiology of the plant is changed and the products of its metabolism are altered to something harmful, so that the animal must expel the plant guest.

Within the coral community there are other strange associations. In the Florida Keys and elsewhere in the West Indian region, a gall crab makes an oven-shaped cavity on the upper surface of a colony of living brain coral. As the coral grows the crab manages to keep open a semicircular entrance through which, while young, it enters and leaves its den. Once full grown, however, the crab is believed to be imprisoned within the coral. Few details of the existence of this Florida gall crab are known, but in a related species in corals of the Great Barrier Reef only the females form galls. The males are minute, and apparently visit the females in the cavities where they are imprisoned. The female of this species depends on straining food organisms from indrawn currents of sea water and its digestive apparatus and appendages are much modified.

Everywhere, throughout the whole structure of the reef as well as inshore, the horny corals or gorgonians are abundant, sometimes outnumbering the corals. The violet-hued sea fan spreads its lace to the passing currents, and from all the structure of the fan innumerable mouths protrude through tiny pores, and tentacles reach out into the water to capture food. The little snail known as the flamingo tongue, wearing a solid and highly polished shell, often lives on the sea fans. The soft mantle, extended to cover the shell, is a pale flesh color with numerous black, roughly triangular markings. The gorgonians known as sea whips are more abundant, forming dense stands of undersea shrubbery, often waist-high, sometimes as tall as a man. Lilac, purple, yellow, orange, brown and buff are the colors worn by these gorgonians of the coral reefs.

Encrusting sponges spread their mats of yellow, green, purple, and red over the walls of the reefs; exotic mollusks like the jewel box and the spiny oyster cling to it; long-spined sea urchins make dark, bristling patches in the hollows and crevices; and schools of brightly colored fishes twinkle along the façade of the reef where the lone hunters, the gray snapper and the barracuda, wait to seize them.

At night the reef comes alive. From every stony branch and tower and domed façade, the little coral animals, who, avoiding daylight, had remained shrunken within their protective cups until darkness fell, now thrust out their tentacled heads and feed on the plankton that is rising toward the surface. Small crustacea and many other forms of microplankton, drifting or swimming against a branch of coral, are instant victims of the myriad stinging cells with which each tentacle is armed. Minute though the individual plankton animals be, the chances of passing unharmed through the interlacing branches of a stand of elkhorn coral seem slender indeed.

Other creatures of the reef respond to night and darkness and many of them emerge from the grottoes and crevices that served as a daytime shelter. Even that strange hidden fauna of the massive sponges—the small shrimps and amphipods and other animals that live as unbidden guests deep within the canals of the sponge—at night creep up along these dark and narrow galleries and collect near their thresholds as though looking out upon the world of the reef.

On certain nights of the year, extraordinary events occur over the

reefs. The famed palolo worm of the South Pacific, moved to gather
in its prodigious spawning swarms on a certain moon of a certain
month—and then only—has its less-known couterpart in a related
worm that lives in the reefs of the West Indies and at least locally
in the Florida Keys. The spawning of this Atlantic palolo has been
observed repeatedly about the Dry Tortugas reefs, at Cape Florida,
and in several West Indian localities. At Tortugas it takes place always
in July, usually when the moon reaches its third quarter, though
less often on the first quarter. The worms never spawn on the new
moon.

The palolo inhabits burrows in dead coral rock, sometimes ap-
propriating the tunnelings of other creatures, sometimes excavating
its burrow by biting away fragments of rock. The life of this strange
little creature seems to be ruled by light. In its immaturity the palolo
is repelled by light—by sunlight, by the light of the full moon, even
by paler moonlight. Only in the darkest hours of the night, when
this strong inhibition of the light rays is removed, does it venture
from its burrow, creeping out a few inches in order to nibble at
the vegetation on the rocks. Then, as the season for spawning approaches, remarkable changes take place within the bodies of the
worms. With the maturing of the sex cells, the segments of the
posterior third of each animal take on a new color, deep pink in the
males, greenish gray in the females. Moreover, this part of the body,
distended with eggs or sperm, becomes exceedingly thin-walled and
fragile, and a noticeable constriction develops between this and the
anterior part of the worm.

At last there comes a night when these worms—so changed in
their physical beings—respond in a new way to the light of the moon.
No longer does the light repel and hold them prisoners within their
burrows. Instead, it draws them out to the performance of a strange
ritual. The worms back out of their burrows, thrusting out the
swollen, thin-walled posterior ends, which immediately begin a series
of twisting movements, writhing in spiral motions until suddenly the
body breaks at the weak point and each worm becomes two. The two
parts have different destinies—the one to remain behind in the burrow
and resume the life of the timid forager of the dark hours, the other
to swim up toward the surface of the sea, to become one of a vast
swarm of thousands upon thousands of worms joining in the
spawning activities of the species.

During the last hours of the night the number of swarming worms
increases rapidly, and when dawn comes the sea over the reef is

almost literally filled with them. When the first rays of the sun appear, the worms, strongly stimulated by the light, begin to twist and contract violently, their thin-walled bodies burst open, and the eggs from some and the sperm from others are cast into the sea. The spent and empty worms may continue to swim weakly for a short time, preyed upon by fish that gather for a feast, but soon all that remain have sunk to the bottom and died. But floating at the surface of the sea are the fertilized eggs, drifting over areas many feet deep and acres in extent. Within them swift changes have begun—the division of cells, the differentiation of structure. By evening of that same day the eggs have yielded up tiny larvae, swimming with spiral motions through the sea. For about three days the larvae live at the surface; then they become burrowers in the reefs below until, a year hence, they will repeat the spawning behavior of their kind.

Some related worms that swarm periodically about the Keys and the West Indies are luminous, creating beautiful pyrotechnic displays on dark nights. Some people believe that the mysterious light reported by Columbus as seen by him on the night of October 11, "about four hours before making the landfall and an hour before moonrise," may have been a display of some of these "fireworms."

＊

Jonah's Dive

The waters compassed me about, even to the soul:
The depth closed me round about,
The weeds were wrapped around my head;
I went down to the bottoms of the mountains.

Book of Jonah

The great novelist's father was a civil engineer, specializing in harbor works and lighthouses. As a lad in Scotland, Stevenson hung around the gantries of the harbor engineering operations and was naturally intended to follow his father's profession. "But indeed I had already my own private determination to be an author," said R.L.S. in Random Memories. *"Only one thing in connection with the harbor tempted me, and that was the diving, an experience I burned to taste of."*

A Dive in Wick Bay

BY ROBERT LOUIS STEVENSON

*I*nto the bay of Wick stretched the dark length of the unfinished breakwater, in its cage of open staging; the travelers (like frames of churches) overplumbing all; and away at the extreme end, the divers toiling unseen on the foundation. On a platform of loose planks, the assistants turned their air-mills; a stone might be swinging between wind and water; underneath the swell ran gaily; and from time to time a mailed dragon with a window-glass snout came dripping up the ladder. To go down in the diving dress, that was my absorbing fancy; and with the countenance of a certain handsome scamp of a diver, Bob Bain by name, I gratified the whim.

It was gray, harsh, easterly weather, the swell ran pretty high, and out in the open there were "skipper's daughters," when I found myself at last on the divers' platform, twenty pounds of lead upon each foot, and my whole person swollen with ply and ply of woolen underclothing. One moment, the salt wind was whistling round my nightcapped head; the next, I was crushed almost double under the weight of the helmet. As that intolerable burthen was laid upon me, I could have found it in my heart (only for shame's sake) to cry off the whole enterprise. But it was too late. The attendants began to turn the hurdy-gurdy, and the air to whistle through the tube; someone screwed in the barred window of the vizor; and I was cut off in a moment from my fellow men; standing there in their midst, but quite divorced from intercourse; a creature deaf and dumb, pathetically looking forth upon them from a climate of his own. Except

179

that I could move and feel, I was like a man fallen in a catalepsy. But time was scarce given me to realize my isolation; the weights were hung upon my back and breast, the signal rope was thrust into my unresisting hand; and setting a twenty-pound foot upon the ladder I began ponderously to descend.

Some twenty rounds below the platform twilight fell. Looking up, I saw a low green heaven mottled with vanishing bells of white; looking around, except for the weedy spokes and shafts of the ladder, nothing but a green gloaming, somewhat opaque but very restful and delicious. Thirty rounds lower, I stepped off on the *pierres per-dues* of the foundation; a dumb helmeted figure took me by the hand, and made a gesture (as I read it) of encouragement; and looking in at the creature's window, I beheld the face of Bain. There we were, hand to hand and (when it pleased us) eye to eye; and either might have burst himself with shouting, and not a whisper came to his companion's hearing. Each, in his own little world of air, stood incommunicably separate.

How a man's weight, so far from being an encumbrance, is the very ground of his agility, was the chief lesson of my submarine experience. The knowledge came upon me by degrees. As I began to go forward with the hand of my estranged companion, a world of tumbled stone was visible, pillared with the weedy uprights of the staging; overhead, a flat roof of green; a little in front, the sea wall, like an unfinished rampart. And presently in our upward progress, Bob motioned me to leap upon a stone; I looked to see if he were possibly in earnest; and he only signed to me the more imperiously. Now the block stood six feet high; it would have been quite a leap for me unencumbered; with the breast and back weights, and the twenty pounds upon each foot, and the staggering load of the helmet, the thing was out of reason. I laughed aloud in my tomb; and to prove to Bob how far he was astray, I gave a little impulse from my toes. Up I soared like a bird, my companion soaring at my side. As high as to the stone, and then higher, I pursued my impotent and empty flight. Even when the strong arm of Bob had checked my shoulders, my heels continued their ascent; so that I blew out sideways like an autumn leaf, and must be hauled in, hand over hand, as sailors haul in the slack of a sail, and propped upon my feet again like an intoxicated sparrow. Yet a little higher on the foundation, and we began to be affected by the bottom of the swell, running there like a strong breeze of wind. Or so I must suppose; for, safe in my cushion of air, I was conscious of no impact; only swayed idly like a weed, and was now borne helplessly abroad, and now swiftly—and yet with dreamlike gentleness—impelled against my guide.

There was something strangely exasperating, as well as strangely wearying, in these uncommanded evolutions. It is bitter to return to infancy, to be supported, and directed and perpetually set upon your feet, by the hand of someone else. The air besides, as it is supplied to you by the busy millers on the platform, closes the Eustachian tubes and keeps the neophyte perpetually swallowing, till the throat is grown so dry that he can swallow no longer. And for all these reasons— although I had a fine, dizzy, muddleheaded joy in my surroundings, and longed, and tried, and always failed to lay my hands on the fish that darted here and there about me, swift as hummingbirds—yet I fancy I was rather relieved than otherwise when Bain brought me back to the ladder and signed to me to mount. Of a sudden, my ascending head passed into the trough of a swell. Out of the green, I shot at once into a glory of rosy, almost of sanguine light, the multitudinous seas incarnadined, the heaven above a vault of crimson. And then the glory faded into the hard, ugly daylight of a Caithness autumn, with a low sky, a gray sea, and a whistling wind.

*

Joseph Smith's Submarine

The Jaredites in their journey to the Promised Land crossed a tempestuous sea: "Buried in the deep there was no water that could hurt them, their vessels being tight like unto dish and also they were tight like unto the Ark of Noah."

The Book of Mormon, CHAPTER SIX

Professor Karo was director of the German Archaeological Institute in Athens for several long periods from 1905 to 1936. As a refugee from Hitler, he taught at Pomona College in California for more than a decade and then retired to a Hitlerless Germany. An amazing postscript to his Antikythera story came in 1958 when an expert on the history of scientific instruments, Derek de Solla Price, went to Athens and examined the fragments of the bronze "astrolabe," or protosextant, noted as the oldest navigational device yet found. Dr. Price mulled long over the corroded and fragile bits of bronze, and announced that the device was actually a digital computor! It could forecast the exact hour of the ascent and decline of stars, phases of the moon, solar eclipses and the courses of the planets, by gear trains that issued the information to three complex indices. This staggering discovery shows that the Greeks had computors on the level of those historians thought were first attained in the Renaissance, sixteen centuries later. What other marvelous things will underwater archaeology tell us?

Art Salvaged from the Sea

BY GEORGE KARO

*I*n the early years of the Emperor Augustus' reign, not long after 30 B.C., a large vessel, loaded with marble and bronze statues, was driving before the wind, off the southernmost tip of Greece, on her way to Italy. The storm must have been too violent for her to risk the dangerous channel between the mainland and the island of Kythera. Farther south, a rocky islet, now called Antikythera, has always offered some slight cover against northerly gales. But as the ship rounded it, her unwieldy cargo was bound to shift ominously, its heavy weight pounding against the sides until the planks gave way. Close to a saving cove in shallow water, she sank to the rocky sea floor.

An unchronicled disaster—no doubt one of very many. For ever since the last decades of the Republic a steadily increasing stream of artistic treasures had been pouring into the capital of the ancient world: sculptures and paintings, precious bronzes and silverware, carved and inlaid furniture. The palaces and villas of emperors and high officials, distinguished collectors and vulgar profiteers, were veritable museums of Greek, Oriental, and Egyptian art, for which sanctuaries and towns were looted, and an army of clever craftsmen in marble copied unobtainable masterpieces. We have detailed accounts of all this: literary sources like Cicero's letters or Petronius' delightful description of the ignorant "collector" Trimalchio, and the ruins of Rome, Pompeii, and Herculaneum, so rich in original Greek works and copies.

As the power and wealth of Rome increased, huge consignments of foreign marbles, columns and cornices and even enormous Egyptian obelisks, were brought across the Mediterranean on ships and rafts. How hazardous such voyages were is best illustrated by the fact that the French steamer which brought the bronze statue of Ferdinand de Lesseps to Egypt, for the opening of the Suez Canal in 1869, nearly foundered when the statue shifted in the hold: a fate which certainly overtook many of the ancient vessels that carried their treasures to Italy. Only one modern case is on record: when Lord Elgin shipped the famous marbles from the Acropolis of Athens to England in 1803, one of his ships was wrecked on the coast of Kythera. It took three years, with the help of divers, to recover the precious cargo. That was all one could tell about such disasters till 1900, when a series of spectacular discoveries by sponge-fishers began.

The Greek sponge-fishers are a race or tribe apart, who have carried on their hazardous profession for generations. Most daring of all Mediterranean seamen, fully aware of the fatal consequences of excessive diving, which doom them to an early death, but do not deter their sons from taking over, they work and play with equal recklessness. After a short but exhausting campaign, mostly in North African waters where the finest sponges grow on the sea floor, they return to their native islands, rich according to their modest standards, and paint the town red, as far as that is possible in the decorous atmosphere of a Greek village. When motorcars were still almost unknown in the Aegean archipelago, and useless anyhow because there were no roads, a group of sponge-fishers in Aegina had one mile of carriage road built along the sea front of their native town, bought an old Ford, and drove up and down that mile, amid triumphant yells and klaxon hoots.

The Aeginetan *sphoungarades* have a good name, but the most renowned for their skill and daring hail from the small island of Syme in the Dodecanese. Such men are heroes, and as such die young; their exploits are told, suitably embellished, in the seaside taverns where fishermen congregate. And their code of honor and courage is high.

Shortly before Easter of 1900, such a Symiote crew left the Tunisian waters for home, on two caïques, cutters which in size, shape and equipment hardly differed from similar craft that had plied the Mediterranean for the last three or four thousand years. There were six divers, and a complement of twenty-two oarsmen for calm days when sails would be useless.

A gale drove the Symiotes out of their course, to the barren, almost uninhabited islet of Antikythera (or Cerigotto, in the Italian lingua franca of the Mediterranean). As they lay some twenty-five yards off the headland which borders the little harbor of the island, they thought they might as well look for sponges on the rocky bottom. When they got down, one of the divers, Elias Stadiatis, to his vast amazement, sighted the remains of a large ship, an enormous heap of bronze and marble figures and various other objects, at a depth of about 150 feet. To prove he was not romancing, he brought up a bronze arm larger than life.

The skipper, Demetrios Kondos, himself an old master diver, promptly corroborated this stunning discovery; then he took some measurements and sailed home to Syme. After prolonged confabulation with the notables of the island, he decided to go to Athens and inform the Greek government, taking Stadiatis and the bronze arm along. There an agreement was reached, promising the sponge-fishers adequate compensation for the treasures they would recover and hand over. A vessel of the Hellenic Navy with the necessary machinery for hauling up heavy weights was to assist them in their difficult task. A government archaeologist would be on board.

When operations at last began, toward the end of November, stormy weather put a stop to them after only three hours. And similar aggravating interruptions occurred after every fresh attempt. So the work dragged on for nine whole months, in those peculiarly unfavorable waters. Only six divers were available, and they could not bear the strain of diving more than twice a day. Nor could they work for longer than five minutes on the sea floor with the very primitive equipment at their disposal: thus their collective efforts only amounted to one full hour's work a day.

And what work it was! Standing insecurely on the slanting bottom, they had to dig and scrape the sculptures out of sand and mud, tie stiff wet ropes around slimy, slippery bodies of bronze and marble, knot them firmly and return to the surface, breathless and exhausted, while the crane of the attendant ship wound up the load. If a rope slipped, at best a day's work would be lost; but the statue might also roll into deep, inaccessible water, and the recoil of the rope could be very dangerous. Under such conditions, it seems almost miraculous that during those three hours of the first day's work, a life-size bronze head, two large marble statues, and several smaller objects were recovered.

This unique archaeological enterprise was doggedly carried on, by fits and starts, with incessant interruptions by storms, extraordinary technical difficulties and the growing exhaustion of the divers. Some days proved rich in results; then a long, disheartening, sterile spell would follow. Much time was lost in clearing away fallen rocks, in the hope of precious finds under them, and in digging through hard, silt-encrusted shale. Such excavations had to be accomplished within a few hurried minutes, in the eternal submarine twilight. The weather continued vile. After a time, four new divers were added to the small original group, and all worked indefatigably, heroically; two were permanently disabled, and one died.

Yet these illiterate fishermen, totally ignorant of archaeological techniques, treated the finds with quite remarkable care and delicacy. I had occasion to examine them, very soon after their arrival in Athens, and was amazed at the insignificant amount of recent damage. Not only had the sculptures been handled with evident gentleness, but even pottery and glass vases had been brought up intact. The results filled a long gallery in the National Museum of Athens. The bronzes comprised a splendid nude statue of a young god or hero, larger than life, excellent work of the fourth century B.C., a couple of fine fifth-century statuettes, and remains of what may have been a group of five or six draped men, Hellenistic portraits of which one head was found the first day. All these must have been looted from some Greek sanctuary; the lead castings under their feet show that they had been torn from stone bases. The missing heads and bodies are undoubtedly still lying on the sea floor, probably at a depth unattainable to Greek divers.

The marbles were far less satisfactory. They have nearly all been terribly corroded by sea water and defaced by encrusted shells. Some are just formless lumps, others have spindly stumps instead of limbs. They look like lepers in advanced stages of the hideous disease. They are mostly commercial copies of famous originals, probably made at Athens for the export trade in the last decades B.C. The date is assured by a broken and incomplete bronze instrument, for calculating the rise of stars, the only extant astrolabe of antiquity. Its inscriptions prove it to have been made shortly after 30 B.C. We owe a debt of gratitude to the divers for having carefully collected what must have seemed to them insignificant bits of broken metal.

The discoveries of Antikythera caused a great stir in archaeological and artistic circles; there was a general feeling that the most modern diving equipment should be procured, to carry the search into deeper waters. But nothing came of it. The only adequately equipped and manned salvage ship of those happy times—when the Mediterranean sea floor was not yet littered with wrecks of two world wars—belonged to an Italian company which demanded half of all the expected artistic finds. The Greek government was forbidden to offer works of art as compensation by law. The negotiations ceased, the initial excitement soon cooled off, and after a few years the sculptures from Antikythera were just a part, and not even the most precious part, of the National Museum's treasures.

*

Starbuck Looks into the Clear Southern Ocean

Loveliness unfathomable as ever lover saw in his young bride's eye! Tell me not thou of thy teeth-tiered sharks, and thy kidnapping ways. Let faith oust fact; let fancy oust memory; I look deep down and do believe.

Herman Melville, MOBY DICK, CXIV

Submarine boat experiences are usually written by the man with the eye to the periscope—the commander—and not by stokers sweating it out in a blind compartment. However, this fetching account is by a Royal Navy stoker in World War II. Sydney Hart was discharged dead, when his name was left inadvertently on the roll of the submarine Triad *the day she sailed from Malta to her doom, leaving him behind in the hospital. He served later in the submarines* Truant, Thrasher, *and* Otus *and had an unusually well-rounded submariner's experience of being torpedoed and sunk in a surface vessel, HMS* Medway; *and of serving in HMS* Byard *when she sank U-Boat 841. Before the United States entered the war, Hart was in New London, Connecticut, for a refit and a U.S. marine asked him how many ships his outfit had sunk. Hart told him and the marine said, "My uncle is a submarine commander and he sank at least four more ships than you." He produced a letter from his relative to prove it: Uncle was Kapitan-Lieutenant of a Nazi Unterseeboot. After the war, the lucky stoker emigrated to Australia, but returned after two years, and now works in a Lancashire automobile factory.*

Trapped!

BY SYDNEY HART

*M*alta gave us a rousing send-off on this next patrol; an air raid was in full blast over the island, creating plenty of stir, as we passed through the boom in the darkness of the moonless night, with surmises as to our next patrol area. To each man his own job! Not that Malta didn't stand up nobly to the numerous pastings it received; we admired the fortitude of all on the island; it richly deserved its George Cross.

Trim dive was satisfactorily completed. *Truant* cruised at a comfortable twelve knots on the surface, and, despite our increasing impatience, no word came from the Captain as to the locality of our immediate activities. And then . . . everybody knew—the Adriatic. Phew! The Adriatic; the much-dreaded Adriatic, well known to all submariners as the worst patrol area of them all. Best thing to do was to shrug it off, and count it a compliment to our previous prowess. It wasn't our business on the lower deck, anyhow; our destinies lay in the competent hands of the commanding officer, and we considered ourselves in as good circumstances as any men afloat. So course was laid for the narrow bottleneck of an entrance that led into the prohibited area—prohibited by the enemy, and wide open to such as dared attempt it. We made a good surface run until the first tinge of dawn lightened the sky, and then we dived.

Being submerged gave opportunity for a chin wag; and all talk centered on this new hazardous patrol area. Questions flew like hail: "Has any other submarine survived an Adriatic patrol?" Someone replied: "I think the *Tetrarch* has been on this beat, and she got back." This news served to ease the strain, to some extent—but, make no mistake, the Adriatic threatened to be a sticky place! When we surfaced that night we received a signal to intercept a convoy in the Aegean Sea, but though several such signals were picked up, and the orders contained obeyed by *Truant*, that convoy was never contacted. So, after several days at sea, we were free to penetrate the entrance to the Adriatic—known to some as The Gate of Hell.

Lieutenant Commander Hugh Haggard took us into his confidence, instead of buttoning up and leaving us guessing. After all, we were in the same boat, and entitled to the information. I'll say this for our Captain, he always treated his crew as men of more than average intelligence. He told us that on the following morning we should dive at break of day as usual, and proceed through the entrance at a depth of 150 feet; and that it would take fully until nightfall before *Truant* was clear of the entrance. In accordance with these orders, the submarine slid gently below the surface with the approach of dawn.

"Shut off shallow water depth gauges!" was ordered as she went down from 32 feet—periscope depth—to 50 . . . 100 . . . 150 feet. Thus we were completely blind until the ship came up to thirty-two feet again, whenever that might be. No one could countermand our orders with any hope of our receiving them. The radio contact with civilization was useless for the nonce. The regular feeling of total isolation oppressed us; we were like lost souls floating in raw space. Not that we felt particularly lost. By this time we were hardened to circumstances, and, indeed, there were times when we genuinely welcomed this aloofness from the outer world.

Take a look at our present situation, perhaps the most difficult we had so far experienced. Inside that trivial steel hull, in a world that was surrounded by mine fields, and liable to be shaken to its depths by chance-dropped missiles of many descriptions, the lawful target of every known device calculated to shatter an underwater vessel, we sat down to a breakfast of tinned bacon and tinned tomatoes as casually as ever we had done at Fort Blockhouse. To give relish to the spartan food, we talked, not without nostalgia, of the huge, toothsome steaks we had wolfed down so recently in the U.S.A. Hungry explorers have said that they staved off the pangs of hunger by dreaming up the most fantastic meals, and thinking of them so hard that to some extent they became half-real. We were in the same category; and I admit we cursed these tinned substitutes for real food wholeheartedly.

It is queer how the comparatively trifling things of life take precedence when shaking hands with death as we were, immediate, unpleasant death. Not that we went in for undue philosophizing; such as were off watch climbed into their bunks and took a stretch off the land without argument—the submariner's most blessed trait is that unlimited capacity for dreamless sleep. The ship's interior was noisy with varied snores as she crept her stealthy way, slowly as a mole, through that defended entrance. At eleven o'clock that morning the call was "Diving Stations!" We were roughly halfway through the narrow Adriatic gateway, and the Captain had brought us up to periscope depth. On our echo-sounding gear we had detected the presence of three surface vessels. Silent liveliness characterized our actions from then onwards.

In the engine room we opened up the shallow-water gauge to follow the proceedings more closely and clearly, when . . . "Buzz, buzz," two torpedoes left *Truant*'s torpedo tubes almost simultaneously. The unshaven face of a seaman came through the watertight door between engine room and control room, his lips shaping the words: "There are two supply ships and an armed merchant cruiser up top!" And before he'd said it all, brrmp . . . brrmp! came the dull thud of a torpedo hitting its target. The very brief space of time between the tinfish leaving its tube and hitting the ship told us we were attacking at extremely close range.

Of all places to attack the enemy we had to pick the bottleneck Adriatic entrance, heavily mined as it was! What followed was rather sensational. *Truant* took a downward plunge with the roar of an express train entering a long tunnel, as the armed merchant cruiser tried to ram her, and missed by only a few feet! Then she leveled out and came up to periscope depth again—immediately the attacker had passed over her. There was another "buzz-zz," and a slight pressure in our ears, as another torpedo left its tube. "What the devil's happening?" queried a voice. Brump . . . brump came the answer;

another hit scored, and this time on the merchant cruiser. Lieutenant Commander Haggard was out for the kill.

It is an eerie sensation to hear the crumple of a ripped-open ship as she sinks deep to the sea's bed. These uncanny sounds are quite audible inside a submarine, and instead of being disconcerting, they create a feeling of triumph. Much the same sensation, I fancy, as a deck gunner feels when his first shell scores a bull on a quick-moving target. Satisfied that we had done our immediate duty, we slid down once again to 150 feet.

"Fall out. Diving Stations!"

Not a bad start. Hardly inside the Adriatic and two ships sent to the bottom. This new venture certainly had the makings of a first-class patrol.

By the time full night came down we were well inside the entrance and making good speed up the Italian coast. We'd won through the barrier, and were at large in hostile, very hostile, waters. Several days passed without much sensation. We crisscrossed from one coast to the other—first Italy, then Albania—but nowhere did a sign of shipping greet our searching eyes and echo sounder. At night, when all was deathly still, we surfaced and set to work to clean ship. All garbage was passed up through the conning tower by a human chain and thrown over the side without unnecessary noise. There was a terrific number of tins to be got rid of, the souvenirs of the plentiful food we'd eaten in the last twenty-four hours. Naturally, we perforated all such containers before they went over, so that they would sink instantly as they touched water, and leave no betraying evidence of our presence.

On the sixth day or thereabouts, inside the Adriatic boom, *Truant* at thirty-two feet depth, her periscope lifted just above the surface, spotted a supply ship of some three thousand tons heading toward her. The familiar call of "Diving Stations!" followed automatically; and was succeeded by "Stand by gun action!" Gun's crews were in the gun tower, shells cradled in their arms, and the gun layer taking quick glances at the target through the periscope on the Captain's orders, to familiarize himself with the general appearance of our impending target. All being in order, "Surface!" came the snapped command, and then, "Blow the main ballast." Up we came like a whale rising from a deep plunge, and the gun's crew were on the gun almost before *Truant* broke surface, so full of zest were they.

Wham—wham! The gun was blazing away at regulated intervals, with every shell fired registering a direct hit. One missile would be high explosive, bursting with a resounding crash as it hit the staggered ship, the next to follow was a semi-armor-piercing, designed to explode as it went through the steel skin of our latest target. All such details were carefully planned in advance, in order that the greatest amount of damage could be done. A comparatively few rounds sufficed to do the trick, and the diving klaxon roared out its significant AHOOA . . . AHOOA . . . AHOOA as the surface action came to an end. *Truant* dipped quickly below the surface with a third victim chalked up to her credit.

So far so good. But our activities were to be extended in a somewhat unusual way. Two nights after destroying the supply ship, our Captain decided to land two Commandos whom we had taken aboard in Malta, hard-headed men who were itching to get ashore somewhere and wreak havoc with their explosives. It may probably interest my readers to hear something of the activities of these gallant Commandos. The two men had, I believe, carried out several other raids from other submarines, and, quite naturally, they took this job from *Truant* as just another bit of necessary duty. In appearance they looked no more like Commandos than Scrooge looked like Father Christmas; both were slender in build, quietly spoken, and outwardly, at least, were of the type whose company would be welcomed at a Sunday school treat; anything less like the desperadoes made familiar to filmgoers could not be conceived.

They landed in full uniform, complete with thick, rubber-soled shoes, so that their movements on shore would be as stealthy as possible, and, if taken prisoner, their uniforms would refute any attempt by the enemy to brand them as spies. They had completed long, exacting courses on how to use their demolition charges to the best advantage, and were conversant with all kinds of fighting at close quarters—how to kill swiftly, silently, and surely. Their weapons consisted of Tommy guns, to be used only in the last extremity, as the noise of the weapons' discharge would give the game away; each man carried one other weapon, a deadly-looking dagger. The hilts of these tools formed the ugliest-looking knuckle-dusters that could well be imagined. These weapons could be used for two purposes at the same time; first, a knock-out blow from the knuckle-duster, then a thrust from the keen blade, with almost the same movement, to make a silent finish of whatever enemy might accost them.

Our passengers were as keen as mustard to get ashore, and as our patrol crept on toward its close, appeared quite worried lest their purpose might be frustrated. They needn't have worried, with a

Captain like ours! Being the kind of men they were, they settled down well in the submarine, and became really chummy with us, their aiders and abettors. The railway line running down Italy's Adriatic coast was a very busy affair, as it connected northern Italy with the southern Italian ports. The decision reached by the Commando officer and our Captain was that *Truant* would creep cautiously close inshore, when the two adventurers were to paddle the last few hundred yards to the beach, and afterward set a demolition charge on the railway line in hope of blowing up a train. When the landing was effected around midnight, *Truant* stealthily went inshore on the surface, and though Diving Stations were ordered, she remained surfaced, ready to plunge at the slightest alarm.

We went so close inshore that we felt that had any Italian been singing "*O sole mio*" on the beach we would have heard him. The rubber canoe was on *Truant*'s casing, ready for immediate launching. When our two daring passengers climbed up the conning tower ladder, whispered "Good lucks!" accompanied them. Unpretentiously they paddled off in that fragile canoe, which was more than scuppers awash due to their combined weight and that of their highly explosive cargo. Darkness, which we prayed might befriend them, swallowed them and not even the drip from the paddle blades was audible.

Suspense stretched our nerves. Men behaved as men do in similar circumstances of tension; a man would aimlessly pick up a spanner, walk a pace or two, turn the thing over in his hand, as if wondering what he'd handled it for, then meticulously put it back again from where he had snatched it. Someone said: "Should be on the beach by now!" Any second that strained, unnatural silence might be broken by the sound of a shot; the darkness split by the dazzling ray of a searchlight. Every second was as long as a minute, every minute as long as an hour. . . . So many possibilities raced through our minds: we listened for the screech of a motor torpedo boat, or the overhead whine of a diving aircraft, or the thunder of a battery of guns opening fire. Sweat poured down our bodies and our scalps tingled. Anything might happen—anything! It was different from the waiting outside Tripoli; that time we had only ourselves to consider; this time two exceedingly gallant friends were relying on us for a chance for life in the final event. My own feeling, shared by my shipmates to a man, was that it would be something little short of murder to have to abandon these heroes to their fate. If the Commandos were trapped whilst on shore, the enemy would instantly jump to the one obvious conclusion, that a submarine had landed them. That meant that the enemy might make things extremely unpleasant for us.

Time dragged on . . . fifty minutes, fifty-five . . . and the climax split the suspense. Bang! That loud explosion ashore meant that the Commandos had got their target; one train would certainly be out of commission for a long time, and the damage to the railway line would take time to repair. Still *Truant* crouched there on the surface, all hands scanning the clock faces. "They're a hell of a long time!" we all said. Why didn't something happen? Why didn't those search-lights flash out in a vengeful brilliance? The Italians must know as surely as we did that a submarine was lying close inshore. Why didn't the fireworks start up? The call through to the engine room, "They're alongside!" was almost as good to us as the declaration of armistice. Only seconds elapsed before the dinghy was stowed inside the submarine's hull, and with that task completed, we sped seaward. We didn't know what material damage was done. We did know that the enterprise must have shaken the morale of the Italian people, because, not having been spotted, there would be uncertainty as to whether it was an inside job by partisans, an enemy raid, or just an act of God. A good show, and we of *Truant* had helped to make it possible, and that's how pride in one's Service is born and grows.

After some fourteen days in the Adriatic we were all keyed up with hope and expectation of hearing the recall. Everything had gone well for us—better than we could have hoped, perhaps—but there was the continuous strain of being incessantly at close quarters with trouble, and eternally on the *qui vive*, and this was taking its toll. The moments of excitement and action were well enough, but the tension of waiting, waiting, began to fray our tempers. All sorts of paltry arguments grew out of trifling words and actions, and there was a growing suggestion of friction. You can get to dislike the same faces when you see them hour after hour, day after day, with no change. The receipt therefore of the signal: "*Truant* return to base at Alexandria," came as a draught of iced water to a thirsty man. But before the cooling draught could ease our tension, the adventurous spirit of Lieutenant Commander Haggard had to be taken into account. No getting away from it, our Captain was out for blood. He was a tireless enemy to Fascism and Nazism, and seemed likely never to be glutted with conquests. Before we left our patrol areas the C.O. glued his eyes to the periscope, through which he was able to see, in one of the several harbors around Ancona, no fewer than five tankers lying at anchor, in perfect safety, as their crews doubtless imagined. That inviting picture was completed by the sight of one enemy destroyer, obviously under a full head of steam, and ready to go into instant action.

Our charts told us that there was seventy feet of water in the harbor, which was sufficient to permit our entry, so the Captain resolved to go in dived, torpedo the destroyer, and then surface, and go into gun action with the five tankers and if possible sink the lot, or set them on fire to such an extent that they would be useless. If this daring venture succeeded it would make a fitting climax to what had already proved a highly successful patrol. The odds were heavily against us, but when did long odds ever deter determined submariners?

It was at four o'clock in the afternoon that *Truant*, at thirty-two feet, crept cautiously into the harbor. The inevitable tension reigned down below, the feeling that something big was pending kept us on our toes. The order, "Diving Stations!" told us the imminence of action was at hand. I've often thought since that these incursions into the guarded harbors were very similar to the stick-and-string Navy's old-time cutting-out expeditions—the sort of thing in which Admiral Cochrane, Lord Dundonald, specialized. The difference was that we couldn't snaffle the prizes and bring them triumphantly out from under the enemy's guns.

"Stand by one, two, three and four torpedoes!" So it had come, then!

All four tinfish were designed for the destroyer. Both motors were at "Slow Ahead" as we felt a cautious way farther and farther into that somewhat cramped roadstead. The Captain was tensed to the last degree, primed for action. He rapped out again, "Stand by one, two, three and four." His eyes seemed actually glued to the periscope. "Stand by—fire one! Fire two! Fire three! Fire four!" And in that instant an unexpected crisis arose. *Truant* took a terrific, dizzying angle, and vibrated. She was aground! Her nose was buried deep in the mud at the bottom of an enemy harbor. That chart had lied. Water was less than thirty feet deep! "Full astern, both motors!" came through the shudders. Our ship vibrated like a frenzied whale that feels the bite of the harpoon. Her screws thrashed angrily as she went into reverse, and tried to snatch herself clear of the gripping bottom.

"Stop both motors! Shut all watertight doors!"

And that order meant that we in the engine room were completely isolated; from then on we should get no information from the control room except by phone or the uninformative orders on the motor telegraphs. We were working blind, only aware of a crisis, equally aware that our Captain would exercise his usual coolness in emergency and do his utmost for all concerned. The bell rang: "Group up on the motors." Every ounce of power was going to be required for the next motor movement. The muffled telegraph rang: "Full astern both!" A shower of sparks flew from the main motor switches as the L.T.O. banged those switches home. Everything was under control, not a hint of panic was evident in the faces around. The situation was obviously serious, but submarines had extricated themselves from worse dilemmas. Why worry?

The propellers thrashed away at a nerve-racking pace. *Truant*'s stern jumped, leaped, bucked like a crazy bronco, but her bows still remained hard and fast in the clinging mud. It seemed to us that she couldn't help but break her back if she kept on like this. We all kept up the pretense of not caring a damn either way; maybe our nonchalance was overdone, but no one noticed. Definite apprehension troubled me, and even a fatalistic outlook couldn't prevent me swallowing a bit faster than usual. The racket was loud enough to drown my quickened heart beats, thank the Lord!

It seemed for all the world as if *Truant* were trying to commit suicide! Maybe on the surface, with a clean get-out possible, we should not have noticed those frantic struggles, but down in that hemmed-in after compartment—phew! Why try to picture the emotions that everyone ever penned in a tight corner knows well enough? Anyhow, what about that Fort Blockhouse training in ways of escape? The real thing couldn't be much tougher than the imitation. The telegraphs rang to stop.

We were trapped and it seemed as if we were finished. The batteries certainly wouldn't stand much more of the punishment they had taken in the two attempts to escape. With the stopping of the motors the silence in that compartment was deathly. And still not a suggestion of panic! "Oh, my country, bless the training that from cot to castle runs!" Queer, how in moments of high tension, tags of half-forgotten verse hum through one's brain!

A typical Navy voice broke that stillness: "I wonder what happened to the torpedoes?" So much unearthly racket had been going on below that we wouldn't know if we had hit or not: torpedoes three and four would obviously be stuck in the mud, but what had happened to numbers one and two? The question was answered by another cool, unemotional voice: "I only hope to God we've hit the

—so-and-so—destroyer!" And then above us we heard "chug-chug-chug." And with one accord we exclaimed: "That's the destroyer, by heck!" Obviously we had missed her, and now she had stopped fairly over the top of us. We knew she could see us: *Truant's* stern was only sixteen feet under water, owing to the angle at which she lay.

Sitting on the polished rails in the speckless engine room, wondering, talking of what the next move might be, every little motion made by our ship, and every trifling movement of the destroyer above, was acutely plain to us in that steel shell that might soon turn into a coffin. Someone made the bright suggestion that the enemy would certainly dredge for us with two ships, swinging a cable between them with high explosives attached, to sign our death warrant. Tension wasn't exactly eased when the clips on the watertight door leading to the control room spun round, and the Navigating Officer came through the slowly opening door. His arms were full of confidential papers, and he said to the Engineer Officer: "We've got to be ready to destroy these instantly." Lieutenant Josefson promptly called me over to him to say: "Stoker P.O. take the door off the drain-oil tank, we'll destroy these papers there when—if the time comes."

I lifted the plate leading into the bilges and climbed down. Bending over the tank top I saw a rat lying on the oil pipes, its eyes bulging, and its whole body trembling with fear. It was unable to move, and the thought came to me that it obviously sensed the danger that menaced *Truant*. My natural instinct was to kill it—rats in a submarine —but for some reason I didn't. A fellow feeling, it might have been. As I climbed out of the bilges I saw Leading Stoker Goldsack giving a demonstration of how he and the Skipper would look if seen to be pulling a plow in an Italian prisoner-of-war camp. The Captain was six foot four high and slim, whilst Goldsack was five foot six and stiffly built; to imagine any such coupling up caused us to laugh, and we needed laughter about as much as anything else life had to offer.

The Navigating Officer told us that the Captain expected an early attack by bombers; he thought that as far as the destroyer was concerned the water was too shallow for her to depth-charge us, and when darkness came down in about two hours' time we should make another stout effort to get free from our troubles. It is to be wondered at that my personal thoughts roamed to the nine o'clock news by the B.B.C. in far-off England, with a short, emotionless announcement at the conclusion of the bulletin: "The Admiralty regret to announce that H.M. Submarine X is overdue and must be presumed lost!" Very shortly, it seemed, they might be reporting this about *Truant*.

Then I thought of the pay sheets I'd seen of *Triad*'s crew, my name standing well to the fore, "D.D., Discharged Dead!" Moldy thoughts, yes, but understandable in the circumstances. It was two o'clock in the morning courage that this situation demanded; and it was only possible to hope, yes, and to pray, that it mightn't ooze out of my fingertips.

It needed something like Leading Stoker Goldsack's next statement to shake such brooding ideas out of one's mind. His dry humor did the trick, and brought the inevitable laugh, that wasn't absolutely bursting with mirth, "There are thirteen of us in this compartment, and if we make our get-out by the Davis Escape Apparatus, there are only twelve sets. Who's likely to be the unlucky one?" Yes, we laughed, all of us, for this type of humor was well understood by the submarine crews. It might be grim, but it fitted the occasion in a macabre way.

For a come-back I said: "Once we're drinking that ice-cold beer in the Fleet Club at Alex, we'll clean forget all about this turn-up, and, anyway, won't it give us something to talk about?" So we all licked our lips, and then started to do a job on the starboard engine. It was an odd place and time to carry out repairs, but we did it, and it helped to pass those two tight-stretched hours away. I fancy, though, that everyone's thoughts in *Truant* must have been the same: "I wish they'd finish the job and get it over and done with." How could we escape? We'd made two determined efforts, and *Truant* hadn't so much as budged.

Never, surely, was a night so slow in coming, but come it did, and as it darkened down on that dismal harbor we were still stuck hard and fast in the clinging mud. The telegraphs rang again with their muffled clang-clang-clang: "Both motors full astern together!" Every pair of eyes turned instantly to the ampmeters as the switches were again rammed home. No one expected the ship to move, and the propellers thrashed futilely at the water. Not altogether futilely though, she plunged and bounced up and down on the sea's bottom. That way she'd break herself up; she simply couldn't stand up to such excessive effort. But our Captain knew his own mind, and the telegraphs remained at "Full Astern!" The motors went on humming . . . humming, with queer little jerks, as if they were trying with human intelligence. You had the idea they were annoyed at their own insufficiency. Again and again we bumped, jolted, stuck, jolted once more. Then she gave an outsize bounce, and an excited voice shouted, "We're moving!"

Something in the nature of a miracle had happened. *Truant* was free of the ground, and her keel was scraping on the bottom as she crept out of harbor, sternwise. We didn't care if she crabbed out sideways, so long as she went! That fresh spasm of hope made us realize how truly scared we'd been. We were lathered in our own sweat. You only realize the weight of a strain when the first suggestion of an easing occurs. We were still in sight of that harbor when we surfaced, a necessary action, of course, as our depleted batteries simply had to be recharged. That stern struggle on the bottom had run them right down, and no wonder.

The atmosphere of the ship changed immediately. The humor was no longer forced but happily genuine. The conning tower hatch was thrown open the instant *Truant* surfaced, and lookouts were smartly on the bridge, both engines started up recharging batteries, and at the same time propelling us toward the Adriatic entrance, and beyond to the joyous Base. The stench of oil, mingling with the air as it rushed down the conning tower, was such that it was pretty obvious one of our torpedoes had sunk a tanker. That most probably accounted for the fact that no attack was made on us whilst we lay helpless in that harbor, whose surface was most probably covered with spilt oil, and one explosive dropped among it would surely have set the whole bay alight. The Italians had apparently decided on the lesser of two evils, which was to let the British bastards go!

*

The Trojan Diver

(Patrocles, the Danaan, knocks the Trojan, Cebriones, out of his chariot with a rock and gloats:)
"Bless my soul, there's a diver! He takes a beautiful header! If he were at sea, he could fill many hungry bellies diving for sea urchins. He'd go overboard in any kind of weather, judging from the way he dives from a car on land. Why, I didn't know there were any divers in Troy."

Homer, THE ILIAD, XVI

The Swedish wanderer Victor Berge has lived a life of peril and wide adventure. He was born in Bollnas, and his wanderlust was stirred by journeymen who worked in his father's tannery. He went to sea in hell ships at sixteen and jumped ship in West Australia, from which he joined the pearling fleet and learned helmet diving. Berge has pearled in a dozen countries, stowed away when necessary, and was once a steeplejack in Texas. During Prohibition he and a friend with two Negro servants drove two cars loaded with Carolina moonshine to New York and set up camp in a park along Riverside Drive. Police molestation was averted when they handed the first cop four fingers of rye whiskey. In 1942, Berge was captured by the Japanese in Java and subjected to torture and solitary confinement for three years. When released Berge weighed ninety-five pounds. His first act was to take back truckloads of rice and fish to his starving fellow prisoners.

An Octopus in Borneo

BY VICTOR BERGE

The four of us had now got money, a grand lugger and the means to fish for pearls, and even if we found no large ones we could make enough to live on from the mother of pearl. We could not hope for more. We called ourselves the "Pearl Vikings" and raved about our coming voyage to the wonderful South Sea coral islands with their beautiful girls. We had not a care in the world and not a tie to prevent us from finding real comradeship. Seldom have youngsters been so carefree and happy as we were during the next few years sailing among the islands. I now considered myself an experienced diver and began to be a bit rash; I thought I knew all about the undersea jungle, but I had a few grim reminders of my mortality and learned that even the finest diver must always be on the watch and always take great care.

I am going to tell of my most dangerous adventure underwater. It happened off the east coast of Borneo, which is one of the most unpleasant coasts in the world. Far out to sea the waters are muddied with the slime from the Borneo rivers. About seven miles north of

Cape Mangkalihat we hit upon a group of small islands. Ro told us that the nearest of them was called Balabalangan and we could find turtles. So we made for it in search of fresh meat, eggs and tortoise shells. As we approached the shore I looked over the rail at the sea bottom. There was every indication that we should find pearl oysters there. Ro dived first while I worked the pump: he soon came up with a basketful of shells. It looked as though we had stumbled on an un-discovered bed. I put on my suit as quickly as I could and dived. Slipping quietly away from the ship I felt my way to the bottom and began to look for the big shells which are the most profitable. I was in about ten fathoms of water. In the middle of a coral forma-tion I saw something that looked like an oyster and worked my way over a big clump of coral toward it. As I was going to pick the object up something caught hold of my left arm. Swiftly I turned round, grabbed the long keen knife divers always carry in case of emergency. I had no idea what was coming at me with swaying arms and I slashed at the point from where it came. It saved my life, for a giant octopus was trying to get me in its grip and the lucky slash with my knife had cut off two of its tentacles. These should have caught me by the upper part of the body and kept me helpless with my arms pressed to my sides.

But at the same time two more tentacles seized my boots and a big jerk threw me off my balance. I saw an ungainly mass and thick waving arms. I cannot describe my fear or how I struggled to try and cut off those tentacles which held my foot prisoner. The monster jerked so viciously that I swayed to and fro. I hit a rock with such force that all the air was pressed from my lungs. My helmet and breastplate banged so hard against my head that I thought I should lose consciousness. The octopus shook me as a cat shakes a rat and banged me backward and forward over the coral reefs. I strained every muscle to right myself after each jerk. If my helmet came down lower than my body the air would get into the suit and I should be finished. At the beginning I could see its body, which was as tall as a man, but the water was soon black with its ink and I was now fighting in pitch darkness. By clutching on to the safety and the life line I managed to keep upright after a jerk that took me down ten feet.

At last I knew that my strength was giving out and that I should soon be unconscious. I had not dared to signal that I was in terrible danger, for I was afraid that the fragile safety line would be torn up on the sharp coral reefs if my comrades pulled it up too sharply.

But now I reached up, my hands gripped the line on both sides and I pulled several times, making the signal: Pull till the line breaks. My body felt as though it was being torn apart and I fainted.

My experienced friend, Ro, saw that something was keeping me down below but he could not see what was happening. He had not wanted to do anything before receiving my signal. At first he hauled me on his own while Jack used the pump. It was no use. Not even the three of them could drag me up.

Ro's presence of mind saved me from a ghastly death. The junk bobbed up and down with the swell. He fastened the line round a capstan amidships and told Charlie and Jack to haul when the boat was in a wave trough. When the next wave lifted the boat it lifted me up on the crest. The octopus was surprised at the hefty heave and at that moment could not have had a fast hold on the coral or else our line would have snapped. I was dragged up and hung about six or seven feet under the water. I came out of my faint and thought my whole body had been torn asunder. The beast's arms were still fast round my boots and far below I caught a glimpse of his thick body. I was helpless, slung as I was between the two men hauling and the octopus which was trying its hardest to drag me back again into the depths. But now Ro could see it. He took a stout rope, hopped overboard and fastened it round my body. The men began to haul and Ro dived down and cut the tentacles from my legs.

There was not much life left in me as they hauled me aboard. Round my boots were traces of the tentacles, now glued to it. My face, neck and shoulders were all bloody from the blows against the helmet and the breastplate; my arms and legs were covered with scratches from the coral reefs. My friends thought I would die, but after an hour I recovered and screamed and cried like a hysterical woman. The giant octopus is the terror of the deep and very few men have ever had an encounter with one underwater and lived to tell the tale.

But a pearl diver's life is not all fights with octopuses and that was the only one I met at unpleasantly close quarters. During my life I have heard a lot of more or less fictional accounts about these monsters and have seen several huge specimens. Often I caught sharks and octopuses and slipped below to see what would happen in their fights. I would go down to forty-five feet so that both contestants should have room to maneuver.

The sight of an octopus arouses the worst hatred and blood lust in a shark, which swims around it so as to bewilder it. The octopus travels on its eight arms and watches its opponent coldly and cal-culatingly. One would think that the fifteen-foot shark could easily gobble it up but the octopus is extraordinarily nimble and adaptable. It maneuvers like a boxer, shoots backward, forward or sideways like lightning and suddenly manages to get a suitable chance. It darts at the shark, slings its tentacles round it and holds fast with the suckers. The shark bucks and rears like a wild horse trying to throw its rider. Sometimes I have seen them bash the octopus so hard against the rocks that both of them were killed. But usually the octopus wins. After about an hour the shark is tamed and sinks to the bottom with the monster on its neck. It holds on fast to the bottom with a couple of its tentacles and begins to strangle the shark. Then the tentacles close the gills and the shark is drowned.

*

"Endymion" (*A passage*)

It was a sounding grotto, vaulted, vast,
O'er-studded with a thousand, thousand pearls,
And crimson-mouthed shells with stubborn curls,
Of every shape and size, even to the bulk
In which whales arbour close, to brood and sulk
Against an endless storm. Moreover too,
Fish semblances, of green and azure hue,
Ready to snort their streams. In this cool wonder
Endymion sat down and 'gan to ponder. . . .

The visions of the earth were gone and fled—
He saw the giant sea above his head.

John Keats

Twenty-two-year-old Charles Darwin on the cruise of the Beagle
*(1831–36) obtained an extraordinary amount of correct information
and insight on the undersea world without going into the water
over his knees. He waded in the intertidal zone in the Maldives and
the Great Chagos Bank. At Keeling Cocos he pole-vaulted across inlets in the fringing reef to peer head down at the line between live
and dead coral. To learn the nature of the sea bottom he lowered
leaden bells filled with tallow. Sand and coral debris stuck in the
tallow and bare rock left a wax impression. Darwin went to sea as a
geologist, and the oceans were a university that shaped him into the
generalizer of nature. In 1839, twenty years before the immortal*
On the Origin of Species by Means of Natural Selection *flowered
from his cogitations on the data from the* Beagle, *Darwin published
a thesis on how coral reefs were formed. It was under attack immediately. Darwin amiably withstood nearly a half-century of challenge
himself, always ready to abandon his theory if the truth were shown
to lie elsewhere. In the last year of his life, he himself proposed a critical test of his idea: "I wish some doubly rich millionaire would take
it in his head to have some borings made in some of the Pacific and
Indian Ocean atolls and bring home cores for slicing from a depth
of 500 or 600 feet." If the core showed only coral and not base rock
Darwin would be correct. Fourteen years later the Royal Society
bored 1,114 feet into Funafuti Atoll in the Pacific. The first 750
feet of the core consisted of powdered coral and the rest was coral
compacted and crystallized into limestone. The core confirmed Darwin's masterpiece of deductive reasoning.*

Coral Reefs

BY CHARLES DARWIN

The naturalists who have visited the Pacific, seem to have had their
attention riveted by the lagoon-islands, or atolls—those singular
rings of coral-land which rise abruptly out of the unfathomable
ocean—and have passed over, almost unnoticed, the scarcely less
wonderful encircling barrier-reefs. The theory most generally received on the formation of atolls, is that they are based on submarine

craters; but where can we find a crater of the shape of Bow atoll, which is five times as long as it is broad; or like that of Menchicoff Island, with its three loops, together sixty miles in length; or like Rimsky Korsacoff, narrow, crooked, and fifty-four miles long; or like the northern Maldiva atolls, made up of numerous ring-formed reefs, placed on the margin of a disk—one of which disks is eighty-eight miles in length, and only from ten to twenty in breadth?

An earlier and better theory was proposed by Chamisso; he supposes that as the more massive kinds of corals prefer the surf, the outer portions, in a reef rising from a submarine basis, would first reach the surface and consequently form a ring. But on this view it must be assumed, that in every case the basis consists of a flat bank; for if it were conically formed, like a mountainous mass, we can see no reason why the coral should spring up from the flanks, instead of from the central and highest parts; considering the number of the atolls in the Pacific and Indian oceans, this assumption is very improbable. As the lagoons of atolls are sometimes even more than forty fathoms deep, it must, also, be assumed on this view, that at a depth at which the waves do not break, the coral grows more vigorously on the edges of a bank than on its central part; and this is an assumption without any evidence in support of it.

No theory worthy of notice has been advanced to account for those barrier-reefs, which encircle islands of moderate dimensions. The great reef which fronts the coast of Australia has been supposed, but without any special facts, to rest on the edge of a submarine precipice, extending parallel to the shore. The origin of the third class or of fringing-reefs presents, I believe, scarcely any difficulty, and is simply consequent on the polypifers not growing up from great depths, and their not flourishing close to gently shelving beaches where the water is often turbid.

What cause, then, has given to atolls and barrier-reefs their characteristic forms? Let us see whether an important deduction will not follow from the consideration of these two circumstances, first, the reef-building corals flourishing only at limited depths; and secondly, the vastness of the areas interspersed with coral-reefs and coral-islets, none of which rise to a greater height above the level of the sea, than that attained by matter thrown up by the waves and winds. I do not make this latter statement vaguely; I have carefully sought for descriptions of every island in the intertropical seas. Enormous spaces, both in the Pacific and Indian oceans, are interspersed with islands, of which not one rises above that height, to which the waves and winds in an open sea can heap up matter.

On what foundations, then, have these reefs and islets of coral been constructed? A foundation must originally have been present beneath each atoll at that limited depth, which is indispensable for the first growth of the reef-building polypifers. A conjecture will perhaps be hazarded, that the requisite bases might have been afforded by the accumulation of great banks of sediment, which owing to the action of superficial currents (aided possibly by the undulatory movement of the sea) did not quite reach the surface—as actually appears to have been the case in some parts of the West Indian Sea. But in the form and disposition of the groups of atolls, there is nothing to countenance this notion; and the assumption without any proof, that a number of immense piles of sediment have been heaped on the floor of the great Pacific and Indian oceans, in their central parts far remote from land, and where the dark blue color of the limpid water bespeaks its purity, cannot for one moment be admitted.

The many widely-scattered atolls must, therefore, rest on rocky bases. But we cannot believe that the broad summit of a mountain lies buried at the depth of a few fathoms beneath every atoll. So highly improbable is this supposition, that the bases of the many atolls did never at any one period all lie submerged within the depth of a few fathoms beneath the surface, but that they were brought into the requisite position or level, some at one period and some at another, through movements in the earth's crust. But this could not have been effected by elevation, for the belief that points so numerous and so widely separated were successively uplifted to a certain level, but that not one point was raised above that level, is quite as improbable as the former supposition, and indeed differs little from it. It will probably occur to those who have read Ehrenberg's account of the Reefs of the Red Sea, that many points in these great areas may have been elevated, but that as soon as raised, the protuberant parts were cut off by the destroying action of the waves: a moment's reflection, however, on the basin-like form of the atolls, will show that this is impossible; for the upheaval and subsequent abrasion of an island would leave a flat disk, which might become coated with coral, but not a deeply concave surface; moreover, we should expect to see, in some parts at least, the rock of the foundation brought to the surface. If, then, the foundations of the many atolls were not uplifted into the requisite position, they must of necessity have subsided into it; and this at once solves every difficulty, for we may safely infer, that during a gradual subsidence the corals would be favorably circumstanced for building up their solid frameworks and reaching the surface, as island after island slowly disappeared. Thus areas of immense extent in the central and most profound parts of the great oceans, might become interspersed with coral-islets, none of which would rise to a greater height than that attained by detritus heaped up by the sea, and nevertheless they might all have been formed by corals, which absolutely required for their growth a solid foundation within a few fathoms of the surface.

Mr. Williams insists strongly that the traditions of the natives, which he has taken much pains on collecting, do not indicate the appearance of any new islands: but on the theory of a gradual subsidence, all that would be apparent would be, the water sometimes encroaching slowly on the land, and the land again recovering by the accumulation of detritus its former extent, and perhaps sometimes the conversion of an atoll with coral islets on it, into a bare or into a sunken annular reef. Such changes would naturally take place at the periods when the sea rose above its usual limits, during a gale of more than ordinary strength; and the effects of the two causes would be hardly distinguishable. In Kotzebue's "Voyage" there are accounts of islands, both in the Caroline and Marshall archipelagoes, which have been partly washed away during hurricanes; and Kadu, the native who was on board one of the Russian vessels, said "he saw the sea at Radack rise to the feet of the coconut trees; but it was conjured in time." A storm lately entirely swept away two of the Caroline Islands, and converted them into shoals; it partly, also, destroyed two other islands. According to a tradition which was communicated to Captain Fitzroy, it is believed in the Low Archipelago, that the arrival of the first ship caused a great inundation, which destroyed many lives. Mr. Stutchbury relates, that in 1825, the western side of Chain atoll, in the same group, was completely devastated by a hurricane, and not less than three hundred lives lost: "in this instance it was evident, even to the natives, that the hurricane alone was not sufficient to account for the violent agitation of the ocean." That considerable changes have taken place recently in some of the atolls in the Low Archipelago, appears certain from the case already given of Matilda Island: with respect to Whitsunday and Gloucester islands in this same group, we must either attribute great inaccuracy to their discoverer, the famous circumnavigator Wallis, or believe that they have undergone a considerable change in the period of fifty-nine years, between his voyage and that of Captain Beechey's. Whitsunday Island is described by Wallis as "about four miles long, and three wide," now it is only one mile and a half long. The appearance of Gloucester Island, in Captain Beechey's words, "has been accurately described by its discoverer, but its present form and extent differ materially." Blenheim reef, in the Chagos group, consists of a water-washed annular reef, thirteen miles in circumference, surrounding a lagoon ten fathoms deep: on its surface there were a few worn patches of conglomerate coral rock, of about the size of hovels: and these Captain Moresby considered as being, without doubt, the last remnants of the islets; so that here an atoll has been converted into an atoll-formed reef. The inhabitants of the Maldiva Archipelago, as long ago as 1605, declared, "that the high tides and violent currents were diminishing the number of the islands": and I have already shown, on the authority of Captain Moresby, that the work of destruction is still in progress; but that on the other hand the first formation of some islets is known to the present inhabitants. In such cases, it would be exceedingly difficult to detect a gradual subsidence of the foundation, on which these mutable structures rest.

Some of the archipelagoes of low coral-islands are subject to earthquakes: Captain Moresby informs me that they are frequent, though not very strong, in the Chagos group, which occupies a very central position in the Indian Ocean, and is far from any land not of coral formation. One of the islands in this group was formerly covered by a bed of mold, which, after an earthquake, disappeared, and was believed by the residents to have been washed by the rain through the broken masses of underlying rock; the island was thus rendered unproductive. Chamisso states, that earthquakes are felt in the Marshall atolls, which are far from any high land, and likewise in the islands of the Caroline Archipelago. On one of the latter, namely Culleay atoll, Admiral Lutké, as he had the kindness to inform me, observed several straight fissures about a foot in width, running for some hundred yards obliquely across the whole width of the reef. Fissures indicate a stretching of the earth's crust, and, therefore, probably changes in its level; but these coral-islands, which have been shaken and fissured, certainly have not been elevated, and, therefore, probably they have subsided. In the chapter on Keeling atoll, I attempted to show by direct evidence, that the island underwent a movement of subsidence, during the earthquakes lately felt there.

The facts stand thus—there are many large tracts of ocean, without any high land, interspersed with reefs and islets, formed by the growth of those kinds of corals, which cannot live at great depths; and the existence of these reefs and low islets, in such numbers and at such distant points, is quite inexplicable, excepting on the theory, that the bases on which the reefs first became attached, slowly and successively sank beneath the level of the sea, whilst the corals continued to grow upward. No positive facts are opposed to this view, and some general considerations render it probable. There is evidence of change in form, whether or not from subsidence, on some of these coral-islands; and there is evidence of subterranean disturbances beneath them. Will then the theory, to which we have thus been led, solve the curious problem—what has given to each class of reef its peculiar form?

Let us in imagination place within one of the subsiding areas, an island surrounded by a "fringing-reef"—that kind, which alone offers no difficulty in the explanation of its origin. Let the unbroken lines and the oblique shading in the woodcut (top p. 209) represent a vertical section through such an island; and the horizontal shading will represent the section of the reef. Now as the island sinks down, either a few feet at a time or quite insensibly, we may safely infer from what we know of the conditions favorable to the growth of coral, that the living masses bathed by the surf on the margin of the reef, will soon regain the surface. The water, however, will encroach, little by little, on the shore, the island becoming lower and smaller, and the space between the edge of the reef and the beach proportionately broader. A section of the reef and island in this state, after a subsidence of several hundred feet, is given by the dotted lines: coral-islets are supposed to have been formed on the new reef, and a ship is anchored in the lagoon-channel. This section is in every respect that of an encircling barrier reef; it is, in fact, taken east and west through the highest point of the encircling island of Bolabola; clearly shown in the woodcut (bottom p. 209) by the unbroken lines. The width of the reef, and its slope, both on the outer and inner side, will have been determined by the growing powers of the coral, under the conditions (for instance the force of the breakers and of the currents) to which it has been exposed; and the lagoon-channel will be deeper or shallower, in proportion to the growth of the delicately branched corals within the reef, and to the accumulation of sediment, relatively, also, to the rate of subsidence and the length of the intervening stationary periods.

It is evident in this section, that a line drawn perpendicularly down from the outer edge of the new reef to the foundation of solid rock, exceeds by as many feet as there have been feet of subsidence, that small limit of depth at which the effective polypifers can live—

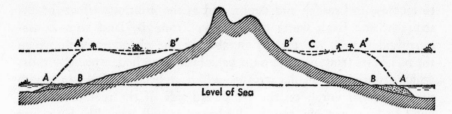

AA—Outer edge of the reef at the level of the sea.

BB—Shores of the island.

A′A′—Outer edge of the reef, after its upward growth during a period of subsidence.

CC—The lagoon-channel between the reef and the shore of the now encircled land.

B′B′—The shores of the encircled island.

N.B.—In this, and the following illustration, the subsidence of the land could only be represented by an apparent rise in the level of the sea.

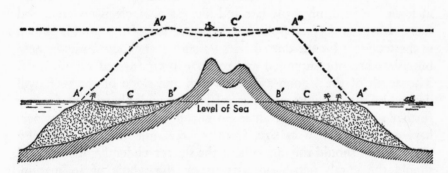

A′A′—Outer edges of the barrier-reef at the level of the sea. The coconut trees represent coral-islets formed on the reef.

CC—The lagoon-channel.

B′B′—The shores of the island, generally formed of low alluvial land and of coral detritus from the lagoon-channel.

A″A″—The outer edges of the reef now forming an atoll.

C—The lagoon of the newly formed atoll. According to the scale, the depth of the lagoon and of the lagoon-channel is exaggerated.

the corals having grown up, as the whole sank down, from a basis formed of the other corals and their consolidation fragments. Thus the difficulty on this head, which before seemed so great, disappears.

As the space between the reef and the subsiding shore continued to increase in breadth and depth, and as the injurious effects of the sediment and fresh water borne down from the land were consequently lessened, the greater number of the channels, with which the reef in its fringing state must have been breached, especially those which fronted the smaller streams, will have become choked up with the growth of coral: on the windward side of the reef, where the coral grows most vigorously, the breaches will probably have first been closed. In barrier-reefs, therefore, the breaches kept open by draining the tidal waters of the lagoon-channel, will generally be placed on the leeward side, and they will still face the mouths of the larger streams, although removed beyond the influence of their sediment and fresh water—and this, it has been shown, is commonly the case. Referring to the diagram shown above, in which the newly formed barrier-reef is represented by unbroken lines, instead of by dots as in the former woodcut, let the work of subsidence go on, and the doubly pointed hill will form two small islands (or more, according to the number of hills), included within one annular reef. Let the island continue subsiding, and the coral-reef will continue growing up on its own foundation, whilst the water gains inch by inch on the land, until the last and highest pinnacle is covered, and there remains a perfect atoll. A vertical section of this atoll is shown in the woodcut by the dotted lines—a ship is anchored in its lagoon, but islets are not supposed yet to have been formed on the reef. The depth of the lagoon and the width and slope of the reef, will depend on the circumstances just referred to under barrier-reefs. Any further subsidence will produce no change in the atoll, except perhaps a diminution in its size, from the reef not growing vertically upward; but should the currents of the sea act violently upon it, and should the corals perish on part or on the whole of its margin, changes would result during subsidence which will be presently noticed. I may here observe, that a bank either of rock or of hardened sediment, level with the surface of the sea, and fringed with living coral, would (if not so small as to allow the central space to be quickly filled up with detritus) by subsidence be converted immediately into an atoll, without passing, as in the case of a reef fringing the shore of an island, through the intermediate form of a barrier-reef. If such a bank lay a few fathoms submerged, the simple growth of the coral without the aid of subsidence, would produce a structure scarcely to be distinguished from a true atoll; for in all cases the corals on the outer margin of a reef, from having space and being freely exposed to the open sea, will grow vigorously and tend to form a continuous ring whilst the growth of the less massive kinds on the central expanse, will be checked by the sediment formed there, and by that washed inward by the breakers; and as the space becomes shallower, their growth will, also, be checked by the impurities of the water, and probably by the small amount of food brought by the enfeebled currents, in proportion to the surface of living reefs studded with innumerable craving mouths: The subsidence of a reef based on a bank of this kind, would give depth to its central expanse or lagoon, steepness to its flanks, and through the free growth of the coral, symmetry to its outline.

*

Above Us the Waves

We shall see, while above us
The waves roar and whirl,
A ceiling of amber,
A pavement of pearl.

Matthew Arnold, THE FORSAKEN MERMAN

The son of Sir Charles Belgrave, former adviser to the ruler of Bahrein, the oil-rich principality in the Persian Gulf, James Hamed Dacre Belgrave was born in Arabia and schooled in England, India, London University and the American University in Beirut. A born Arabist, Hamed Belgrave has studied the history and people of Bahrein in sympathetic detail, as indicated by this account of the immemorial pink pearl industry of the Persian Gulf. He is now director of public relations and broadcasting for the Bahrein government.

Jewels of the Deep

BY JAMES H. D. BELGRAVE

*P*earl diving is probably the oldest industry in Bahrein and is the reason why a small and comparatively unproductive group of islands has been the scene of so many bitter wars and has been overrun by so many invading armies. From earliest times Bahrein has been renowned for its pearls; in an Assyrian inscription around 2000 B.C. a parcel of "fish eyes" from Dilmun is believed to be the first reference to Bahrein pearls. Pliny stated that Tylos, the classical name for Bahrein, was "famous for the vast number of its pearls." Suliman, an Arab traveler of the ninth century, mentions the pearl fisheries of Bahrein. In the tenth century we have the first description of the actual methods of diving by Abu Zaid Hassan.

At the turn of the sixteenth century the Portuguese had firmly established themselves in India and were expanding into the Persian Gulf. In 1514 Don Albuquerque, Governor of India, visited Bahrein and noted with envy its pearl fisheries, and on his return to Hormuz, he ordered Bahrein pearls sent to the King of Portugal for the "pontifical of Our Lady." The subsequent Portuguese seizure of Bahrein in 1522 was probably due to the wealth of pearls, for the Portuguese were firm believers in monopolies and wanted to ensure control of the industry. This is confirmed by a Dutch traveler who said, in 1598, that "The King of Portugal hath also his factor in Bahrein, that stayeth there only for the fishing of pearls."

In the seventeenth and eighteenth centuries the pearl fisheries became better known to Arabs, for Bahrein pearls attracted the al-

Khalifah from Kuwait, first to Zubara and then, after their victory over the Persians, to Bahrein. In the nineteenth century the British became politically supreme in the Persian Gulf, but did not interfere in the industry. They helped to preserve the rule that only inhabitants of those countries bordering on the Gulf could pearl on the banks. Recent laws passed in Bahrein and Saudi Arabia forbidding the use of diving suits are aimed at giving all an equal chance to fish, without richer merchants gaining an unfair advantage by the use of mechanical equipment.

The "Gaus al-Kabir" or main diving season takes place from June to early in October, but before and after the season there is the "Gaus al-Bard" or cold diving season, the duration determined by weather conditions. In former days the departure of the Bahrein fleet for the pearl banks was the occasion of great excitement; with drums playing and small boys cheering, the boats would sail from Muharraq. Joined by boats from other coastal villages, the fleet would proceed to the pearl banks, where each boat would choose an anchorage and prepare for diving.

Formerly the boat built especially for pearl diving was the sambuk, but today the common craft is the jalibut. Many smaller boats with crews of a dozen men also go out to the banks. The pearlers carry special oars with square blades, and on arriving at the banks these are lashed so they project over the water. At each oar, two ropes are thrown overboard, one attached to a stone or metal weight and the other to a net bag, although the bag is sometimes hung around the diver's neck. The divers then strip to the buff, or a loincloth, put on nose clips of bone or tortoise shell and protect their fingers with leather guards. Standing in loops of the weighted rope, the divers are swiftly let down, each by his Saib or puller, who holds them with the careful hand of a fisherman, for more is at stake than a trout or a salmon. If the Saib fails to hoist the diver to the surface directly he feels his pull on the rope, the diver's life is in danger. When the diver reaches the sea bed the weighted rope is pulled up while the diver keeps hold on the second rope. The diver cuts out as many oysters as he can, usually about ten shells in the minute and a half he spends below the surface, then tugs sharply and is hauled to the surface. Seventy feet is about the maximum depth to which he dives, and it is easy to picture his frantic exertions to collect shells. Upon surfacing, the diver rests on the weighted rope, while the Saib tips the bag of shells inboard. In colder seasons the divers spend two-thirds of the time resting on the deck of the boat, sucking cigarettes or sipping bitter Arab coffee, but when the water is warmer a longer period is spent below. Food is not eaten during diving hours as it is considered bad for the diver's health.

The splash and swirl of the blue waters of the Gulf, often as smooth and clear as glass, the glistening bodies of the sunburnt divers, the deep-throated chanting of the Saibs, and the mounting piles of dark encrusted shells, are sights and sounds never to be forgotten. From time to time the cabin boy bags the shells and piles them along the gunwales. As the sun sets the crew eat a light meal of dates, fish, bread and coffee and then sink with pleasure into deep sleep along the decks. Then all that disturbs the silence of the night is the crackling of the fire burning on the portable mud hearth, the creaking of ropes and the splash of the midnight fisherman's line, catching tomorrow's meal.

Next morning the crew arises early and gathers around the heaps of shells which are more easily opened after having been left in the night air. With deft flicks of little curved knives, the pearlers examine the meat so that not even the smallest seed pearl is missed. The shells are tossed aside, later to be thrown back into the sea. Those who find pearls stick them between their toes and later hand them to the nakhoda or captain. He stores them in a great wooden chest, studded with brass nails, after tying them in small squares of red cloth, the color which is believed to show pearls to their best advantage. The decks are swabbed down and the day's diving commences.

From time to time, boats return to Bahrein for provisions and medical treatment. Fresh water, surprisingly enough, is less of a problem, for near many of the pearl banks there are submarine springs, some of which have been controlled by pipes affixed by the Bahrein government. The monotony of the diver's day is also broken by visits of "Tawawish," pearl buyers, who come out in launches to the banks to offer ready cash for their purchases, and by visits of hospital and police launches.

Despite the tales of travelers, sharks and saw fish are not a great menace to divers; they are in fact a rarity and for many years no diver has been attacked by either fish. The blue jellyfish is more feared than either, for its long tentacles can deal a most unpleasant sting. In the jellyfish season many divers wear cotton clothing covering them except for the hands and eyes. With better diet and medical treatment divers of today are as healthy as workers in other industries.

The financing of a pearl boat is a complicated affair. Formerly most boats were owned by their captains, but today the majority

of the larger boats belong to land merchants. Where boats belonging
to captains are financed by merchants, the latter make a profit of
about 10 per cent but when merchants both own and provision the
boats they receive 20 per cent. After deducting costs, the remainder
of the profit is shared in fixed proportions, the captain receiving
five parts, the diver two, and the Saib one.

When the nakhoda sells the catch he must always be accompanied
by two members of the crew, to see fair play. Sales are carried out
in an unusual way. The nakhoda and the purchaser or broker do not
want interested bystanders to know the amounts offered for the
pearls, so they spread a cloth over their hands and dicker by a sort
of deaf-and-dumb language. Once they have agreed on the price the
nakhoda must obtain consent of his two crewmen before the sale
is valid. Ordinary pearls are sorted for size in graded sieves, and
weighed and counted for their value in "chows," a traditional measure-
ment determined from a book. Once a pearl or pearls have been
assessed, the value per chow is settled by bargaining, the price
depending on the shape, texture and color. The value of paired pearls
depends on how well they are matched. Seed pearls, the smallest form,
are sold by weight, while a single large Bahrein pearl has been sold
for as much as $42,000, to a well-known American lady.

✤

Two Frenchmen Get the Same Idea

Could submarine landscapes constitute a revelation an-
alogous to that of the East under the brush of Delacroix?
The answer is that one needs a Delacroix.

Philippe Diolé, THE UNDERSEA ADVENTURE, 1953

I must think about getting a palette that could be put
into water.

Eugène Delacroix, JOURNAL: 11 AUGUST, 1855

One of the ablest historians of the U.S. shoal in the Pacific was Captain Edward L. Beach who made ten combat patrols in USS Trigger. *Later he was executive officer of* Tirante *during one of the war's epochal patrols, and subsequently he commanded the submarines* Piper, Amberjack *and* Trigger II. *Following this he served as President Eisenhower's Naval Aide during his first term, commanded the fleet oiler* Salamonie, *and is now skipper of the nuclear submarine* Triton.

Wahoo

BY CAPTAIN EDWARD L. BEACH

To tell the story of USS *Wahoo*, it is necessary also to tell the story of Mush Morton. More than any other man, Morton—and his *Wahoo*—showed the way to the brethren of the Silent Service. He was positive, intolerant, quick to denounce inefficiency if he thought it existed; but he was precise by nature, absolutely fearless, and possessed of a burning desire to inflict damage upon the Japanese enemy.

Just why Morton felt that destruction of the Japanese merchant marine was his own private job will probably never be explained, for he and *Wahoo* sleep forever somewhere in the Sea of Japan. But all that is immortal of both of them is indissolubly paired in the archives of a grateful (but forgetful) nation and in the minds and hearts of a few men who knew them.

Morton died, perhaps believing that his message had not been received by those for whom it had been intended, perhaps with a bit of bitterness that he could convince no one to follow where he led. But he need not have worried, for after him came a host of names which, by their very fame, proved that his ideas had fallen upon fertile soil. *Trigger, Tang, Barb, Tirante, Harder*—these were some of his disciples: the school of "outthinking the enemy"; the believers in the coldly logical evaluation of chances, followed by the furious, slashing attack; the devotees of the competition to bring back the most ships.

Morton believed that there was a certain way in which the job

216

should be done. He would have nothing to do with any other way. There is no question but that his search for perfection in his science brought about his own undoing.

On the last day of 1942 Lieutenant Commander Dudley W. Morton took command of USS *Wahoo* at Brisbane, Australia. There was nothing particularly outstanding about the new skipper during the first few weeks of his command, except perhaps an almost fanatical determination to get the items of the refit completed and checked on time, so that there would be no unnecessary delay in starting upon patrol.

Finally, on January 16, 1943, all repairs had been completed, and *Wahoo* was ready for sea for her third war patrol—Mush Morton's first in command. In company with her escorting destroyer—necessary in view of the "shoot on sight" order directed against any submarine in those "friendly" waters—the submarine got under way and headed for the open sea. At nightfall the escort turned back, a dimmed signal light blinking the customary farewell: "Good luck . . . good hunting!" Perhaps the captain of the destroyer wished that he, too, could go forth on his own, like some ancient sea rover, to seek out the enemy. Undeniably there was always a strong element of romance at the sight of a small ship setting out alone for enemy waters, bravely inviting the worse the enemy could offer, confident in her ability to best him in all encounters. Perhaps the destroyer skipper sensed this as he watched his signalman flash out his valedictory; perhaps Morton knew a momentary sense of understanding, also, but his answer was an equally simple: "Thank you!"

Wahoo was on her own.

It wasn't long before the first plan churning around in the restless brain of *Wahoo*'s new captain became evident to the crew, now that the need for secrecy had passed. Only recently had it become known that the Japanese for some time had been using a harbor known as Wewak as a major staging area. The location of this harbor was loosely determined to be somewhere on the northeast coast of New Guinea, but its position was known to our forces only by whole numbers of latitude and longitude. Morton planned to find Wewak, enter the harbor unsuspected, and raise as much fuss as possible.

The preparations he and his officers made for this little expedition were thoroughly characteristic of the man. The only available chart showing even in vague degree the location of Wewak was contained in a school atlas. Using a camera lens and the ship's signal light, a homemade projector was rigged up for the construction of a large tracing, designed to exactly the same scale as the ship's charts of that section of New Guinea. Much study of the *Notices to Mariners* and of other publications resulted in the accumulation of a considerable body of information which aided in the location of the correct spot. After several round-table discussions, the most likely area—between and behind several small islands off the coast of New Guinea—was selected. A large-scale chart was then made showing all pertinent information, and this chart was the one Mush Morton proposed to use for his entry and egress.

All this time *Wahoo* was proceeding at the best practicable speed toward the general area where Wewak was known to be. Obviously this new skipper was a bearcat, at least insofar as getting into action with the enemy was concerned.

Eight days out of Brisbane, *Wahoo* silently dived, at 0330, just a couple of miles north of the suspected anchorage. As dawn broke, her periscope made continuous and wary observations while her plotting party carefully noted down all landmarks and other data which might aid the attack or the subsequent exit.

If there were any lingering doubts that the new skipper meant to follow through with his daring plan, they must have been dispelled by this time, for he calmly ventured right into the anchorage area, deftly avoiding a patrol of two antisubmarine torpedo boats which had just got under way for their daily sweep. Nothing was seen here, however, except a tiny tug and barge which Mush did not consider worth bothering with.

Some tripod masts on the far end of one of the islands excited his interest, for they might belong to a ship, and a warship at that. An attempt to circumnavigate this island was frustrated by a low-lying reef connecting the island to the next in the chain and thus effectively keeping *Wahoo* from getting around to where the masts had been spotted.

It is difficult to describe the situation in which Morton had deliberately placed himself. He had entered, submerged, but in broad daylight, a suspected enemy harbor. He was in shallow water—a very bad place to be if your presence is detected. Moreover, there were enemy craft about, and in a position to do something about the submarine once its presence became known.

But far from worrying Morton, the fact that there were two Japanese patrol vessels active on antisubmarine sweeps in the area actually encouraged his belief that he had indeed found Wewak. So he spent the whole morning quietly cruising about the harbor area, nosing (submerged, of course) into all the suspected and possible anchorages, one after the other. By one o'clock he was quite disgusted, for he had seen nothing to show for his pains except a tug, two *Chidori* class patrol boats, and those unidentified tripod masts which he was unable to approach, and which, later observations showed, had disappeared.

But a few minutes after one, the situation changed. A ship was sighted, about five miles farther into the harbor, apparently at anchor. She was too far away to be clearly made out, because of the mirage-like effect of the glassy bay waters, which also forced *Wahoo* to expose only an inch or two of her periscope per observation for fear of being sighted.

Wahoo alters course, heads for the unknown ship. Two or three quick observations are taken, and the target is identified as a destroyer at anchor, with some smaller vessels alongside—apparently the tug and barge first sighted at dawn.

One of Mush Morton's unorthodox ideas, later adopted to some degree in the submarine force, was to have his executive officer make the periscope observations, while he, the skipper, ran the approach and co-ordinated the information from sound, periscope, plotting parties, and torpedo director. Thus, so ran his argument, the skipper is not apt to be distracted by watching the target's maneuvers, and can make better decisions. But you really have to have the courage of your convictions to carry out this stunt! And you also have to have an exec in whom you have complete confidence, and who can so work with his skipper that the two think and act together as one. Fortunately Morton had such a man in Dick O'Kane. They have thoroughly discussed and planned how everything should be done in case a chance comes their way—and here it is!

Battle stations submerged! The word is quietly passed through the ship. O'Kane and Morton have both been up in the conning tower of *Wahoo* for hours, looking over their quarry. Now O'Kane keeps the periscope, while Mush handles the rest of the attack details. The plan is to sneak up on the destroyer while he is still swinging around his hook, and to blast him right then and there. *Wahoo* will start shooting from about three thousand yards' range. All is in readiness as the submarine creeps into position. Fully aware of the unprecedented risks they are taking, *Wahoo*'s crew tensely stand to their stations. The temperature inside the ship wavers around a hundred degrees, for the air-conditioning plants have been shut down for some time to avoid unnecessary noise. As a concession to morale, however, and in the interests of having at least a bearable atmosphere inside the boat, the ventilation blowers and fans have been kept running—but now even these are stopped. A ship with all auxiliaries stopped can be eerily quiet indeed, and it is with this unnatural, deadly silence that *Wahoo* works into position for her attack.

"Up periscope! One more observation before we let him have it!" The voice is the skipper's.

Rising slowly from his haunches as he follows the 'scope up, his face pressed against the rubber eyepiece, O'Kane sees only greenish-yellow muddy water for a moment until the tip of the instrument breaks clear of the surface. Then bright sunlight strikes the objective lens of the periscope and reflects in multicolored hues as the tiny rivulets of water drain swiftly off the glass. O'Kane voice rasps out:

"He's under way! Coming this way! Angle on the bow, ten port!"

"Right full rudder! Port ahead full!" The skipper is almost instantaneous in the command. "Standby aft!" You have to be quick in this business, if you expect to be good, or if you simply hope to survive. Morton's intentions are immediately obvious to everyone: swing around to the right, and let him have a salvo from the stern tubes as he goes by. Still no thought of avoiding action.

"Dick! What speed do you give him?" Mush has to have this information. "Sound! Get a turn count on the target's screws as soon as you can!"

The sound man, intently watching his bearing dials as though by divination they could give him the information sought, shakes his head even while, with one hand gently pounding his knee, he is attempting to count. O'Kane runs the 'scope down without comment, then speaks over his shoulder.

"He's just got his anchor up, and he's speeding up. Not a chance in hell of getting his speed!"

"Well, try again! We've *got* to have some idea of it!"

The 'scope starts up again. O'Kane's voice "He's zigged! To his left! Crossing our bow! Bearing-mark!"

"Three oh three!"—this from the sailor intently watching the scribe marks on the periphery of the azimuth ring overhead, as the etched hairline on the periscope barrel matches that relative bearing.

"Down 'scope! Give him fifteen knots, Captain. That's just a guess, though!"

Mush Morton has not been idle during this periscope observation period. He has shifted preparations for firing torpedoes from the after room to the forward torpedo room. He has also made a swift approximation of enemy speed, from the meager information available. Quickly he supervises the insertion of the new situation into the Torpedo Data Computor (TDC). In a matter of seconds *Wahoo* is ready to fire with a third completely new setup.

"Sound bearings!" The command starts the chant of numbers from the sweating sound man.

"Three two oh!—Three two five!—Three three oh!—Three four oh!—Three five three!—" It's difficult to stay on a target going by at such close range and such relatively high speed, and the sound man has his troubles, but he does the best he can.

"Standby forward. Standby one!"

All is in readiness. All is quiet. The skipper nods to his exec. "Give us the bearings, Dick!"

Up goes the periscope again. Firing torpedoes on sound bearings is not for *Wahoo*. To make your shots good, you must get the target's exact bearing as shortly before shooting as possible. You take a chance on his sighting your periscope! If you really make them good, you won't have to worry whether he sees it or not!

"Bearing—mark!"

"Three five eight!"

"Set!" The TDC operator reports that he is, at that precise instant, on the target.

The clipped commands, the staccato syllables, are a natural result of the tension generated in the confines of the conning tower. About twelve feet long by eight in diameter, the conning tower is like a cylinder lying on its side, where, during general quarters, ten men must work.

"Fire!"

"Fire one!" repeats the firing key operator into his sound power telephones, as he presses the firing key.

In the forward torpedo room, the torpedomen are standing anxiously by the tubes. The tube captain wears the telephones and stands between the two banks of torpedo tubes, his eyes glued to his gauge board, his hand poised to fire the torpedo by hand if the solenoid firing mechanism fails to function electrically. But everything operates as it should. The click of the solenoid and the rush of air into the firing valve sound unnaturally loud in the stillness. The whine of the torpedo engine starting is heard momentarily as it leaves the tube, and the ship lurches. The pressure gauge for number one tube impulse air flask dies rapidly down to zero, and just before it reaches the peg at the end of the dial there is a sudden rush of air into the bilges under the tube nest, followed immediately by a heavy stream of water.

The Chief Torpedoman waits an agonizingly long time, then reaches up to a manifold of valves and levers and pulls one toward him. The roar of the water stops with a tremendous shuddering water hammer, and immediately a sailor, stripped to the waist, vigorously turns a large chromium-plated crank attached to number one tube, thus closing the other torpedo tube door.

Up in the conning tower, the firing key operator has been counting to himself as he holds down the firing key, but suddenly he is interrupted by a report in his earphones and sings out, "Number one tube fired electrically!" He then releases his firing key—actually a large brass knob fixed to the bulkhead beneath the ready-light and selector switch panel—reaches to the selector switch for number one tube, turns it to "Off," and then, very precisely, turns the selector switch under the number "2" to "On."

Meanwhile the TDC operator, who is the ship's Gunnery and Torpedo Officer, has been watching a stop watch and at the same time turning a crank set low in the face of the director before him. This introduces "spread," causing successive torpedoes to follow slightly diverging tracks. When his stop watch indicated ten seconds after the first fish has been fired, the TDC operator snaps, "Fire!"

"Fire two!" repeats the firing key operator into his phones, pressing his brass knob.

"Number two fired electrically!" reports the firing key man.

Roger Paine, operating the Torpedo Data Computor, waits until his stop watch again indicates ten seconds, and then repeats, "Fire!" Three torpedoes churn their way toward the unsuspecting destroyer.

Cautiously Dick O'Kane runs up the periscope. Suddenly he curses. "They're going aft! The bastard has speeded up!"

At the same moment a report from the sound man: "Two hundred turns, sir!"

"That's eighteen knots," says Morton. Then to Roger Paine, "Let's lead him a bit. Set speed twenty knots!"

"Bearing—mark!" from O'Kane.

"Zero one zero!"

"Set!"

"FIRE!"

A fourth torpedo heads for the enemy.

A cry from O'Kane—"Cease firing! He's seen the fish! He's turning away! Down 'scope!" The periscope starts down.

"*Leave it up, by God!*" Mush's voice has taken on a new quality, one not heard before by *Wahoo*'s crew. A raging, fighting, furious voice—the voice of a man who will always dominate the fight, who will lead and conquer, or most assuredly die in the attempt.

As the periscope starts up again, all eyes in the conning tower instinctively turn toward their skipper. This is something entirely new and unorthodox. "*Why, that will make sure he sees us, and will surely bring him right down on top of us! What can the Captain be thinking of?*" As if in answer to the unspoken thought, Morton speaks again, in the same reckless, furious tone as before. "We'll give that son of a bitch a point of aim all right. Let him come after us! Wait till he gets close, and we'll blast that goddamn tin-can clean into kingdom come!" At the full import of these words, the atmosphere in the tiny conning tower is electric. Striving to keep his voice calm, the telephone talker relays the plan of action to the rest of the ship, so that every man is apprised of it, and, of course, aware of the most extreme danger in which it places *Wahoo*. But not one of them falters, not one quails; although some may be mentally saying their prayers, they loyally go through with their skipper all the way.

Morton's plan is indeed unprecedented in submarine warfare, although obviously it has not been thought up on the spur of the moment. *Wahoo* is going to remain at periscope depth, instead of going deep and trying to evade the working over with depth charges she has invited. She will leave the periscope up in plain view—it being broad daylight, remember—to make sure that the enemy destroyer knows exactly where the submarine is. Seeing the periscope, of course, the Jap will also know the exact depth to set on his charges. But as he rushes in to make this apparently easy kill, *Wahoo*'s bow will be kept pointing toward him, and at the last possible minute, so that he will not have a chance to avoid it, a torpedo will be fired right down his throat!

This, rather obviously, is a pretty risky way to operate. Four torpedoes already have been fired, and there are only two more ready forward. All four after tubes are ready, of course, but there is no time to turn the submarine around. So Morton is shooting the works with only two fish, and one of them had better hit!

Grimly, O'Kane hangs on to the periscope, watching the Jap ship complete his evasive maneuver—turning away and paralleling the last torpedo, and then, after it has safely passed, turning around once more and heading for the source of the sudden attack. Smoke belches from his stacks as his firerooms are called upon for full power.

Around he comes, a full 180 degrees, until all that O'Kane can see is the destroyer's sharp, evil-looking bow, curiously now rather fat in appearance. Men are racing around the decks, and at least a hundred of them take stations in various spots of the topside, on top of turrets and gun shields, in the rigging, and along the rails on both sides of the bow.

Sweat pours off the face of the Executive Officer as he stares at what looks like certain destruction. But he does not forget his primary mission. "I'm keeping right on his bow!" he growls. "Angle on the bow is zero! You can get a bearing any time!" Occasionally he twirls the periscope range knob, and a new range is fed into the TDC. All is silent—except for the muttered bearings and ranges of the quartermaster, and the Captain's terse commands, and the hoarse breathing of the ten men in the conning tower, and the creak of the hull and the murmur of water slowly passing through the super-structure. O'Kane becomes conscious of a drumming sound and realizes that it is only the racing beat of his own heart.

"One five double oh yards"—from the quartermaster. Paine looks inquiringly at his skipper. Surely he must fire now!

Morton's jaw muscles bulge, and his face assumes even more vividly that prize-fighter expression which was to become well known —and even feared—by his crew. But his mouth remains clamped shut.

The dials of the Torpedo Computor whirl around: 1,400 yards' range!—1,350 yards!—1,300!—1,250!

As the range reaches 1,200 yards, the Captain's lips part at last, and a roar bursts from him, as if pent up within him until there is no containing it.

"FIRE!"

Wahoo's fifth torpedo starts its trip toward the rapidly approaching enemy. The men in their cylindrical steel prison feel a tightening of the suspense; the tension under which they are all laboring rises to a nearly unbearable pitch. But O'Kane is still giving bearings, and the TDC dials are still racing. Torpedo run for that fifth fish should be about thirty-two seconds. Morton waits a full ten seconds.

"FIRE!"

The sixth and last torpedo leaves its tube.

Dick O'Kane continues to watch at the periscope. A curious feeling of relief, of actual detachment from the whole situation, wells up within him. He now has the role of spectator, and there is nothing he or anyone else can do to change the outcome of events. He makes a mental reservation to pull the 'scope down if the torpedoes miss, so that the destroyer will not break it off passing overhead.

Two white streaks, almost merged into one in the murky water, swiftly draw themselves toward the onrushing Jap. Twenty seconds since the first one was fired. Dick notices much activity on the bridge of the destroyer. He starts to heel to port, as his rudder is evidently put hard a-starboard. The first white streak is almost there now—is there, and goes beyond, evidently a miss by a hairbreadth. But the second white chalkline is a little to the left of the first—it is almost there now—it is there. My God, we've missed! What? WHAM! A geyser of dirty water rises right in the middle of the destroyer, breaks him exactly in half, holds him suspended there like a huge inverted V, his bow slanted down to the right. The white-clad figures crowded all over his topsides are tumbling ridiculously into the water, arms and legs helplessly flailing the air. A cloud of mingled smoke and steam billows out of the broken portion of the stricken hull, rises hundreds of feet into the air, a continuation of the original geyser. Then, swiftly, the halves separate, and each slides drunkenly beneath the once-smooth surface of Wewak Harbor, now roiled up by the force of the explosion and the splashes from hundreds of particles of metal and other pieces of gear from the doomed vessel.

Within *Wahoo*'s thick steel hull the force of the explosion is terrific, something like a very close depth charge, as heavy a blow as if the destroyer had actually succeeded in completing his run upon her. Some of the crew, in fact, do believe they have received the first of a series of such depth charges. But in the conning tower there is wild exultation. Always kept ready for an opportunity such as this, the camera is broken out, and several pictures are made of the bow of the enemy vessel which, for a moment, remains to be photographed.

Then, and not until then, *Wahoo* goes to deep submergence—obviously not very deep in an anchorage—and starts for the entrance of the harbor more than nine miles away. The trip out is punctuated by numerous shell splashes on the surface of the water, sporadic bombing, and the patter of several distant machine guns. No doubt the Japs in the shore batteries would like to cause the undersea raider to lie "doggo" on the bottom until some antisubmarine forces, perhaps the two patrol ships sighted in the early morning, can get to the area. But *Wahoo* doesn't scare worth a damn, and late that evening she surfaces well clear of the harbor.

When asked later how he had managed to keep his nerve in the face of the attacking destroyer, Morton is reputed to have answered:

"Why do you think I made O'Kane look at him? He's the bravest man I know!"

So it was that *Wahoo* gave the submarine force her first lesson on one way to dispose of enemy destroyers. Needless to say, that method was seldom sought deliberately, even by the more successful sub skippers, but it is worthy of note that Sam Dealey in *Harder*, Roy Benson in *Trigger*, and Gene Fluckey in *Barb* at one time or another attempted similar shots.

Three days after Wewak, *Wahoo*'s lookouts sighted smoke on the horizon. This was to be a red-letter day. The minute smoke is sighted, or radar contact made at night, it is necessary to determine the approximate direction of movement of the contact. Otherwise, the submarine might track in the wrong direction, lose contact, and never regain it. So *Wahoo*'s bow is swung toward the smoke, and several successive bearings are taken. This takes time, for it is not easy to determine the approximate direction of motion of a wind-blown cloud of smoke when the ship making it is not visible. You don't want it to be visible, either, for that might enable an alert lookout to sight you. The smoke resolves itself into two freighters on a steady course, no zigzag—which makes the problem easier. Shortly before 0900 *Wahoo* dives with the two vessels "coming over the hill," masts in line. Then she lies in ambush, her crew at battle stations, torpedoes ready except for the final operations, always delayed until the last possible moment before firing.

Wahoo's plan is to lie a little off the track of the two ships, and fire at both almost at once in a single attack, so that torpedoes fired at the second ship will have nearly arrived before hits in the leading ship might give the second sufficient warning to maneuver to avoid. As the targets finally show up, however, Morton realizes that he is too close to the track to carry out his original intention of firing three of his six bow tubes at each ship. You must allow enough range for your fish to arm and reach running depth. So Mush regretfully reverses course, and now plans to shoot stern tubes. Since there are only four tubes aft, he will have to be content with two fish per ship and consequently less certain of sinking them.

Closer and closer come the two unsuspecting ships. Submarining is exactly like hunting, for you stalk your prey, lay a trap for him, and then wait for him to fall into it. Granted that merchant ships do not have an equal chance against a submarine, a skillfully handled ship can escape once the submarine has been detected, and an exceptionally well-handled one might even do damage to the undersea craft. Of course any submarine caught on the surface, by no matter what agency, is in trouble. So there is an element of danger in the hunt, and it is accentuated if defensive vessels, such as escort ships or aircraft, are about. Tension mounts as the game draws nigh. Periscope exposures become briefer but more frequent, to prevent a chance sighting as the firing point approaches. O'Kane is still doing the periscope work—excellent training for the skipper-to-be of the USS *Tang*.

Twenty degrees to go. Since the two ships are nearly in column and not far apart, it is planned to hit the first one just after he has passed astern of *Wahoo*, and immediately get the second just before he crosses her stern. Thus there will be the minimum interval between all fish, and it will be more like a single salvo.

"Make ready the stern tubes! Set depth ten feet!"

"Tubes ready aft! Depth set, ten feet!" The telephone talker repeats the report from the after torpedo room.

"Match gyros aft!" The TDC operator cuts in the gyro regulator for the after torpedo room, and a quick telephone check is made to insure that the angle transmitted from the conning tower is actually being reproduced at the tubes. It is the third time this particular check has been made this morning, but this is the time you want it to count.

"Standby aft!" Sound indicates there are only a few degrees to go. Plot and TDC indicate the same thing. O'Kane puts the 'scope back up.

"Continuous bearings!" The periscope bearing reader commences a singsong chant:

"One seven nine—one seven nine and a half—one eight oh—one eight oh and a half—one eight one . . ."

"Set—set—set!" from Rog Paine on the TDC.

Mush takes a final look at all dials, checks the bearings, and pronounces the word they have all carefully avoided saying until this moment:

"Fire!" The first torpedo speeds on its way. Ten seconds later, "Fire!" again, and the second torpedo is ejected, to follow nearly in the path of the first.

"Check fire! Shift targets!" Morton is taking no chances that an excited sailor might shoot off the last two torpedoes aft.

At the same time from O'Kane on the periscope, "Check fire! Shifting targets!" These two know each other's thoughts, know exactly what is expected and desired. Dick spins his periscope a few degrees to the left, picks up the second target, a somewhat larger freighter.

"On target! Bearing—mark! Continuous bearings!" And the chant resumes:

"One six nine, one six nine and a half, one seven oh—"

"Fire!" and, ten seconds later:

"Fire!"

Total time to fire all four torpedoes has been thirty-seven seconds.

The skipper orders left full rudder and full speed in order to get the bow tubes around in case the stern tubes prove to have been not enough.

Wahoo has barely started her wing to the left when—

"Whang!" and then, almost exactly ten seconds later, "Whang!" again. The first ship.

O'Kane had lowered his periscope to avoid being seen. Knowing the approximate time required for the torpedoes to reach the first target, he now raises it just in time to see the two hits, one near the bow of the leading ship, the other in his stern. He swings to the second ship, and sees a thudding hit in the stern of that one also, an instant before the sound and shock wave of that explosion reaches *Wahoo*. Three hits for four torpedoes. Not bad shooting, Mush. Now let's see if they sink, or if you have to polish these cripples off.

Down periscope again. *Wahoo* continues her swing, to bring her bow tubes to bear. Shortly before the circle is complete, up goes the 'scope, and a sweep around is made, to take stock of the situation.

Wonder of wonders! Now three ships are seen, instead of the original two! The newcomer is a large transport-type vessel, and troops can be seen crowding the decks. He must have been behind the larger freighter, hidden from the limited view of the periscope eye. So there are two damaged ships and one undamaged.

"Standby forward!" Bow tubes are ready, outer doors opened. There is no time to track this new target—only time to make the tubes ready, put the bearing into the TDC, and shoot. The same speed as for the original targets is used, because there is no information indicating a difference in the transport's speed, until this moment anyway.

"Fire!" after ten seconds. "Fire!" and then "Fire!" for the third time. Three torpedoes flash out toward the transport, and the last two hit him, with the familiar tinny, high-pitched explosion. The sound of water pouring into his damaged hull comes clearly over the listening gear, and his screws can no longer be heard. That will hold *him* for a while. Now back to the other two ships!

A quick look around shows that one is dead in the water, listed to starboard, and down by the stern. Nothing much to worry about there. He's evidently on his way to Davy Jones' locker right now.

But that second target is still under way, and has turned toward *Wahoo*. Give this Jap skipper credit for trying his best to fight his way out of the tough spot he is in. He has turned toward the place where the torpedoes came from, probably in the hope of ramming the submarine, or, at least, of interfering with further shots. He achieves his intention, too, for *Wahoo* is forced to fire two torpedoes quickly at him—another "down the throat" shot—in hopes of cooling off his combativeness. One hit, but even this doesn't stop him. Closer and closer comes the wounded hulk, yawing slightly as the Jap skipper and helmsman try to keep on course. Too late to fire another fish. The range is too close to allow proper functioning, and it would simply be a torpedo wasted. Nothing to do except duck.

"Flood negative! All ahead full!" The orders crack out like a whiplash. "Left full rudder! *Take her down!*"

Down plunges *Wahoo*, to get out from in front of that tremendous bow on which O'Kane has been counting rivets for the past fraction of a minute. Eighty feet, by conning tower depth gauge, and everyone breathes easier. Nothing can reach you down here. And listen to what's going on topside! Explosions, bangings, cracklings, water gurgles, a whirling and a thumping all over the place. *Wahoo* has certainly raised hell with this convoy!

But this is not the time for compassion. The job now is to get the rest of those ships down, and quickly before they get help from somewhere. "Up periscope!" Though the submarine is below periscope depth, and the range of visibility under water is not very great, a quick look will tell O'Kane whether they are coming up under the dark hull of one of the ships up there. The periscope breaks surface to show nothing in sight, and Morton heaves an involuntary sigh of relief. Only two ships can be seen now, while a large area covered with dirt, coal dust, and debris marks the end of the first target. The freighter which had attempted to ram is still under way, but the transport is stopped dead in the water, his topsides boiling with soldiers. *Wahoo* bores in, lines him up, and shoots one torpedo.

A bull's-eye! The wake heads straight for the target, now looming big in the periscope field, and passes harmlessly beneath him. No explosion. Morton grimly orders another fish fired. It follows the path of the first, but this time the depth mechanism does its job, and the torpedo goes off right under the tall, sooty stack of the doomed vessel. A blast of water momentarily hides his amidships section from view, reaching up higher than the top of the stack itself. Then it subsides, showing the ship broken in half, sinking rapidly by the bow, with men clad in olive drab jumping off into the water, or trying desperately to lower the lifeboats they should have gotten ready long ago. Two down out of three, and time out is taken to get a few pictures. Besides, the remaining torpedoes have to be loaded into the tubes and checked, a job much better accomplished submerged than on the surface. It is now noon, and *Wahoo*'s crew is sent individually, as they can be spared, to get what food the harried cooks have been able to get up on short notice. In the conning tower, Morton and O'Kane continue to watch the fleeing ship, munching sandwiches and drinking coffee between looks.

Suddenly, a pair of heavy masts is sighted over the horizon. This is beginning to look like old-home week for the Japs—and for Davy Jones, too, if the instantly laid plans of *Wahoo* bear fruit. This fellow looks like a warship. So much the better! There are a few more torpedoes left, and his name is on one of them. *Wahoo* proceeds at maximum sustained speed in the direction of the unidentified vessel. Unfortunately, she has so badly depleted her storage battery during the morning's action that she cannot chase at high speed, and hence cannot get into position to attack the new arrival. In the meantime, the crippled freighter has been staggering away from the scene as rapidly as his engines can drive his battered hull. The plotting parties check his speed at about six knots, quite respectable for a ship with two torpedoes in him. You really have to hand it to that Jap skipper. It is soon obvious that *Wahoo* cannot hope to catch either vessel. She continues to watch through the periscope, and sees the newcomer revealed as a large tanker, instead of a warship. He joins up with the cripple, and the two proceed away at maximum speed of the latter, black smoke pouring from stacks of both ships. All this time the undersea raider watches helplessly, too far away to interfere and too low in battery power to give chase.

There is a hasty council in the conning tower. Morton, O'Kane and Paine do some rapid figuring. Then, their computations completed, *Wahoo* changes course and proceeds directly away from the fleeing ships as rapidly as her waning battery power will permit. A continuous watch is kept on the quarry until finally the tops of their masts have disappeared over the horizon. Then *Wahoo* commences some maneuvers which are rather strange for a submarine anxious to avoid detection in enemy waters. The periscope rises higher and higher out of the water as the submerged vessel comes closer to the surface. As the height of the tip of the periscope increases above the surface of the sea, O'Kane and Morton can see farther over the horizon, and sight is thus kept on the escaping ships as long as possible. Finally, with the hull of the submarine only a few feet below the water and the periscope extending a full fifteen feet into the air, contact is finally lost. The periscope twirls around rapidly, scanning the horizon and the skies for any sign of other enemy activity. Then, swiftly, it starts down.

There is a moment's hiatus, and suddenly a long black shadow, visible beneath the waves, becomes sharper and more distinct. A moment later a sharp bow breaks the surface of the water at a large angle, plowing ahead through the waves like the forehead of some prehistoric monster, and within about ten seconds the whole low dark hull, cascading water from her decks and through freeing ports along the sides, has appeared. Up on the bridge there is sudden activity. The crash of metal on metal is heard as the conning tower hatch is flung open. The head and shoulders of a man appear, shortly to be joined by another. Morton's robust voice: "Open the main induction!"

There is a loud clang as hydraulic mechanism opens the huge engine air-induction valve. Instantly the exhaust roar of a diesel engine starting explodes into the stillness. Simultaneously, a small cloud of gray smoke pours from a half-submerged opening in the after part of the hull. This process is repeated three times, at rapid intervals, until four streams of exhaust vapor, two from each side, are sputtering and splashing the water which attempts to flow into the half-submerged exhaust pipes. The speed of the submarine increases through the water. A high-pitched screaming sound can be heard distinctly over all the other noises, as though a hundred cats had caught their tails in a wringer simultaneously. This noise is made by the low-pressure air blower, which is pumping atmospheric air into the ballast tanks, completing the emptying job which had been started submerged by high-pressure air.

All this time *Wahoo*'s speed through the water has been increasing as the diesel engines take the place of the battery for propulsion, and she rises higher and higher out of water as the ballast tanks go dry. Soon she is making a respectable seventeen knots—considering that one engine must be used to recharge the nearly empty storage battery so that *Wahoo* will be ready for further action submerged if necessary—which, of course, is exactly Mush Morton's intention.

While other members of the crew are relieved from their battle stations, there is no rest or relaxation for the plotting parties. But not one of them thinks of being relieved, nor would he accept relief were it offered. The plotting parties are busy with a problem which, by virtue of nearly incessant drill, has become second nature to them. You have a target trying to get away from you. You have his approximate bearing, and you have a good idea of his speed. Also, you have a lot more speed available than he has. Problem: Find him. Problem: Keep him from sighting you. Problem: Dive in front of him so that, despite his zigzags, he will run near enough to the spot you select to give you a shot! So *Wahoo* chases her prey from the moment of surfacing, shortly after noon, until nearly sunset. This is known as the "end around," and is to become a classic maneuver in the Submarine Force. You run your periscope up, barely maintaining sight of the tips of the enemy's masts, so that he will not have a chance of spotting you, and you run completely around him, traveling several times as far as he does, in order to arrive at a point dead ahead of him.

Half an hour before sunset *Wahoo* dives, once more on the convoy's track. This approach is much more difficult than the previous one. The enemy remember only too vividly the fates which befell their two erstwhile comrades, and consequently are zigzagging wildly. Then, too, *Wahoo* wants to attack the tanker first, since he is as yet undamaged. Finally, one hour after diving, *Wahoo* sees the tanker limned in her periscope sights in perfect attack position. The old routine procedure is gone through. As always, there is still the same breathless hushed expectancy, the same fear that, somehow, at the last possible moment, your prey will make some unexpected maneuver and frustrate your designs upon him. And you never forget that your life, as well as his, is in the scales. O'Kane is at the periscope . . . Paine is on the Torpedo Computor . . . Morton is conducting the approach, as always, blind.

Bearing! Range! Set—FIRE!

And three torpedoes race out into the gathering dusk. One minute and twenty-two seconds later, "WHANG!"—a single hit. The tanker stops momentarily, then gets under way again, at reduced speed. *Wahoo* spins around for a shot at the crippled freighter, but that canny Jap has already started away from there, and his change of course has spoiled the setup. It is still fairly light, though too dark

to see effectively through the periscope. There are only four torpedoes left in the ship, all aft. A moment's reflection, and Morton
gives the command to carry the fight to the enemy. "Surface!" Three
blasts of the diving alarm, the traditional surfacing signal, sound
raucously in the confined interior of the submarine. Up comes *Wahoo*,
ready to try her luck on the surface, under cover of what darkness
there may be.

In this she has the advantage of a much lower, darker hull, and
since there is as yet no moon, the shadows of night, growing pro-
gressively thicker, conceal her more and more from the Japanese
lookouts. Another advantage lies in the fact that the two damaged
ships choose to stick together instead of separating. But having torpedoes in the after tubes only is a tremendous disadvantage in a night
surface attack and *Wahoo* maneuvers unsuccessfully for two hours,
trying to get lined up for a shot. In desperation Morton even tries
to back into attack position, but is frustrated by the submarine's
poor maneuverability while going astern. So he must outguess the
enemy, despite his radical zigzag plan. *Wahoo* gets directly behind the
tanker, which in turn is behind the freighter. Then, as the two Japs
zig to the right, *Wahoo* stays on the original course, and when they
zig back to the left, the submarine is about a mile on the beam of the
unfortunate tanker. Suddenly *Wahoo*'s rudder is put full left, and her
port propeller is backed at full power, while her starboard screw is
put at full ahead. In this manner Morton is able to twist his ship,
get her end on to the broadside of the now-doomed Jap, and let fly
two torpedoes.

One hit amidships. The sound of the explosion cannot be heard,
but its effects are spectacular. The vessel folds in the middle and
plunges from sight almost instantly. "All full ahead!" Now for
that freighter! *Wahoo* has played around with him long enough. But
the skipper of the lone remaining Jap ship has other ideas. He keeps up
a continuous fire with his guns and steams in even more radical and
haphazard fashion than before. Now and then he sights the ominous
shape of the sea wolf stalking him, and places a few well-aimed shells
alongside, forcing her to turn away and once even forcing her to dive.

For an hour this cat-and-mouse game keeps up. Finally, a powerful
searchlight beam is sighted over the horizon. An escort vessel or
destroyer, probably sent to succor four vessels who had reported
being under attack by submarine. *Wahoo* had better do something to
end this stalemate fast! Again Morton puts on his thinking cap. What
would he do, if he were the skipper of the Jap freighter! "Well,"

thinks Mush, "there's no doubt at all what I'd do! I'd head for that destroyer just as fast as ever I could!" And he heads *Wahoo* toward the destroyer, full speed. Sure enough, the lumbering hulk of the wounded cargo vessel is soon sighted, headed in the same direction. Only *Wahoo* has preceded him, and now lies in wait for him and two torpedoes come out of the night to put finis to a gallant defense.

Four ships sighted and four down was *Wahoo's* record for January 27, 1943. The whole one-sided battle lasted thirteen hours, and after its conclusion one Jap destroyer was left fruitlessly searching the area with his searchlight.

Like everything else she did, *Wahoo's* entrance into Pearl was dramatic, for lashed to her full extended periscope was—a broom!

On her next patrol, which she spent in the Yellow Sea between China and Korea, *Wahoo* ran the entire distance to the patrol area, deep in the heart of Japanese-controlled waters, on the surface, diving only for necessary drills. When the patrol was completed she surfaced, still in the middle of the Yellow Sea, and headed for home, digressing only to track and sink one lone freighter sighted on the way. Only this attack, incidentally, prevented her from making the same "no dives" boast on her return trip as well. During the patrol, which covered nineteen days in the assigned area, *Wahoo* sank nine ships, one trawler and two sampans, and again expended all her ammunition. Once again the broom was lashed to the periscope. And again, in April, 1943, *Wahoo* and Morton made their third war patrol together sinking three ships and damaging two.

But she fell upon bad days, and Morton was a stubborn man; to these circumstances, and their unfortunate combination at just the wrong time, we may lay the responsibility for the sad loss of USS *Wahoo* and her fighting skipper.

After Mush Morton's third war patrol in command of *Wahoo*, an inspection of the ship showed that an extensive overhaul was needed to replace the worn-out battery, to repair damages, and to install new apparatus. So the vessel was ordered to Mare Island Navy Yard for two months. While there, the fine team Morton had built up suffered serious injury with the detachment of Dick O'Kane, who received orders to command the brand-new submarine *Tang*, then under construction at the Navy Yard. Roger Paine moved up to the position of Executive Officer. Mush Morton, though he regretted the loss of his very capable second officer, was overjoyed to see him finally get the command which he had longed for, and for which he, Morton, had repeatedly recommended him.

In late July, 1943, *Wahoo* arrived back at Pearl Harbor, after the completion of her overhaul. Then bad luck struck, for Paine developed appendicitis, and had to be removed to a hospital for an operation. Morton had been deprived of the two officers he depended upon most, but, nonetheless, confident, he proceeded on his fourth patrol.

Now Dudley W. Morton was a man of original ideas and independent thinking. Submarine doctrine called for shooting several torpedoes at each target, in a spread, in order to take into account possible maneuvers to avoid, errors in solution of the fire control problem, or malfunction of torpedoes. No quarrel could really be had with this procedure, so long as a submarine was apt to see and be able to shoot only a few ships per patrol. But in three successive patrols *Wahoo* had returned before the completion of her normal time on station, with all torpedoes expended. Morton knew he had the knack of searching out targets where other men could not find them. If you know you are going to see plenty of targets—so ran his argument—why not shoot only one torpedo at each ship, and accept those occasional misses? If a submarine fires three fish per salvo, and sinks eight ships with her twenty-four torpedoes, is that as effective in damaging the enemy as a submarine which fires single shots and sinks twelve ships with twenty-four torpedoes? Yet in the first case the sub should be credited with 100 per cent effectiveness in fire control; in the latter with only 50 per cent. The problem, according to Mush, lay simply in the number of contacts you could make. So he asked for, and received his fourth patrol, the hottest area there was—the Japan Sea!

The Japan Sea is a nearly landlocked body of water lying between Japan and the Asiatic mainland. It can be reached from the open sea in only three ways—through the Straits of Tsushima, Tsugaru, or La Perouse. The only other possible entrance is through the Tartary Strait, between Sakhalin Island and Siberia, which is too shallow for seagoing vessels and, anyway, under the control of Russia. It was known that the Japanese had extensively mined all possible entrances to "their" sea, and that they were carrying on an enormous volume of traffic in its sheltered waters with no fear whatever of Allied interference. If *Wahoo* could only get into this lush area, Mush figured, she should find so many targets that she would have an ideal opportunity to try out his theory. He knew the entrances were mined but he also knew that it takes an awfully good mine field to completely close up such a large passage as La Perouse or Tsushima, and that his chances of running through on the surface

above the anti-submarine mines (which, of course, would be
laid at depths calculated to trap a submerged submarine) would be
good. He also was banking on probable laxness and inattention on the
part of the Japanese defenders, and on taking them by surprise. So
on August 2, 1943, *Wahoo* departed Pearl Harbor for the Japan Sea,
carrying with her a determined captain and an entirely new team of
officers, some veterans of her previous patrols, but practically all of
them in new jobs as a result of the drastic changes at the top. On
August 14 *Wahoo* transited La Perouse Strait, on the surface at night,
at full speed. Though detected and challenged by the shore station
on Soya Misaki, she remained boldly on her course, ignoring the
signal, and having done his duty the watcher in the station went back
to sleep, leaving all navigational lights burning as though it were still
peacetime.

Mush Morton was certainly right about one thing. He entered the
Sea of Japan on August 14; that same night *Wahoo* sighted four
enemy merchant ships, steaming singly and unescorted. In all, she
carried out four separate attacks, three of them on the same ship, firing
only five torpedoes in all. And here Fate dealt Morton her most
crushing blow! *Faulty torpedoes!*.

There is nothing in the world so maddening as to bring your
submarine across miles of ocean; to train your crew up to the highest
pitch of efficiency and anticipation; to work for weeks getting into
a good fertile area; to assume heavy risks in arriving finally at an
attack position—and then to have the whole thing vitiated by some
totally inexplicable fault in your equipment. Time after time *Wahoo*
sights the enemy's vital cargo carriers and tankers. Time after time
she makes the approach, goes through all the old familiar motions
which have previously brought such outstanding success—and time
after time there is nothing heard in the sound gear, after firing the
torpedoes, save the whirring of their propellers as they go on—and
on—and on! Once indeed, the sickening thud of a dud is heard, but
most of the time the torpedoes simply miss, and miss, and miss!

Desperately, Morton tries every conceivable trick in his book. He
does not lack for targets—that he had foreseen correctly—so he has
plenty of time to try everything he knows. But he is still stubborn,
and mutters savagely something to the effect that there is no use in
firing more than one torpedo at any target until he has found out
why they don't go off. For four days *Wahoo* valiantly fought her bad
luck, and made, in all, nine attacks upon nearly as many enemy
ships. Results achieved, zero! Heartbreaking, hopeless, utter zero!

And then Mush Morton finally broke down. After four nightmarish days in the area, during which he became increasingly silent, moody, and irascible, sometimes venting the smoldering fury which possessed him with outbursts of a fantastic, terrifying rage, Morton decided that there was only one thing left to do. Characteristically, it took him only four days to reach this decision and to implement it. Fate had been able to make him do something no Jap had ever succeeded in doing—cry "Uncle." A message was sent to the Commander Submarines, Pacific, informing him of the complete failure of the torpedoes of his most outstanding submarine. The reaction from Admiral Lockwood was instant: Orders to proceed immediately to Pearl Harbor, and Mush Morton's action was equally decisive: *Wahoo*'s annunciators were put on "All ahead flank," and were left in that position until the submarine reached the entrance buoys off Pearl. The only exceptions to this performance were caused by appearance of a neutral merchant ship, which was identified as *Wahoo* maneuvered in for an attack; and two Jap sampans, whose captured crews found their final destinations to be somewhat different from what they had expected.

On August 29, only eleven days from the Japan Sea, Mush Morton and his *Wahoo* stormed into Pearl Harbor and tied up at the submarine base. This time there was no broom tied to an extended periscope, and the booming exuberance with which this sub had been wont to return from patrol was totally lacking. But such was the fame of *Wahoo* and her skipper that there was quite a crowd of men and officers on the dock to greet her and to tender the usual congratulations upon safe return. On this occasion there was a cloud over the normally lighthearted feelings of those present, for all knew that there was something radically wrong. One or two made an effort to say something cheerful to the obviously suffering Commanding Officer, but nothing they could say or do could allay the fact that Morton, who up to this time had been the most successful skipper of the whole force, had returned from his last patrol empty-handed. As soon as he decently could, Mush strode away from the crowd and hurried to the office of ComSubPac.

Once there he gave voice, in no uncertain terms, to the anger which possessed him. Virtually pounding his fist on the table—after all, you don't pound your fist at an admiral, even one so understanding as Admiral Lockwood—he insisted that something was radically wrong, and that corrective measures had to be taken immediately. The Admiral and his staff listened thoughtfully, for this was by no means the only report they had received about malfunctioning of the submarine's major weapon, and Morton was not the first man to cry "Damn the torpedoes!" Half-formed thoughts about sabotage, inefficiency, or improper preparation hovered above this gathering, and the upshot of it was that the Commander Submarines, Pacific Fleet, gave his word to Commander Dudley Morton that he would find out what was wrong with the fish if it killed him. In their hearts, the members of his staff echoed his sentiments—for, after all, every man there was a veteran submarine skipper himself. The interview with *Wahoo's* skipper at an end, Lockwood asked the question which Morton had been waiting for: "Well, Mush, what do you want to do?" Knowing his man, the Admiral was prepared for the answer he got, but it must be admitted that he would hardly have been surprised had Morton indicated that he had been taking a beating lately, and would like a rest. A rest was farthest from Mush Morton's mind at that moment. "Admiral," he said, "I want to go right back to the Sea of Japan, *with a load of live fish* this time!"

The two men took stock of each other. Morton saw a seamed, genial face, normally weather-beaten from years at sea, now showing signs of the strain of keeping his boys going and solving their problems for them—of holding up his end of the larger scope of the war plan—of defending and protecting his operations from those who, not knowing of the phenomenal results being achieved, would encroach upon, limit, or circumscribe them. With a small shock, however, he realized that at the moment there were only two emotions showing in the Admiral's eyes—worry, over him, and—*envy*.

On his side, the Admiral saw a young, virile officer, proud in his profession with the pride that comes only from a sense of accomplishment, and which will support no criticism. A fiery man, a fighter, and a leader. But burning in his steady eyes was the shining light of the crusader, now doubly dedicated, because his latest crusade had failed. They shook hands. "We'll get you ready as soon as we can," said Lockwood. Morton stood up gravely, thanked him shortly, and departed. As he watched that straight, tall figure stride out of his office, the thought flashed across the Admiral's mind: *"I shouldn't let him go. I ought to take him off his ship and let him cool off a bit. But I just can't do it!"*

So *Wahoo* was given another load of torpedoes, which were most painstakingly checked for perfect condition, and immediately departed for the Japan Sea to redeem her previous fiasco. She stopped at Midway en route, but nothing more was ever heard or seen of her, and what information we have been able to gather, consisting of reports of losses which could only have been due to depredations made by *Wahoo* on her last patrol, has come from Japanese sources. According to these sources, four ships were sunk by *Wahoo* in the Japan Sea between September 29 and October 9, 1943. Knowing the Jap tendency to deflate records of losses, it is probable that the actual number of ships sunk was eight or more, instead of four.

Wahoo never returned. Surprisingly, however, among the 468 United States submarines which the Japs claimed to have sunk, there was not one record, or any other information anywhere discovered which, by any stretch of circumstances, could explain what had happened to her. The enemy never got her. They never even knew she had been lost, and we carefully concealed it for a long time, knowing how badly they wanted to "get" *Wahoo*.

Like so many of our lost submarines, she simply disappeared into the limbo of lost ships, sealing her mystery with her forever. This has always been a comforting thought, for it is a sailor's death, and an honorable grave. I like to think of *Wahoo* carrying the fight to the enemy, as she always did, gloriously, successfully, and furiously, up to the last catastrophic instant when, by some mischance, and in some manner unknown to living man, the world came to an end for her.

*

To Sir Henry Wotton

And in the world's sea, do not like a cork sleep
Upon the water's face; nor in the deep
Sink like a lead without a line: but as
Fishes glide, leaving no print where they pass,
Nor making sound; so closely thy course go,
Let men dispute, whether thou breathe, or no.

John Donne

"Gorgonian" is the pseudonym of a retired Scottish clergyman, who became interested in marine science through student exposure to Sir John Murray's Challenger Office in Edinburgh a half-century ago.

The Undersea Gods

BY "GORGONIAN"

Before the pre-Homeric Greeks installed the gods of the Pantheon, they revered the Father of All, old Oceanus, the very river of creation. He lived at the furthest west of the world, amidst a court of sea monsters, and stroked his white beard with his red crab claws as he watched with universal eyes the struggle of man against nature.

Three of the twelve gods who were subsequently enthroned on Mount Olympus came from the sea: Aphrodite, born of the brine, debarked from a scallop shell as the goddess of love: Crookleg Hephaestus, the deity of invention and engineering, lived beneath the waves; as did blustering Poseidon, ruler of the oceans. Poseidon shared the sovereignty of the universe with the landsman, Zeus, and Hades, the lord of hell. The Sea King proclaimed "the gray sea as my inalienable realm," and posted it, according to Homer, with the challenge, "I am not going to let Zeus have his way with me. Powerful as he is, let him stay quietly in his own third of the world."

The sea-girt Greek imagination created shoals of submarine divinities. Oceanus' daughter Doris married Nereus. They lived in the bottom of the Aegean Sea and produced two hundred amiable diving daughters, the Nereids, or sea nymphs, who wheeled and sounded like porpoises. The most desirable Nereid, Amphitrite, was won by Poseidon after he sent his fastest porpoise to catch her. Their son, Triton, was a well-equipped diver. From the waist up, he was a man, and below he was fitted with flukes. Triton carried a trumpet conch which he blew sweetly to quiet stormy seas and blasted loud when he wanted a gale. From this salty clan have come two names for divers: *Ichthyotauri*, or fish-centaurs; and *Oceanides*, the descendants of Oceanus. Hera, the earth mother, bore a son with deformed feet, Hephaestus, and threw him out the window. Hephaestus fell from Olympus into the sea, where a charitable spinster, Thetis, took him into her submarine chambers, where also lived Joy, Bloom and Brilliance—the Three Graces. They gave the boy a tool kit, and he was soon fashioning marvels. He made a sword for Achilles, a scepter for Agamemnon, a necklace for Harmonia, and two walking, talking girls of gold to help him about on his crippled legs. Then he made an instrument of revenge upon his mother—a dazzling throne of beaten gold which he sent up to Olympus anonymously.

Hera sat on the golden throne and invisible chains clamped her down. The court locksmiths could not release her. Zeus sent another son, the ingratiating Dionysus, god of wine and merriment, to fetch a specialist to release the Queen. Dionysus put out to sea with his decks laden with grapevines growing in tubs as trading goods for the voyage. Hearing of the reputation of a clever boy who lived with four beautiful sea nymphs in a submarine grotto, Dionysus called one day, got the lad drunk and carried him off to Olympus. Hephaestus freed his mother of the invisible chains and was permitted to take her side in family arguments. Zeus, the Earth Shaker, became annoyed and this time, *he* threw Hephaestus out the window.

The engineer landed on Lemnos Island whose populace was in daily dread of a volcano called Old Mosychlos. The lad spit on his hands and plugged the volcano. The grateful islanders set him up in a new smithy, where he built two more walking, talking girls of gold, having mislaid the original pair somewhere. Dionysus, often came to see him during the wine harvest. They sat late with the farmers, sampling and resampling the new wine from the amphorae. These all-night drinking bouts were called *symposia*, from which the modern scholarly *symposium* takes its name, if not its inspiration. The ancient Greek labor day was dedicated to the deformed submarine engineer: smiths, smelters, carpenters and joiners, potters, wheelwrights, shipwrights, masons, and sculptors drank to Hephaestus and ran wild torch races.

The engineer's foster mother, Thetis, was a clever lass. She hid Hephaestus for nine years beneath the wine-dark sea, and often sheltered Dionysus when he was in trouble on the peak. She also fended with her quarrelsome admirers, Zeus and Poseidon, who visited the sea nymph while on "business trips." Nereus, the father of the good-hearted Thetis, pressed her to marry a substantial god, and hired a fortune-teller to find out whom. "Thetis' first son will be greater than you," said the seer. The jealous Nereus thereupon forced his daughter to marry a mere man. She tried to clothe her newborn son with immortality and succeeded in every part save the left heel. His name was Achilles and he gained mortality from Hector on the plains of Troy.

Many of the simple-hearted Nereids had romantic troubles. Galatea fell in love with a beautiful chap named Acis, which infuriated her gigantic admirer, Polyphemus, who had one eye in the middle of his forehead and slept in a cave with sheep. Polyphemus crowned poor Acis with a boulder. The mourning Galatea changed Acis into a river, an obituary notice that still flows through Sicily. Polyphemus later got his just deserts from a skipper named Odysseus. The cyclop took Captain Odysseus captive in the cave, and inquired his name. "Nobody," replied the canny mariner. In the night Odysseus put out the sleeping Polyphemus' eye with a burning brand, clutched the belly wool of a huge sheep and drew himself up into covert. The blinded monster cried to his gang, "Catch that man!" They said, "Who?" and Polyphemus said, "Nobody!" In the confusion, the sheep carried Odysseus from the cave to freedom.

The giant, Atlas, "knew the depths of the whole sea," said Homer, who also termed him "the thinker of mischief." Atlas did not find time for underwater practical jokes, however, due to his singular occupation, which was standing in one place and holding up the universe. He married an ocean nymph, Pleione, and their seven daughters form the constellation known as the Pleiades. Homer asserts that Atlas was also the father of Calypso, one of the most accommodating of the water maids. She dwelt on an island in the navel of the sea, and once entertained Odysseus for seven years. The sea rover made no complaint upon her hospitality, but Calypso at length began to feel that perhaps he should be thinking of returning home to the wife, and showed him how to build a boat. Odysseus took the hint.

Castalia was an unfortunate Nereid. In trying to elude the pursuit of Apollo, she fell into a spring on Mount Parnassus. The fountain still flows in that immortal glen at Delphi and if you take a glass of water from it, you become a poet.

The diver's mount of mythical times was the *hippocampus*, a horse with a fish tail. The gods often rode porpoises as well. Once a porpoise happened upon a woman named Ino who had fallen in the sea with her infant son, Melicertes. The helpful mammal carried them both ashore, where Ino and Melicertes were elevated to godhood as the protectors of distressed mariners. (The porpoise did not even receive a Trinity House medal.) The Romans rechristened Ino as Matuta and Melicertes as Portunus, their god of harbors.

The Romans as well changed Poseidon to Neptune and reduced

the Sea God almost to his present low estate as a buffoon in equatorial-crossing ceremonies on shipboard. It was harsh degrading for a god who had lived in a glittering palace deep in a lagoon and rode the waves in a chariot drawn by horses with bronze hooves and golden manes, whilst sea-monsters gathered in homage. No wonder then, that the Romans proved poor seamen for trifling with Poseidon in this churlish way.

Poseidon was an avid balcony climber and his wife, Amphitrite, formed a great jealousy of one of his inamoratas, the fair Scylla. Amphitrite dropped magic salts in Scylla's bathing pool, and the wretched creature emerged with six heads and a ravenous appetite for porpoises and sailors. Scylla took up a station in the Messina Strait and began to eat passing porpoises and seals. When a ship ventured by, she sometimes gulped the entire bridge watch in one bite, including dozing admirals and their cocked hats, sashes and claymores. It is a recorded fact that when Odysseus forced the Strait, she removed six men from his muster roll.

Amphitrite maintained a fold of domesticated seals, which were guarded by a moist shepherd named Proteus. The playwright, Euripides, asserts that Proteus was actually her son, but this may have been mere theatrical gossip. On the other hand, Proteus owned undeniable divine talents. He was a clever soothsayer and had the knack of turning himself into any shape he pleased, an art shared by many of the Greek sea gods.

Submarine deities usually married outside the profession, save Hephaestus, the ill-favored metallurgist, who won the hand of the radiant Aphrodite, goddess of love. Their marriage was not a success, perhaps because she resented his two golden secretaries. Later the Romans kidnaped Hephaestus and Aphrodite and changed their names (without deed poll) to Vulcan and Venus. The blacksmith is a persistent figure in mythology and reappears later as the Vulcan of Rome and in the Norse Saga as Loki, the fire god.

Although many Greek gods dived occasionally in the course of their duties, the only true professional diver among them was Glaucus, born a mortal. He was a sponge and murex diver in the Euboean Gulf. One day, whilst ascending quite spent from his seventh plunge, he noticed fish nibbling on a seaweed which stimulated them into all manner of pretty capers. Glaucus picked the weed and ate it. It drove him insane, and like some of our "frogmen" who sustained oxygen convulsions during the late war, Glaucus jumped into the sea and drowned. But there was a benevolent witness to the incident:

from the end of the earth Oceanus was watching. Out of compassion, he reanimated the diver as a god.

The sponge-picker joined the merry Nereids in their perpetual tour of the Mediterranean Sea, often going ashore to carouse and tell fortunes, even in the Sacred precinct of Apollo in Delos. Apollo was no green hand at prophecy himself and it was a plucky seer who dared invade Delos or Apollo's other booth at Claros. It was at Claros that quiz programs, like the ones with which we are familiar on the BBC, were introduced by a vain soothsayer named Calchas. He came with an impressive record gained in camp shows during the Trojan War: he had predicted the struggle would last ten years and was exactly right. Calchas announced that his own death would occur when he met a man smarter than he was. At Claros, he met another diviner named Mopsus and they bandied riddles about for several days until Mopsus stumped Calchas and the ex-champion fell dead. Glaucus was partly responsible for the first oceanographic expedition. He built the research vessel, the *Argo*, for Captain Jason, who sailed out with his band of technicians, the Argonauts, in quest of the Golden Fleece.

Even so, the old sponge-fisher retained a human failing from the days before his translation by Oceanus. He was subject to ennui. He became bored with diving, love, and prophecy, and complained, "I cannot die." All soon learned to avoid the gaffer with the fish tail, blue scales, gray beard, and oysters and barnacles nesting in his hairy chest, who kept repeating, "It's not fair. No matter how hard I try, I cannot die." Oceanus watched this long enough and once more felt pity for the diver. Glaucus went ashore one day, and as he stood confused in a busy street, the Father of All raised his red claw and permitted a chariot to knock him down and kill him.

Born in 1899, Commander E. R. Fenimore Johnson is an accomplished and publicity-shy explorer, a howling contradiction in terms. Since 1928 he has been taking underwater movies and developing submerged cameras in his own laboratories. He served in the field artillery in the First Great War and in the U.S. Navy in the Second and has conducted many marine explorations, including the Smithsonian Deepsea Expedition in 1932. His scientific reports include Studies on the Absorption and Scattering of Solar Radiation by the Sea *and one whose title we like very much:* The Preservation and Abuses of Motion Picture Film by Scientific Institutions. *His few popular writings have mostly appeared anonymously, but this rare signed piece will give the reader an idea of the caliber of our modest friend.*

Surrounded by Piranhas

BY E. R. FENIMORE JOHNSON

Of all the fish that propel themselves by means of fins, probably the most sinister reputation is held by a small denizen of fresh waters, variously called the caribe fish, the parai, and piranha, depending on what part of the world one may happen to be traveling in or reading about. The Latin name is *Serrasalmo piraya*. Mostly they are only twelve to eighteen inches in length but sometimes grow up to four feet. They have deep, compressed bodies and rather small mouths. When the lips are pulled back and the teeth are exposed their jaws are simply terrifying to the beholder. The teeth are triangular, sometimes like a shark's, and are so set that they interlock. The piranha is common in the Orinoco and Amazon and Paraguay rivers but is not found as far south as Argentina nor on the Pacific Coast of South America. Some species range up into Central America. All, to the best of my knowledge, live in fresh water. Everywhere one goes within their range one hears the same two grim stories. The first one is that a man who went swimming was emasculated by them, and walking out onto the bank, he picked up his revolver and shot himself through the head. The other is that if you throw the carcass of a cow into the water the piranha will reduce it to a skeleton within twenty minutes.

245

My own introduction to the piranha occurred in April, 1931, in the State of Matto Grosso, Brazil. At that time I was president of a corporation which had sent out an expedition for the purpose of making motion pictures, collecting animals, and carrying on scientific research. We had our headquarters in Matto Grosso at a little ranch village named Descalvados on the headwaters of the Paraguay River. On our staff was a medical student. One day he called me to look at a native who had met with an accident. The native was bleeding profusely from the big toe, which had been sliced away by a fish that had such effective biting equipment that part of the toenail and flesh had been cleanly removed. The big toe bone gleamed whitely when the blood was washed away. The radius of the bite was about equal to that of a silver dollar. The native had been riding his horse belly-deep in the waters of the nearby flood plain. The general belief was that he had scratched his toe on a piece of vegetation and that the blood had attracted a piranha.

In this day and age it is more popular to debunk than to exaggerate dangers, so I am going to do a little debunking; but I am going to be careful not to overdo it, because I still firmly believe that the piranha is a very dangerous little fish. In fact, I rate him as more dangerous than the shark, because he is more often met in schools than are the larger sharks; and while a man might have a chance to fight off a single large shark while swimming under water and equipped with self-contained breathing apparatus, his chance of fighting off a school of piranhas once they attacked is, in my opinion, absolutely zero.

The Descalvados water tank and pump were continually getting out of order, and we would be deprived of showers for days at a time. In that country one gets pretty sticky and dust covered and, consequently, pretty desperate for a bath. In July, under the leadership of Sasha Siemel—the "Tiger Man"—Dr. Petrullo, Julian Duguid and I went for a swim off the ranch dock in the main stream of the Paraguay. The water was so turbid we couldn't see more than an inch or two. Sasha claimed we were in no danger from the piranhas as long as we didn't bleed; and, in truth, none of us was bitten. I cannot honestly say that I enjoyed that or the subsequent brief dips which the heat drove us to take. Aggressive fish were so numerous that we used to amuse ourselves by tossing oranges into midstream where they would be repeatedly struck from below and sometimes driven several inches into the air, until some fish with a large enough mouth to sink his teeth into the oranges would finally win the prize. Casting plugs were chewed to splinters by the fish after very little use. A large part of our catch were piranhas. So! We did not swim around; we dove in and scrambled out fast.

Well! Let's get back to the debunking. In late May or early June the crew of our floatplane was completely demoralized by the spectacle of all the women in Descalvados coming down in a mass to the water's edge, stripping themselves naked, and going bathing. They took their time about it and came out of the river with nary a bite.

One day Dr. Petrullo and I made a special trip to the nearest city, Corumba, especially to confer with General Candido Rondon and offer him the courtesy of an airplane ride to his private ranch. The general was delighted to accept. On June 12 we had duly embarked on the airplane, when, much to my embarrassment, we couldn't raise the anchor. It was hooked onto the city's water supply pipe. Now, I do not count myself a brave man, but I have my principles. I don't order other people to do things that I'm scared to do myself. The water was only about twelve feet deep, but in view of the piranha and the jacares, a kind of crocodile or cayman, not to mention the anacondas that we often saw swimming around, I was not at all happy about ordering anyone to go over and free the anchor. There seemed to be nothing for it, so I stripped down to a pair of shorts, and over I went.

The underwater visibility was fairly good, and going hand over hand down the anchor rope I soon made out the anchor. Coming to it, I stood on the bottom and carefully lifted it free of the water pipe, then jammed a fluke into the bottom downstream so that the anchor would not drag while I was going up. I had not seen any fish on the trip to the bottom, but upon turning around to follow the anchor line back up to the plane, I glanced upward along the line and felt my entire body change from warm to that icy-cold feeling which instantly possesses one when shocked by mortal fear. Around the anchor line above me, arranged like spokes in a wagon wheel, was layer after layer of full grown piranhas!

Instinctively I reached the conclusion that a sudden move might precipitate an attack. Fortunately I had plenty of breath left, so I started slowly hand over hand up the anchor line, squarely through the center of the coldly staring fish. A most prominent feature of the piranha is its large, round, light-colored eyes, with their dark, pea-sized pupils. Believe me, the stare of a multitude of any living thing which is unfriendly has the power to heighten the fear of anyone who is the subject of the stare. By the time I climbed aboard the plane I was in such a state of shock I couldn't speak. It was at least a half-hour before I could relate my experience to my companions.

If I were thirty years younger I should make a trip to the Orinoco, the Paraguay or the Amazon to photograph the life story of the piranha and give it a good windup punch by photographing the fish in schools as they devoured a full-size steer carcass. Unfortunately, I have many responsibilities and am no longer able to spend four to six hours a day under water as I used to do.

*

From the Heights of Capri

"Look," he said, pointing down to the clear depths of the sea a thousand feet below. "Didn't your Tacitus tell you in school that when the news of the Emperor's death had reached the island, his palaces were hurled into the sea?"

I wanted to leap down the precipitous cliffs at once and plunge into the sea in search of my columns. "No need for such a hurry," he laughed, "for two thousand years corals have been spinning their cobwebs around them and the waves have buried them deeper and deeper in the sand. They will wait for you until your time comes."

Axel Munthe, THE STORY OF SAN MICHELE

A pioneer free diver and superb underwater photographer, Hans Hass has explored beneath the Caribbean, Mediterranean and Red seas. He remains faithful to oxygen rebreathing apparatus, for which he has an amazing individual tolerance. As in these Red Sea dives, he swims far below the permissible limits of oxygen, which are about thirty feet for the average diver. Dr. Hass is an Austrian-born marine biologist now living in Lichtenstein.

Coral Magic

BY HANS HASS

I had a regular program each day now. I was awakened by Achmed at seven; at eight Mahmud arrived and took my equipment to the boat; by ten we were already lying at anchor over the Wingate Reef. The weather was exceedingly favorable. In the mornings the sea remained almost perfectly smooth, with a long ground swell; the usual northerly wind did not rise until shortly before midday, and it took us back to Port Sudan in the late afternooon under full sail. Mahmud and O Sheik soon got used to my methods of work. While I swam and dived, they squatted in the boat or gossiped or else pulled the sail over their heads and slept. I saw them several times at their prayers, their bodies rising and bending in the little craft that floated in solitary state at the edge of the reef.

During these days I often had the feeling that every muscle in my body was enjoying itself on its own initiative. Wherever I dived, an endless new world lay before me. Every abyss which I explored beckoned me on to the next, which lay even deeper, even more sinister, below me. I came upon views so lovely that they took my breath away. And all my impressions took on a special spice from the fact that I was entering forbidden ground. I never allowed myself to forget that a shark might be waiting behind the next rock; I could never so lose myself in the beauty of a view as to forget to keep a sharp lookout.

A diver's greatest danger lies within himself; it is the sudden onset of fear. So long as he keeps calm and encounters hazards with full realization of all the dangers inherent in them, everything is all right.

249

But it is fatal to allow himself to be disconcerted by some unexpected occurrence. He is then in the position of a tightrope walker who loses his balance. Up to then his hands have automatically performed all the manipulations necessary to keep the respirator and other equipment in action, but after the onset of fear they seem helpless.

Breathing becomes twice as fast. He feels he is getting too little air. He pumps in fresh in a hurry, but too much of it. He makes for the surface and has to puff to regain his balance. Meanwhile, he bumps into a rock, or cuts himself, till it burns, on a coral; he turns around, but the string holding the yardstick has gotten tied up around the respirator and the camera is thumping ominously against the oxygen cylinder. Water has penetrated the mask and he has to lie down on his back and pump air hard into the thing.

Why was it he got so excited? It may have been only some unimportant trifle. An unexpected contact behind him. At once tautly stretched nerves slacken, an incautious movement is made—and a whole series of blunders ensues. It may be possible to resume his coolness and inner equilibrium; or there may be nothing but to make a dash, with a wildly beating heart, for the surface. With the feeling that it may already be too late and he will never reach fresh air and daylight in time, at last he bursts through to the sparkling surface of the water, hurriedly turns off the mouthpiece tap, and spits out the mouthpiece, breathing in deep drafts of liberating air. Then with trembling knees he climbs up a short slope of rock, and gradually the shock subsides as he lies in the warm sun.

The very fact that I had still not yet met any fair-sized shark got on my nerves. As soon as I saw the first one, I should immediately know what I was about; I should know whether the sharks here were really of a different type, more aggressive than those I had encountered in other seas. Where the deuce had they gone to? Were they deep down somewhere or off some outlying island, assembling for their mysterious mating ceremonies, leaving only the little ones, not yet of ripe age, at home? I had seen quite a number of small sharks of that sort, some of them absurdly long and thin. But the really big ones, against which I was continually being warned, had so far only shown up in my imagination.

It also occurred to me that I should not be able to count on anyone's assistance if anything really did happen. Mahmud and O Sheik were sitting up there in the boat, and I could easily guess how they would behave if I didn't reappear after an hour. They would row round and round in desperate anxiety and look down through the waves, but they would never be able to see right down to the depths at which I usually disported myself.

From below, one's upward range of vision is much longer. I could still see, from the depths of ninety and one hundred feet, the silhouette of the boat lying at anchor off the edge of the reef. But if I reached a still lower submarine chasm, I could only see at most fifty or sixty feet up. The deeper I went, the grayer and grizzlier the water became. Here were missing the bright solar reflections which continuously altered all the shades of color nearer the surface. Stale and oppressive, the motionless water hemmed in my body and the coral formations about me. I felt that I had to push this inert mass of liquid out of my way. My hands, when I caught a glimpse of them, were as pallid as those of a dead man. Not the slightest glimmer of red penetrated this depth.

Thick, serrated-type groupers, speckled black, glided up before me and turned to sink back again, their forms fading into greenish water. An enormous fish of angular shape, looking as though cut out of paper, hung motionless in the distance. Close to me a small recess had formed in the rock. So as to protect my back for a minute, I sat down in it and pulled myself together. Then a chill slowly began to rise up my legs. It was not a natural chill, for even at this depth the water was still relatively quite warm. It was a chill of uneasiness.

If there are two of you, diving is a pleasure—and fun for experts. If you are alone, you are at the mercy of your worst enemy, your own imagination. What might be approaching my recess from both sides? And what might there be in the recess itself, in the dark hole behind? The only thing to do was to think of something else. How was the camera focused? How many photographs had I taken up to now? Was everything still watertight? I forgot the depth and gloom and began to wonder whether I could photograph that fish that looked as if it were cut out of paper. I started swimming again. I had captured a new stronghold, for the next time I came to this neighborhood, it would already be familiar to me and the unknown would have lost its terrors.

So as to be able to recognize, later on, the separate types of coral I photographed, I broke a small piece off each stem and kept these specimens in the boat, preserved in little vials of alcohol. The form in which these pieces grew was quite distinct in each case, according to the environment. I had therefore to be able to recognize individual polyps, which varied amazingly in size: in the case of the stinging fire corals, belonging to the jellyfish family of polyps, they were only visible to the naked eye as tiny points; the star corals were about a half-inch in diameter; and the remarkable mushroom-shaped corals grew to the size of one's hand.

These mushroom corals form, it is true, an exception in every respect. While all other corals combine, like plants, with the soil beneath, the mushroom corals only do so at the very early stage of their growth. They then resemble a mushroom in the course of developing a continually widening head on its delicate stem. The polyp is carried on this head, which later breaks off and thereafter lies among the corals like a dumpling; it is picked up by the waves and tossed about; but the polyp thrives perfectly well on this treatment and grows out in all directions. The stem is also content with its fate. It at once starts developing a new head, which after a certain time, at the right moment, breaks off in its turn.

The weird thing about reef-forming corals is the fact that there seems to be absolutely no limit to their span of existence. If a stem grows too big, other grubs attach themselves to it and new colonies overgrow and displace it; but here and there one of them continues to grow and expand, regains its youth, and in its turn starts displacing the others. The oldest trees in the world have lived for some thousands of years; how many tens of thousands of years has this or that family of corals existed, growing up out of the bright maze of colors behind it? In this submarine world, there is no distinction between young and old, only an endless surge of new sprouting, which takes its building material—chalk—from the sea itself, in order to erect indestructible strongholds against that very sea.

How did the reef grow up, how did it turn into a solid wall? Up on its flat top it was hardly possible to see how the rock, worn smooth by the waves, could have been formed. But here below I could see the platelike structure was hollow underneath. Everywhere pockets and fissures led downward, creating entries to a system of grottoes which were undermining the plate of the reef from the depths. I found grottoes that ran far below the solid block of the reef for over fifty yards, and wildly meandering sidetracks and crossways which I followed underground.

Ghostly pairs of eyes gleamed out from the darkness of these grottoes. Pallid, hideous crayfish glided by like phantoms. I met cuttle-fish and there were slimy halls of the sea where a beam of light fell from some lofty window and played over the walls, unveiling the structure of the reef.

While, up above, the towering stems had been built into walls by calcareous insects, fragments of coral, and tiny chalk-isolating organisms, here below the sea was nibbling away the cement again and the buried stems were reappearing. Like spirits from the other world they brandished their dead arms from the rock. Jagged points, resembling stalactites, hung from the vault. I took a closer look at them: they were the lower ends of the corals growing upward. Upward . . . into the rock!

When I left these caverns of the past for daylight once more, my eyes were blinded by the dazzling brightness of the living corals, and I had again to get accustomed to distinguishing the multiplicity of details.

The bright fluttering, as of a butterfly's wing, over the bluish-violet bloom of the cluster yonder—was that caused by fish or by sunbeams which had grown heads and graceful fins? One of them drew nearer and became interested in a small crab hiding, apparently, in a nosegay. As the fish remained motionless for an instant I noticed that every scale in its body presented a different hue of the rainbow. All the colors were there. Blue, red, golden, and silver decorations and patterns traversed the graceful fins and encircled the head. He was gone! The little crab, too, had vanished. It was the old, sad story of eat and be eaten.

The myriad hues reached quite shallow water, where I was collecting, under the breaking waves, dainty little snails—the dove and Pharaoh varieties. Violet and purple snake stars curled among the twigs of the flower-like clusters. Blue-black and dark-red sea urchins seemed to be playing a crafty game with their spiteful prickles. Nile-green, azure, and orange-yellow water lilies unfolded their gorgeous starry crowns. And in the calyxes themselves strangely tinted, shell-less snails were posted, feeding on the corals like caterpillars browsing on flower petals in a garden.

If I moved, butterfly fish came gliding up in a panic, some with a huge eye outlined on the body, which examined me timidly as they scampered off like goblins. Soft, scaleless sea jumpers glided high up on the rocks and sprang, when I chased them, like grasshoppers to the next stone. But, look out! It would be better to be very careful where I put my hand. My fingers jerked back just in time! There lay a Synanceje, the ugliest of all fish. It lay close to a coral, like a bunch of seaweed, and slowly rolled the skin back from its dorsal prickles. Its sting is said to be as painful as that of a scorpion. Sometimes it even proves fatal.

But the blue and brown surgeonfish, which swam so harmlessly and nimbly about over the flowery meadows of the sea, also carried weapons I had better steer clear of. They are so named on account of two little daggers which can be snapped open at the root of the tail —reminiscent of the lancet once applied to the veins by the barber-surgeon. On the other hand the spindly-thin filefish, weird squadrons of which ride their patrols beneath the waves, were harmless. Despite their wicked-looking, crocodile-type jaws they were timid, and when I chased them, they dashed off over the water in long leaps into the distance.

If I wanted to see any more peculiar-looking shapes, all I had to do was to smash a pen coral and out came, like the residents of a hotel on fire, a number of little creatures, fleeing from their hiding places in all directions. Grotesquely patterned trapeze crabs ran races with a bright-green grasshopper-crayfish. Tiny little spotted fishes, no bigger than one's thumbnail, came floundering out of the wreckage. A date mussel, which had been living inside the coral, lay helpless, broken from its moorings. A small, reddish scale star wriggled under an iridescent annelid worm, which curled up and fled.

Even the rocks lying in the shallows were full of life. Their tops had been selected as sitting accommodations by sea squirts, moss animalcula, and sponges. When I caught hold of them, my hands were filled with numbers of little worms. They were embedded in the narrowest of crevices and channels; many had built themselves tiny houses out of sand and fragments of mussel shells; others merely used the rock as a temporary refuge and went out hunting at night. Brick-red scale worms adhered to the rocks like snails, by suction; others extended slimy threads, or stung me, when I touched them. The entire reef was nothing but a sponge of inordinate size, thronged with life. Creatures could live on it in a thousand and one ways, and they were adapted, in a thousand and one ways, to live in the fashion they did.

The reef had developed in exactly the same way as a human city. In a city, too, there are a thousand and one ways of living, which are exploited by human beings in their vocations. Each of the latter requires a particular equipment and a special kind of adaptation, and each has its effects on the rest in the great economic machine. One trader's business expands, another's is ruined. And this was precisely what happened among the crustacea, fish, and worms of the reef. Those that were advantageously endowed spread and became important wheels in the clockwork. Those that could not adapt themselves to the given conditions were destroyed, and other wheels took their vacant places.

Another time I was swimming at the foot of a precipice of the reef when I saw a double movement at a considerable distance. It rose vertically up the wall of the reef and glided over its top in the shallow water. At first I thought it was a couple of large panther (or spotted-eagle) rays, swimming close behind each other in an impulsive courtship.

I darted upward and saw both creatures, in quite shallow water, performing a round dance over the top of the reef, as they beat the water with their long whip-shaped tails and speckled lateral flippers. I took a photograph, then I tried to get nearer. But at once both got on the move again and swam off so fast through the shallows that I had all I could do to keep them in sight.

Suddenly the foremost doubled like a hare and swam for the top of the reef again, its partner following closely. I tried to cut them off, but by the time I myself had gotten to the top of the reef, they were already beneath me, in deep water, swimming on in a straight line, so that they were bound to disappear from my field of vision during the next few seconds.

Perhaps they both heard my sigh of disappointment; at any rate the foremost, the somewhat larger of the pair, evidently the female, doubled in its tracks as unexpectedly as before and made straight for me in a diagonal drive, while the smaller male came fluttering hastily after her.

I took a photograph, then concentrated my whole attention on the camera. It looked as if the rays, in their amorous frenzy, would come up quite close to me; I should have to take advantage of this unique opportunity. Range I put at one meter. Exposure could stay as it was. For speed a hundredth part of a second would do. Parallax? I should have to keep the upper point of the finder a little below the center of the crosslines. Ready!

I was just in time. The foremost ray had come right up to me and was just turning and gliding off sideways over the corals of the top of the reef. I waited till she raised her flippers, and then I took the photograph. Actually, the result was twofold. On the one hand the picture, with two others, won me a gold medal later on, and on the other hand the barely audible sound of the release catch was enough to send both rays dashing off in a panic.

If I hadn't seen it myself, I wouldn't have thought it possible that such clumsy creatures could attain such incredible speed. In their sudden fright they shot off like two great bats and it could not have been five seconds before they were swallowed in the distance.

*

Sea Change

Full fathom five thy father lies;
Of his bones are coral made;
Those are pearls that were his eyes;
    Nothing of him that doth fade,
    But doth suffer a sea-change
    Into something rich and strange.
    Sea-nymphs hourly ring his knell:
        Ding-dong.
    Hark! now I hear them—
        Ding-dong bell!

William Shakespeare, THE TEMPEST

Prior to building his famous steamboat, Robert Fulton spent twenty years trying to induce Britain, France and his own country to commission one of his practical submarine designs. In 1800 at Rouen, France, Fulton built a submarine called the Nautilus, *which he successfully dived to twenty-five feet and navigated for thirteen hundred feet submerged by the power of four crewmen turning the propeller. He turned the boat around underwater, proved that compasses work below the surface, and devised a primitive snort tube to the surface which permitted one dive of six hours. In a demonstration for the French Navy, Fulton blew up a sloop with a trailing mine and scared the admirals out of their wits. They turned down the invention with the comment, "Citizen Fulton's submarine boat is a terrible means of destruction because it attacks in silence in a manner nearly inevitable." No Admiral—French, British or American—wanted to encourage this fearsome weapon. When spies reported to London on Fulton's submarine the following warning went out from the Admiralty. It led to Britain enticing Fulton from France to deprive Napoleon of his alarming talents.*

The Secret Admiralty Circular

Adml. Lord Keith Sheerness
Admiral Montagu /20th/ Portsmouth
Rear Adml. Montagu Downs.
Honbl. Adml. Cornwallis/20th/at Sea
Adml. Sir Jno. Colpoys, K.B./20th/Plymouth.

Admiralty Office
19th June, 1803

My Lord,

My Lords Commissioners of the Admty. having been informed that a plan has been concerted by Mr. Fulton, an American resident at Paris, under the influence of the first Consul of the French Republic, for destroying the Maritime Force of this Country; I am commanded by their Lordships to send you herewith the substance of the information they have received relative thereto, that you may be appraised thereof, in order to your taking such measures as may appear to you necessary for frustrating any attempt on the part of the Enemy, connected therewith.

I have the Honour to be, etc.
Evan Nepean

(*Enclosure*)

Mr. Fulton, an American resident at Paris, has constructed a Vessel in which he has gone down to the bottom of the Water, and has remained thereunder for the space of *seven* hours, at one time—that he has navigated the said Vessel, under water, at the rate of two Miles and a half per Hour; that the said sub-marine Vessel is uncommonly managable, and that the whole plan to be effected by means thereof, may be easily executed, and without much risk; That the Ships and Vessels in the port of London are liable to be destroyed with ease, and that the Channel of the River Thames may be ruined; and that it has been proved that only twenty-five pounds of weight of Gunpowder was sufficient to have dashed a Vessel to pieces off Brest, tho' *externally* applied.

*

Plongeur Libre

He would swim in deep water on his belly, on his back, on his side, with his whole body, or only with his legs, or with one hand in the air holding a book. Indeed he would cross the whole breadth of the Seine without wetting that book, dragging his cloak in his teeth as Julius Caesar did. Then with one hand he would powerfully lift himself into a boat, from there dive headforemost back into the water, sound the depths, explore the hollows of the rocks, and plunge into the gulfs and abysses.

François Rabelais, GARGANTUA 1:23

The unusual prospects of northern ship archaeology are dramatically shown by Anders Franzen's discovery of a seventeenth-century warship surprisingly well preserved in Stockholm River. The author is a member of the United States Liaison Committee for Oceanographic Research, and was assisted in her report by Captain Edward Clason, R.S.N.

The Wreck of the Vasa

BY RUTH LONERGAN

*I*t was a beautiful Sunday afternoon in August 1628, during Sweden's Great Power Era under King Gustavus Adolphus. The King was fighting in Poland, with half of his navy blockading the Polish Coast, but heavy reinforcements were on their way. The people of Stockholm stood in festive ranks around the Royal Dockyard to watch the maiden sailing of a mighty sixty-four-gun ship, the *Vasa*, with 120 seamen and 300 marines aboard. The huge three-decker was 170 feet long with a 40-foot beam. The crowds watched the seamen loading stores and trundling new bronze guns into the ports. Their barrels bore the crest of the Vasa dynasty and the letters G.A.R.S., for *Gustavus Adolphus Rex Sueciae*. Late in the afternoon, as vesper bells rang from the Great Church, the *Vasa* raised topsails and glided into the river in a light southwest breeze. She was a proud and dazzling demonstration of seventeenth-century naval might. Gilded and brightly painted carvings ranged along her sides from beakhead to poop. Above the array of shining gun muzzles, the red doors of the gun ports were drawn up, revealing on their insides golden lion heads in high relief, with red tongues lolling and fangs bared. Ranks of marines, shined and pipe-clayed, stood at attention along the rails. She was a sight to terrorize the Baltic.

The great ship, still carrying only topsails and mizzen, paraded between cheering spectators, toward the Sodermalm, the high rocks forming the southern coast of Stockholm Harbor. When she left the lee of the rocks, without a perceptive increase in wind, the *Vasa* suddenly listed heavily to port. Erik Jonsson, the chief ordnance officer, raced below to truck the heavy guns to starboard to counter

259

the list. It was too late. Water poured into the open gun ports on the low side and the warship went down with flags flying, a hundred yards from the horrified patriots on shore. Flag-dressed boats, which had been escorting her, now gathered survivors of the catastrophe. About forty men were drowned. Her captain, Sofring Hansson, was thrown in jail and interrogated, and an inconclusive court martial ensued. The man who designed her, Chief Naval Architect Henrik Hybertsson, was beyond questioning. He had died the year before.

Three days after the disaster a British engineer, Ian Bulmer, was awarded a salvage contract on the basis of "no cure, no pay." There was immense value in the ship—the bronze guns, the stores for a whole campaign, and it is likely the pay chest of the fleet of which the *Vasa* was the flagship. The Englishman did not cure and was not paid. The wreck lay in ninety feet of water. Repeated attempts at salvage in the next decades did not succeed. The divers in their primitive suits "frequently came to the surface coughing out blood and then died," say contemporary accounts.

Thirty years after the sinking, a Swedish engineer, Lieutenant Colonel Hans Albrecht von Treileben, started work on the wreck with one-man diving bells four feet high with a sort of stirrup hanging twenty inches below for the man to stand on. The divers took down long poles with hooks, spears and grabs on the ends and began poking in the maindeck. The previous salvors had left it so littered with chains, anchors and abandoned rigging that it took a year to clear the decks in order to begin operations. The divers remained down fifteen minutes at a time, but their stay was later extended by lowering weighted barrels of fresh air, which were released into the bells. The ship stood upright and her oaken construction did not deteriorate during all these years, due to the fact that the Baltic is cold and rather brackish and cannot support worms and marine diatoms that destroy organic material in other seas. In 1664 the first gun was recovered—a two-ton cannon somehow handled by the cramped men in the bells. By the following year, more than fifty guns had been slung to the surface. Large-scale operations ceased and the *Vasa* was left in the cold and dark, in gathering obscurity, for centuries.

In 1920, several unidentified cannon were found in Stockholm Harbor. The historian, Professor Ahnlund, in seeking an attribution for them, came upon the accounts of the disaster in legal archives: Colonel von Treileben and his salvage partner had fallen out and their consequent lawsuit had left a rich deposit of *Vasa* data. Ahnlund's report fascinated a Stockholm wreck hound named Anders Franzen. He started probing both in the archives and in the harbor for the *Vasa*. In 1956, after thirty-five years of pursuit, his divers found a big oaken hull standing upright twenty feet above the floor. Commander Edward Clason of the Royal Swedish Navy came to Franzen's aid. Helmet and Aqua-Lung divers from the Navy Experimental Diving Unit were assigned to conduct their testing and training exercises in the wreck area. Although visibility is very poor—not more than five or six feet—and any contact with the bottom or the silted-over decks produces a cloud of zero visibility, the divers, in the first thousand (modern) descents to the wreck, proved that the hull is standing virtually intact with the exception of holes smashed through the main deck by their predecessors. There are any number of serious people in Stockholm who believe the 1628 ship can be raised and floated as she stands. The ship was largely fastened together with oak pegs, which have survived in good shape. Specimens of oak brought up show a tensile strength about 60 per cent that of new oak. In 1958 all doubts that the wreck was the *Vasa* were dispelled when divers raised a bronze twenty-four-pounder with the Vasa-dynasty crest emblazoned on it.

To orient themselves in the turbid waters, the divers tacked measuring boards along the ship's sides. They removed fifteen anchors from other ships that were fouled and lost in the *Vasa*. Hundreds of important and revealing finds came from the hulk: a beautifully carved head-rail still showing traces of gilding: eight of the ferocious lion's heads from the gun ports, and many sections of her decking and upperworks. The divers are taking great care not to destroy her integrity and hamper an actual lift of the inglorious ship.

Transverse tunnels have been jetted under the ship to pass lifting cables. She is settled seven to ten feet deep in stiff clay with an upper layer of slimy mud. Commander Clason's group is gathering the money and technical support to move the hull gently to shallow water, where the *Vasa* can be surveyed and, if necessary, strengthened before refloating her. If he succeeds, we will look upon the oldest capital warship yet found and learn whether Henrik Hybertsson, the silent chief naval architect, was woolgathering when he carried out the King's commission in 1625.

The South African L. A. J. "Peter" Keeble was originally a captain in the merchant marine, then a flier, commander of a Royal Navy antisubmarine vessel, and, throughout most of World War II, Fleet Salvage Officer in the Mediterranean and Red Sea. He wrote a wonderful book, Ordeal by Water, *about his wartime underwater effort. It started when the Italian port of Massawa in the Red Sea was captured in 1941. Keeble was ordered to clear the port, which was to be the most important Allied base east of Alexandria. Keeble found that the departing Italians had sunk sixteen ships and two floating dry docks in the Harbor. He had one Royal Navy diver, an Italian diver prisoner-of-war who could not be trusted underwater, and some Eritrean workers. Keeble himself had been underwater only once before and had panicked on that occasion. Nonetheless he dived. He and Captain Edward Ellsberg, USN, and a civilian contractor, cleared the port. Later he was called on the Top Secret Dive he describes so vividly in our selection. We regard the exploit and his superb description of it as one of the greatest things to come out of the war.*

N.B. "Boffin"—British service slang for scientist and technologist.

Top Secret Dive

BY PETER KEEBLE

*W*ith news of fresh casualties pouring in almost every day, we were kept steadily on the hop in Alex. A swift excursion to sea would be followed with a few days' hard labor in the office to bring myself as nearly up-to-date as I could ever hope or contrive to be. During one of these spells of clerical convulsions, I was sent for by Vice-Admiral Sir Bernard Rawlings and instructed to take a quick trip to Medway II, the submarine base at Beirut. I was promised "something of interest." It turned out to be the toughest and certainly the most dramatic operation I had yet embarked on.

I took passage by air to Beirut and reported to Senior Officer, Submarines. He quickly outlined the position. The corvette *Gloxinia* and destroyer *Petard* hunting together had depth-charged a U-boat and forced her to surface. She had wallowed for a minute in a heavy swell, long enough for about half her crew to scramble up on deck and throw themselves overboard, before dipping at the head and sliding down to the depths in a welter of flotsam-spotted air bubbles. Whether her last dive had been caused by damage from depth-charging, or whether one of her officers had performed his ultimate duty to the Reich by opening the vents and scuttling her, was not known; but, Captain (S) said, *Petard* had got a pretty good fix on where she went down. He laid a finger on the chart:

"There, Keeble. She's pretty deep."

I looked over his shoulder and whistled. The soundings marked nearest to the circle and dot indicating the position of the sunken U-boat read thirty-eight fathoms—about twice as deep as I'd ever been. "And you want us to raise her, Sir?" I asked. "Well—yes. We'd like to have her up, of course; but more than that we want something out of her." Involuntarily Captain (S) lowered his voice. "This is top secret, Keeble. If the enemy gets wind of what we're up to, the operation doesn't stand a chance. D'you understand that?" I nodded.

"Jerry's been getting on top lately with his U-boats. Our backroom boys think they know why, but they're not sure, and from what we've gathered from the survivors from *Petard's* victim, *U-307* can probably give us the answer. Our guess is that the new technique is for the U-boat to surface at night and lie awash, presenting a cluttered or negative radar echo, and wait for a target to present itself. There'd be no point in this if they had to depend on ordinary night vision for seeing it, and so the boffins have deduced that they are using some sort of infrared gadget which will pierce the darkness and give them a clear view of what they're shooting at. Survivors have admitted that *U-307* is fitted with something of the kind. We've got to get it."

I interrupted with a question. "Do we know what the thing looks like, Sir? Where it's located, how it's rigged? We'll be working absolutely blind down there—assuming we can find the sub, in the first place."

"Oh, yes. The boffins have given us a good conjectural picture of the machine, and they've flown one of their chaps out to advise on the spot. You'll be thoroughly briefed. And you realize, of course, that there will be an explosive charge embodied in the gear?" The Captain smiled shortly. "The diver will have to remove that before dismantling the instrument. Any questions, Keeble?"

"Rather a lot, Sir, I'm afraid. We'd better bring *Prince Salvor* over from Alex. I'll send a signal for her at once; but she's an extremely valuable ship, and I'd like to know what our chances are of getting air cover for her."

"That's all right," Captain (S) answered. "I'll take care of that. We'll give you an air umbrella and an antisubmarine escort. The escort'll help you to sweep for the wreck."

"Good! Now what about the interior of the U-boat? Can you provide any dope on her layout? The less we have to discover for ourselves the better our chances of getting what you want. Working time at that depth will be strictly limited."

"Pilot's thought of that," the Captain said. "The gadget's in the U-boat's control space, and he's got together a good collection of photographs of the layout of the space while we were waiting for you to arrive. We're making a mock-up of the whole issue for you to practice in. I take it you'll be doing the job yourself? Understand you're an experienced diver."

"I was going to ask you about that, Sir. Naturally, I'd like to have a shot at it; but one ought to be pretty fit to work at two hundred feet. More fit, probably, than I am. I've been turning over in my mind whether it would be better to send my chief diver down instead of me. C.P.O. Devonshire is a first-class man, younger and fitter than I. What do you think, Sir?"

The Captain looked at me and said slowly, "There must be no leakage of any kind about this operation, Keeble. I think you'd better go."

During the week that followed I spent many hours "working up" in the caricature of a U-boat's control room the carpenters and engine-room artificers had rigged for me. It was built of plywood, lifesize, and followed accurately the layout of a submarine—sawn off a few feet fore and aft of the conning tower. The first question was whether it would be possible to get a fully dressed diver, complete with front and back weights, through the two hatches leading to the control space. We decided it could be done. I had innumerable dummy runs, with a bandage around my eyes, groping for the reputedly cylindrical gadget that was the object of our exercise. Lowering myself solemnly through the conning tower hatch, down through the lower hatch, I would inch my way along inside the belly of the "submarine." Broom handles, lengths of hose, blocks of wood, anything that had caught the chippies' fancy, simulated the miles of piping, the valves, manifolds and the thousand and one parts of a sub-

marine's gear that I had to know by heart before I penetrated the
U-boat. Quite soon I could find my way about by touch alone and
almost without thinking.

Meanwhile, *Prince Salvor* had arrived. At once the First Lieutenant
set about checking on all equipment, a routine preliminary to any
operation, but when a working party was turned to for the disinter-
ment of the seldom-used recompression chamber, the mess deck
hummed and buzzed. Obviously there were some deep dips ahead,
and this was quickly confirmed by a steward's report that the young
Quack had been seen brushing up on "the bends" over a gin in the
wardroom. Rumor reached fantastic proportions and must have
greatly excited enemy Intelligence, for security was always rocky in
in the Levant.

When I was satisfied that the equipment was in order and that I
should be able to find my way about *U-307* if we were lucky enough
to strike her, I hauled Walters, our tame boffin, on board, and we
pushed off. Less than a day's steaming brought us to the search area
and our rendezvous with the antisubmarine escort Captain (S) had
laid on for us.

We went at once into a prearranged box sweep, crossing and re-
crossing a great square of ocean on parallel courses a quarter of a
mile apart. With our fathometer searching the ocean bottom, we
watched its stylo trace an undulating line across the graph paper, following every lift and fall of the sea bed. If our luck was in, if
Petard's navigator was as good as he should have been, if the floor
of the ocean wasn't strew with great rocks, if all our calculations
were correct, a sudden lift of the stylo, a sharp peak on the graph,
would pin-point the U-boat we were looking for. Or some other
wreck. Or some submarine obstruction. Taking the great waste of
the sea bed and the fallibility of men and their instruments, the odds
against our getting on to *U-307* seemed colossal; and as the hours
passed they lengthened.

Throughout the long night as *Prince Salvor* traced the monotonous
pattern of her sweep I dozed on the chart room settee or paced the
narrow bridge house, stopping at intervals to peer at the scrawly line
of the fathometer's graph. It pursued its placid course, echoing the
roll of the ocean bottom, but never for a moment lifting to the
peak which might indicate the sunken U-boat. It clattered indiffer-
ently on as hour followed hour.

Then, toward dawn, when I was flat on the settee drawing dispiritedly on a cigarette, the even clacking of the fathometer changed to a quick fretful clatter that told of a sudden change in depth. I leaped to my feet and almost collided with the Officer of the Watch as with one mind we sprang at the graph. There it was: the jump in the spidery blue line that meant *something* on the bottom. Something! But what?

"Stop both," I yelled into the wheelhouse, and out of the corner of my eye saw a hand go to the engine-room telegraph. The Officer of the Watch darted to the bridge telephone and cranked rapidly. "First Lieutenant! First Lieutenant! Wanted on the bridge—right away, please."

The stylo had resumed its steady line. Forty fathoms—just about right. From the wheelhouse the quartermaster called, "Ship's losing headway, Sir."

"Right!" Action Stations were shrilling through the ship, and the watch below burst up on deck. I nodded at the First Lieutenant panting at the head of the bridge companionway: "Get a dan buoy over the side as soon as you can while the way is off her, Number One. And Yeoman—make to Escort: 'Have contact—proceeding with sweep.'" A Signalman jumped to his platform in the wing of the bridge and the Aldis lamp clattered its message to the destroyer just beginning to show in the dim morning light on the horizon.

I drew Number One into the chart room and together we inspected the pinnacle. "Could be," I said. "Looks too sharp for a rock. Might be another wreck, of course; but it could be what we're looking for. Now that the buoy's planted, get your sweep over the side and start praying." The First Lieutenant slid joyfully down the ladder bellowing for the Petty Officer of the Watch.

The sun grew steadily out of an almost calm sea. Hull down, the silent escorts carried out their Asdic patrol and up in the void above three Spitfires wove their effortless patterns, the roar of their engines rising and falling. Under my feet *Prince Salvor* wove her own pattern, the sweep wires vibrating to the pull of the bight on the sea bottom far below. Nobody spoke on the bridge as we steamed back on a reciprocal course. I faced the fathometer again, staring at it in mute appeal while I waited for the rise in the trace line as the invisible pulse fled to the object on the bed of the sea and ricocheted back to the receiver. I saw the stylo lift sharply, hesitate for a split second, then swoop down again to the mean line.

Four times I watched the fathometer record our passage over this lump on the bottom and four times my heart sank when I realized the sweep was still trailing free behind us. Then the fifth time it happened. Simultaneously I felt the slight tremor run through the ship and heard the bridge telephone rattling. The Signalman, stammering in his excitement, gasped: "S-s-s-sweep's fast, Sir!"

"Stop engines!" I ordered, and gripped the bridge rail hard in my hands as if I could slow the ship with my personal strength. Slowly, all too slowly, *Prince Salvor* lost way and eased quietly to a standstill. A hoarse voice from the bottom of the companionway called, "Captain, Sir! We've got her, Sir! The First Lieutenant's compliments and she's taken nearly all the wire, but we're well fast and nothing's broken!"

Then began the slow, nerve-wracking maneuvering of the ship into position for further investigation. Working with strained care we recovered the kite at the end of the light-wire sweep, gently easing it up, coaxing it toward us so that it would not snap or break free from the obstacle on the bottom it had wrapped itself round. With the kite safely inboard, we bent on a light but strong flexible wire rope and, hauling on the sweep, ran the heavier wire down and round the obstacle. I eased *Prince Salvor* astern, taking the strain on the wire, aiming at getting the ship right over whatever was lying on the bottom. When the wire had straightened to an angle of seventy degrees or so I felt we had tempted fate far enough. I stopped engines and sent Number One away in the launch with a mooring party. The four three-ton anchors *Prince Salvor* carried were lowered into the boat and one at a time carried out and dropped in a square at a respectable distance round the wreck, if such it was. With the ship spread-eagled by her anchor cables I was then able to work her right over the point where the sweep had snagged. Easing off on two cables, shortening in the wire on the third mooring, we inched the ship into position. When the line from the wreck had righted itself almost to ninety degrees, I decided we could start diving. Six hours had passed since the fathometer had recorded our first contact with the obstacle.

Devonshire, working with his diving party in the waist, had a shot line with a two-hundred-pound sinker attached rigged to one of the derricks. The weight was swung outboard and the chief diver, hanging on to a stanchion, stretched out over the water and hacked with an ax at the marline lashing, racking the wire shot-line under the derrick snatch-block. The lashing parted and, with a twang like a bowstring, the heavy weight disappeared into the ocean, the coils of wire on the deck snaking over the side after it. Devonshire leapt nimbly back inboard, and with his elbows on the rail thoughtfully watched the white painted marks on the descending line steadily telling off the depths through which it was plummeting. A sudden slackening in the shot line showed that the sinker had reached the bottom, and Devonshire's hand went up to stop his party paying out more wire. "Hold it," he ordered. "Take in the slack. Make fast." He squirmed over the rail to see the reading on the wire.

I joined him in the waist. "What's the score, Devonshire?" I asked.

"Two hundred and thirty feet, Sir."

We looked at each other for a minute. They weren't far wrong, I thought to myself. "All right, Devonshire, get dressed and go down and have a nose round. As you may have guessed, we're looking for a wreck. It's a sub. If you can find it, we'll lower a second down-line to you. Shackle it as close to the sub's conning tower as you can. When you've positively identified whatever's down there, come up and we'll recompress you. I want to free the sweep, but not till you're clear."

Devonshire and a stand-by diver dressed quickly, while his team coupled up the necessary lengths of diving hose. Once Devonshire's helmet was on I tested out the telephone set. We were working with a combined mike and speaker in the helmet connected to a loudspeaker on deck. Remembering the secrecy of the operation, I substituted a pair of headphones for the amplifier and clamped them over my cap. I settled down on a canvas chair while Devonshire, standing on the steel diving grid, was lifted clear of the deck and swung overboard. In a few minutes Devonshire's voice rasping over the roar of air in the telephone told me that he was on to the shot line. We waited tensely as he descended.

The telephone came to life again. "All right, Devonshire?"

"O.K., Sir. Visibility not bad. Wreck of some kind not far off."

Minutes passed.

The line crackled. "Captain, Sir. This is . . ." The words that followed were drowned in a splutter of atmospherics. Probably a leak in the telephone cable. I leaned forward, bellowing into the mouthpiece on my chest, asking for the message to be repeated. Devonshire's voice came through at intervals, unheeding: ". . . dark blue sides . . . damage not extensive . . . nearly on even keel."

"Devonshire," I shrieked. "For Christ's sake, *what is it?*"

"Whassat, Sir?" The voice was faint, wandering away. It came back. "It's the sub all right. I'm on her deck now. . . . Conning tower hatch's open. . . . Permission to enter, Sir?"

"No. I'm lowering a shot line to you. Make it fast and come up."

Devonshire's voice trickled through plaintively. He didn't want to come up. Instead, he was trying to get his distance rope round the bight of the shot line he had gone down. A running commentary interrupted by bursts of static told us that he was hauling it in now to the conning tower; had lashed it up; was asking for a shackle.

We lowered the shackle to him and he made the shot line fast to the U-boat's gun platform. We had a direct line from *Prince Salvor* to *U-307*. It was almost incredible. I relaxed in my chair, sweat breaking out with relief.

Devonshire came through again, giving instructions to warp the ship right over the wreck, guiding us steadily, calmly, as the capstan rattled and hissed and the anchor cable groaned under the strain. When he was satisfied the ship was in the most advantageous position he consented to come up.

I looked at my watch and at the sky. By the time Devonshire had been recompressed and I had had a chance to talk to him it would be dark. The crucial stage of the Operation would have to wait till tomorrow. I thought with loathing of the dragging hours ahead.

The next morning Devonshire and I dressed side by side in silence.

The Chief Petty Officer had been speechless with fury when I told him that I was going to enter the sub. "At your age!" he had said, his eyes telling me plainly that there was no fool like an old fool. And of course he was right. Two hundred and thirty feet was no depth for a man of almost forty, of not better than middling fitness, to be playing about at. The fact came home to me very clearly during the hours of waiting. I was fatalist enough not to worry about the effect on me, but I was desperately worried lest physical weakness on my part robbed the operation, brilliantly successful so far, of a triumphant ending. So was Walters. The scientist had spent hours the previous night going over the routine of dismantling his precious device, and always I had felt his eye on me, coldly calculating. He was standing by now, waiting to help if I got into difficulties down below. He was especially anxious, and not for my sake, about the demolition charge. I shared his anxiety fully.

I spat out a cigarette and jerked my head at the attendants. They lowered the helmet over me and it settled heavy on my shoulders as they twisted and locked it into position. My crew hooked the big front- and back-weights on to me, over the corselet lugs. Under that load it needed the usual effort to get off the stool and on to my feet, which felt as though my enormous boots were anchoring them to the deck. While the air hissed into the helmet I squinted through the opening at the gauges on the instrument panel. In front of me somebody held up the small tools which I had selected for the job of getting the gadget off its mounting on the bulkhead: I nodded and felt the tools being slipped into the bag lashed to my belt. Here goes, I thought, without appetite.

I raised one hand, and a couple of inches in front of my nose the thick glass of the front port was screwed into its place, leaving me alone with my hard breathing coming back noisily off the curved walls of the helmet. Out of the side glass I could just see Devonshire. His half-sulk had worn off and he was on his feet grinning in at me, holding up two fingers in a jaunty Victory sign.

My suit was bellying out with the pressure building up inside. I fumbled awkwardly for the exhaust valve and opened it a couple of turns. Then I shuffled to the steel grid and grabbed hold of the wire bails. Number One's voice crackled in my headphones.

"Hold on, Sir. Taking you over the side, now."

"Go ahead," I told him. It was a relief to be on the move. The grating trembled under me as the winch took the weight and swung me up high enough to clear the rail; then I felt the swing sideways and I was being lowered gently toward the sea, gently down. The twill suit pressed in against me as I sank and the pressure rose sharply. Opening the exhaust valve another turn and a half, I felt more comfortable as the helmet's weight lifted slightly off my shoulders. The water line trembled silver up across the glass in front of my face and then it was green, gentle gloomy green and I was on my own, and on my way down and more alone with every foot of the grid's lowering.

The platform stopped; it swung slowly under me while I checked my suit for leaks, and tested the valve. Everything seemed to be as it should be. "Lower away," I said into my microphone. The shackles began to grate again on the wire down-line, and as I sank deeper into the sea the light from the surface faded and the deep green closed in. Suddenly, so hard and sharp that I almost cried out aloud, a stab of pain shot through my head. I gasped into the microphone urgently, "Hold on—hold it!" At once the platform stopped, and panting under that savage pain, never less for being expected, I closed the exhaust valve a bit and rose slowly up the wire bails with my feet clear of the grating. I yawned hard and swallowed, grimacing, and with the click of the distending tubes the pain left my eardrums. Clawing down the wire, back to the platform, I bent my knees and shook my head, swallowed, inviting the pain to return. But it held off and I told them up top: "All right, surface. Lower away."

Once again I was on the move downward with the pressure increasing every second and that greenish dark closing in to match it. The only sounds were my own breathing and the creak of the shackles. I kept my eyes on the down-line and presently the white-painted ninety-feet mark rose to the level of my helmet and the platform stopped. This was where I got off. I maneuvered my air pipe and the telephone cable clear of the sling, grabbed hold of the slimy wire shot-rope with both hands and swung myself off the grating. As I went on down I gave the platform one last look. Each part of it was outlined in massed and sparkling bubbles, clear and bright as diamonds. I slid away down the line, only slowing occasionally to let the air pressure build up to counteract the increasing outside pressure. The deep green was changing now, turning from green through gray to a bluish twilight, blue-gray, blue-black; and infinitely silent and menacing in its depth and weight. At the other end of the shot line people talked and smoked. They belonged to another world. I had left them and it for this vast loneliness, this solid void, so different because of an extra hundred feet that I felt as if I had never dived before. There was a coldness inside me unconnected with the temperature of the water, and I shook my head briskly to clear my brain of the terrifying impressions that were edging in on it. No good panicking at this early stage.

One of my boots struck something solid and, forgetting now to be afraid, I checked myself and eased down another couple of feet. My boots slid off whatever it was and found some sort of ledge: peering down, I realized that I had landed on the edge of the U-boat's bridge gun deck. I could make out the dim shape of the mounting with its twin machine guns swinging loose, unclamped, and looking up and for'ard I could just see the periscope standards and a pencil-thin quiver of black which I knew must be the jumping-wire. Very cautiously I clambered round the gun mounting and, squeezing my bulk between the after periscope standard and the side of the bridge, I found the conning-tower hatch standing wide open, the brass hatch itself thrown back. I stared down at the black circle of the hatchway, morbidly comparing it to the entrance to a tomb—which in fact it was. Or it might, for my part, be a trap, baited and set. Whatever way I looked at it the opening seemed excessively uninviting. I rested for a minute, leaning against the after standard, trying to get my breath to come more or less evenly, and the hatch gaped back at me, daring me to enter.

I did not want to let any air go; the pressure was bad enough without that. So instead of reducing my buoyancy to get down the ladder, I left the valve alone and hooked my boots *under* the rungs and pulled myself down. When I stepped into the hatchway my boots looked even bigger than they were. Each one seemed about the size of the hole, and it struck me that for all our calculations back in Medway I was not going to be able to squeeze myself in. I cannot pretend that the idea upset me very much. At this stage I think I might have accepted the impossibilty of access as divine intervention, reprieve. I dragged myself hesitantly down into the black hole and sure enough my front and back weights jammed on the rim of the hatch. Without them I could have slipped through fairly easily. Well, I thought, is this as far as we go? I stopped where I was, panting under the effort of movement which, with my heavier breathing, was producing a lack of oxygen and a surfeit of nitrogen, and looking down and feeling the brass ring of the hatch about my middle I realized, suddenly, that it was not round but oval. I should have remembered that from my exercises in the dummy. Anyway, it meant no excuses after all. I swung my body sideways, turning, and felt the weights come clear in the side width of the hatch. Groping with my feet for the next rung of the ladder, I pulled downward again, and then I was inside *U-307*. But suddenly it was bad, worse than it had ever been. The panting come harder and faster, and I couldn't do a thing to control it. It shook my whole body and I choked for the want of air, and the more I tried to get the less there was to breathe. Specks of light exploded in front of my eyes and shot away in brilliant white streaks. The pound of my own heart was like some detached force which I could not stop in its efforts to drag my chest apart. Sweat ran down my face and the sickness started, too, acid in my mouth and—well, it is not possible to be sick properly against pressure, you just feel sicker and sicker and retch pointlessly and the breathing gets worse and worse. Relax! I told myself. If you don't, you've had it. You won't last another two minutes. Forget that it's hard to breathe. The performance hasn't started yet, and if you don't take it easy it never will. It's not pressure that's bothering you; it's not lack of oxygen: it's plain bloody panic. Just take it easy and save yourself for what's coming.

The panting slowed and my breathing came more gently, although it was still jagged. I listened to it as though it belonged to someone else, and I was just trying to help. Still trembling from the attack, I clung to the ladder with my boots and with my left hand, and I brought up my right hand to open the spitcock on my helmet. Sucking, I drew in a mouthful of salt water, swilled it round to clear away the acidity of sickness and then spat it all out at the inside of the glass port in the helmet's front. It cleared the misted glass as well, two birds with one squirt. Not that it made much difference whether or not the glass was misted. Here in the tower it was pitch black, darker than any night I had ever known. When I pressed one finger against the outside of the glass port, right in front of my eyes, I could only just make out faintly the whitish blob of my fingertip. My microphone crackled, and a voice which might have been a thousand miles away asked, "Sir—can you hear me?" It wouldn't have been much use trying to talk back. The chances were that they wouldn't hear me up top, and instead of trying to speak I pressed the chin-switch, and at once the voice crackled back at me.

"Jolly good, Sir. You've thirty minutes more. Are you all right?" I wondered what was so jolly good, but anyway I chinned the switch for a second time and that must have satisfied them, because the crackle died out of the speaker. All the same, down there in the pitch dark with the steady hiss of air escaping from the vents I could not help grinning to myself: once I had got myself down and off this ladder into the submarine's control room, what would they be able to do about it on top even if I *wasn't* all right? Phone for an ambulance?

I rested again and braced myself once more to go on down. The brass toe-caps of my boots scraped on the rungs of the ladder as I shuffled, extending one leg to hook myself a step further down. Instead of the cheerful clang I had expected to indicate I had found the next rung, something soft stopped my leg. Something so soft that is seemed more like my leg refusing to straighten than anything underneath its way. Through the solid weight of the boot there was no question of any sort of feeling, only I had an impression of resilience in whatever it was that I was forcing down on physically. What the devil was going on? I kept the toe of my right boot jammed under a rung and held tight to the sides of the ladder. Then I raised my left leg in the small space left to move in and stamped downward with all the force I could muster. The same soft but determined resistance stopped my foot again.

I tried to feel with the boot, to feel where this started and how wide it was. I moved my foot sideways, pressing down: it slid over and down and I lodged it under a lower rung, jamming the toe there while I shifted my hands lower on the ladder and pushed my other leg down. There it was again—that soft, solid resistance to pressure. It seemed to be right across the middle of the tower and somehow part of or mixed up with the ladder itself. Pulling myself down still lower I groped out and down with the other boot until I had a leg on each side of the obstruction: I kicked at it from the side, swinging my leg like a pendulum, but that did not budge it either. I got my hands low on the ladder and dragged myself down astride of the blockage, hooked myself there with my boots locked under the rungs so that my hands would be free to pull the thing out of the way.

Bending was a fiendish effort, and I felt the lack of air again and had to rest where I was for a minute or two. I was wondering how much time I had left and to forget my growing sickness I concentrated on the thing below in childish petulance. I leant downward and found it with my hands. At first it felt like a mattress in some sort of mackintosh cover. Then the fingers of my right hand moving across it found some small, hard object: my hand was swollen, by now, and insensitive, and it was a little time before I realized what I had found. It was a zipper. I dragged it open and forcing my hand through the gap I felt buttons—the metal buttons of a naval uniform. This was a dead German I was sitting astride. He was fat with swelling inside his waterproof suit—the sort our submariners call an Ursula—and he was completely jammed-up in the ladder. When the submarine made her final dive with the vents open he must have been starting up the ladder behind the others who had already got out, and halfway up he had met the sea coming in and had been there ever since. Of course, he could have drowned inside and been washed up into the tower afterward, but I do not think he would have been as tightly mixed up with the ladder if it had been that way.

Well, now I had to get past him: no good *thinking*. I opened the valve as far as it would go and forced myself down. I did not make an inch. I grabbed hold, and pulled; jerked sideways; it made no difference at all. Time was running out and the sickness rose suddenly in an overwhelming wave and left me reeling, half-conscious and fighting the same old white lights. I made myself rest and my senses told me urgently to take it easy again, easy or there'd be two of us for Devonshire to clear.

I knew perfectly well, now, what I would have to do. It was not a very pleasant thing to ponder over, and I tried not to think at all as I slid my right hand around my waist to the haft of my diver's knife. The knife was a heavy weapon designed for anything from sharks to hemp and rope, and it had a serrated back edge, to saw with. I set my teeth and, reaching down, began to cut my way through. I was not a human being, I was just a diver doing a job. Up top there were several hundred men backing me up: all I had to think about was the object of the operation and the value of its achievement. Not about the feel in my hand when my saw-edge got to bone.

The thing began to sag and then it fell away except for something which I kicked, and that went too. I let the knife fall on its lanyard and pulled myself down through the lower hatch onto the control room ladder, then slowly down another ten rungs. I felt the deck plates under my boots and a moment later I was off the ladder, standing close to the for'ard periscope where the U-boat's captain would have been during an attack. I felt the periscope barrel with my hands and it was still greasy. The wires on either side of it were still bar-taut.

Standing by the periscope and resting there with a hand on each of the wires, I summoned into my mind the sketches of a U-boat's layout and the interior of the mock-up I had spent so many hours fumbling about in. Now patience has its reward, I thought. I am between the ladder and this periscope and its lifting wires are athwartships, to port and starboard of it. I am square behind them, so I can only be facing for'ard. There cannot be any mistake about that. Now if I turn ninety degrees right and move three paces ahead I will come up against the control panel on the starboard side. I reached up and pulled in a bight of airline and telephone cable, enough to let me get over to the submarine's side plus another three feet or so to give me enough slack for the short journey for'ard to where the gadget was supposed to be.

I turned what I reckoned to be ninety degrees right, and checked the way I was facing by feeling to my left for the periscope and its wires. This was the way I had planned to do it and so far there were no snags. Everything seemed right. I moved straight ahead with both hands stretched out in front of me. Three normal paces to go—that'll be about six of my shuffles. All the same I moved more slowly and cautiously than I need have done. I forgot to count, and I could only have covered about a few feet of distance before I began to think that by now I should have found the ship's side, that something was all wrong and upside down—my memory or my sense of direction had failed me. I controlled a quick flare of panic, an urge to turn and try another tack, and in the next moment my fingers touched the steel bars which protected the vent levers. Now it was all right, I knew where I was. If I had given way to that pressing, unreasonable urge a few seconds earlier I would probably have ended up circling into the port for'ard corner of the control room and then I would not have known where the devil I was. I would have had to follow my lines back to the hatch and start all over again.

I was close up against the ship's starboard side now, and my hands ran over the vent levers and the high pressure valve wheels. The vents were open, all the levers pulled right back and loose. I shoved them in, one by one, thinking of the possibility that they would decide to raise this wreck and give the job to me. If I could shut the vents now it might save me a second trip. One excursion of this kind was enough, I felt. But there was no reaction from the vents; no thumps of their closing, not even a hiss of telemotor pressure. Just the same, I pushed all the levers home, thinking that in any case it would not do any harm to have them the right way. Then I realized that I was dawdling, wasting time, *getting sleepy*. I was losing sight of what I was here for. And this drowsy feeling, my eyes heavy, worries fading, that lovely idea of *relaxing*. Just leaning up against something and letting it all slide . . .

I pulled myself together. That would have been a quick way out, that snooze. You've overstayed your time as it is, I reminded myself, and if you let yourself slide now you'll be here for keeps. I talked to myself as if I were talking to a child, and with an effort forced my eyes wide open and turned left to face for'ard, which was the way I had to go. . . .

Now this was the chart table. Its top was smooth, greasy, or perhaps my hands were greasy and everything they touched had that feel. After those ghastly minutes in the tower with that knife my hands felt filthy enough to be burnt. I took hold of the edge of the chart table with the fingers of my right hand and as I pulled myself forward the top of the desk rose in my hand. It was hinged at the back like a school desk, and sliding my hand in I felt around—out of curiosity, or perhaps because I was sleepy again and vague in the real purpose of my being here at all—and my hand found a sodden mass of paper, slimy bulk, then a metal parallel rule, a pair of dividers; something bigger, heavier—perhaps a course and drift calculator or a station-keeper. Where was the man who had used them a few weeks ago?

Just for'ard of the chart table was a short section of thwartships bulkhead. I had expected it, but it was a comfort to find it right there where it was supposed to be. My fingers gripped its edge, and I realized that my hand must be within a foot of the box of tricks I had come to get. I felt no excitement; not even the excitement of fear. I was as sleepy as a baby, and I wondered why the sickness had held off for so long. Out of a dreamy awareness that it was vital to stay awake I heard the voice again in my headphones. I realized suddenly that I had heard it before, but it had not penetrated. I had accepted it as part of the sluggish growing sleep, and I had neither listened nor tried to answer.

"Can you hear me? Captain, Sir—can you hear? Chin-switch if you can, chin your switch if you can hear. Do you hear me?"

I couldn't recognize the voice. It was so faint it might have been Snow White calling long-distance from Buenos Aires. I bumped the switch with my chin and the tinny jangle of its bell whispered back out of the telephone. The voice came again, and it sounded less excited, easier.

"Your time's up, Sir. More than up—more better you come up pronto!"

"More better"—the phrase identified Number One. Stupid bastard, I thought. Talk English *and for the love of God leave me alone!* I turned my face to the helmet microphone and forgetting the value of saved exertion, I cursed them personally and I cursed the times and tables which I had always enforced myself. I cursed the whole lot nastily and crudely using words I would normally regard as outside even a seafarer's vocabulary. I didn't know I was doing it, and I didn't remember doing it, even afterward when I was told the whole story.

I dragged myself on, up to the steel partition. My fingers found the junction box exactly where the scientists had said it would be, and I traced the thick metaled lead out of that and through another box and then—how simple!—I had my hands on the Thing itself! Its size and shape were right and the connections were in the right places, and I could feel the securing screws. I almost grinned to myself as I reached down into the canvas bag at my waist and picked out the screwdriver, took it in my right hand and with the fingertips of my left hand guided its point into the groove of the first screw. Then everything seemed to slip and before I had realized what had happened the tool was away down there in the dark and of course I could not bend to pick it up. I should have had the damned thing on a lanyard, but it was too late to think of that. Much too late!

Groping among the odd tools in my bag, I found a pair of pliers. Perhaps they would do—with a monkey wrench. Using them was not easy because my fingers were stiff, slow and fumbling. But after what seemed an age of blind effort the nuts and studs dropped away, and as the last pair went rattling down I felt the whole thing swinging loose. Searching above it, my hands felt the unions and the cable piping stretching up, exactly as the scientists had sketched it in that drawing that I had been shown—several ages ago—in Medway. Now —last lap!

Bit by bit the monkey wrench loosened the union nuts. I battled on at them, and then something broke in on my concentration, tapping on the back of my helmet! I'd ignored the first couple of raps, but now it happened again, and I began to feel angry to the point of losing my temper. A silly thing to get heated about, but I suppose under circumstances like these a man's thoughts and feelings get to be exaggerated. I stopped work and turned sideways to feel around for whatever it was up there behind my head. At once my hand closed on what was unmistakably an arm. Less angry now but somehow not shocked or surprised I ran my hand down along the arm: the hand at the end of it was puffy, obscene to the touch. On one finger was a thick metal ring, the sort of ring that our own stokers used to file up out of odd bits of metal when they were off watch and had nothing better to do. I realized that this was what had been rapping on my helmet—almost as if the owner of the hand had been trying to attract my attention. But I had no time, now, to be sociable: I reached up with both hands to the body floating face down with its hunched back brushing the deckhead and its arms drooping out and down like a bat's wings, and I moved him a couple of feet for'ard, where we would be out of each other's way. He moved easily enough. And he was probably more comfortable than I was. I forgot him, went back to work on that blasted pipe.

Another minute's work, and the nuts were free enough for me to be able to move them up the cable. I dropped the monkey wrench back into the tool bag, and pulled at the piping. It moved a little way, then stuck fast. I tugged again, but it would not budge. Wild with anger, frustration and a sort of panic from knowing the wasted value of these slipping minutes and the danger of overstaying my time as I had already done by a wide enough margin, I dug out the monkey wrench again, stuck it in behind the joint, and heaved. Grunting and sweating in the slippery stifling darkness, I struggled until suddenly the wrench slipped, throwing me off balance. I gashed my hand badly on some projection, tried to clutch the falling wrench, missed it and heard it a moment later as it hit the deck. I thought of trying to bend down to pick it up, but I knew that even if I managed to get down that far I certainly wouldn't be able to straighten up again. So I tried using my knife, forcing its blade into the gap and levering: the knife snapped in two and I let the useless haft drop down on its lanyard. I thought: That's about the bloody lot! That finishes it. I'll have to come down again tomorrow. Or as soon as I'm fit for it again. But the idea of going up there now, without the thing I had come for, seemed somehow impossible. I felt the joint on the cable with my torn fingers and racked my brains for an answer. And the answer came. *That parallel rule!*

I groped my way back to the chart table, opened it and pulled out the heavy ruler. I took it back to the gadget, and even in this urgency I couldn't help thinking with a navigator's mind and regretting this barbarous misuse of a navigational instrument. But pushing away any such technical and professional qualms I worked in an edge under the bulged and battered conduits, took a firm grip with both hands, and, knowing it was this now or nothing else but an admission of defeat, I put all that I had and perhaps a bit more into one savage, maniacal heave. The pipes came free. I clutched for a hand-hold to stop myself going over backward, found one, and found at the same time that the gadget was now lower down and apparently held by another stud.

I took the thing firmly under one forearm, shoved the rule under the flange and pulled. Something parted, and I had the gadget, free, right in my arms! For the moment, though, I was too exhausted to cheer, even mentally. I rested the studs of my front glass on a bulkhead I could not see and lowered my face onto the cold metal of the helmet. All I needed now was the strength to get this box of tricks, and myself too, up into the sunlight. We had a little way still to go.

I straightened up, made sure of my grip on the gadget, groped aft to the control panel and there turned right to the ladder. I was glad to find it in the same place—there had already been so many snags that it would not have surprised me overmuch to find that the thing had moved off. I leaned against it, chinned the bellpush and called the surface. My words came back at me off the walls of the helmet, and to me they sounded like the pantings of a dog that should have been put down years ago.

"On deck—on deck! Take up the slack—easy. I am on my way up. Send down a weighted bag on the shot." A distant voice crackled back an answer.

"Send bag on shot—aye, Sir. Taking up your slack. You—long way—overtime—Sir. Sending down—diver—to —help."

That really got me on the raw. I tried to shout though probably it was only a jagged whisper.

"Keep your blasted diver! Keep him where he is!"

"Aye aye, Sir," the voice said regretfully. Probably Devonshire had been agitating for an hour to be sent down after me. I thumbed the valve with my free hand and waited for buoyancy to build up— the suit distended and the load lifted off my shoulders as my feet left the plates. I guided and checked myself with my hands on the sides of the ladder, but passing the place where the ladder had been blocked I tried not to touch it more than I needed to. Then my helmet scraped against the edge of the top hatch and I heaved and wriggled my way through into the submarine's bridge. With the toe of one boot locked under the hatchway's rim, I opened my exhaust valve by a turn and a half, to keep myself heavy. Then with my fingers on the spindle I called the surface.

"Up top! I've got the bag. Stand by." I grabbed the canvas, brass-eyeleted bag which swam just over my head in the gently moving current, and as soon as I had it fast I tipped the weights—old nuts and bolts—out of it. I settled the precious object-of-the-operation into the bottom of the bag, and told them up top: "It's all yours— take it away!" I watched it rise and vanish where the streak of the shot line vanished too, and I told them, happily, "I'm coming up."

Reaching for the shot, I closed the exhaust again. As the corselet rim rose to my chin, the filling dress took me steadily up the line, while my hands, not feeling much now, slipped loosely over the oily strands. The black became green and the green lightened, brightened. I could see tiny shining bubbles clinging to the line as it passed my front glass; I could see my magnified hand sweeping those bubbles aside into brilliant fading showers, like fireworks at a distance. The voice came again out of the speaker.

"Sir, you're coming up to the stage. Better rest there a bit." The suggestion puzzled and irritated me.

"Put the First Lieutenant on the line."

"Sir?" Number One's voice rattled down.

"Cut out the stage party. Forget the bloody stage—I want to get out of here. Bring me up and I'll go straight into the chamber. Got the bag inboard?"

"Yessir. Walters has locked himself in your cabin with it. We'll bring you up from the stage when you're ready."

And here *was* the stage. I handed myself over to its rusty grating and swapped the shot rope for its wire bails. I was thinking that the nonsensical idea of my waiting down here would have been Doc's doing. Been reading up too thoroughly on the bends—but let him worry about me when I get up top. That's all I want—*to get up top*.

I jerked the breast line four times and the shackles started squealing as they began to haul me up. I leaned back against the bails and watched the silvery, glittering surface coming down to meet me. A minute later I was face to face with *Prince Salvor*'s rust-scabbed plates. It was a sailor's dream of home.

Inboard, hands quickly freed me of my weights, helmet, corselet and boots, and for a moment I tasted air, real air. Then I was bundled, still in my suit, through the manhole into the recompression chamber. I felt awful beyond words, and the Doctor, who had followed me into the chamber, confirmed cheerfully that I looked it. I sagged down onto a mattress and gave up.

When I came round again, the Doc was bending over me with a syringe. "What's this in aid of?" I asked.

"Anti-tet injection," the Doctor told me. "I don't suppose you know it, but you came aboard looking like a pork butcher. It was quite obvious that you'd been doing a bit of dissection down there— and not very scientifically. Thought you might have got a bit of infection through these gashes in your hands. Now don't get up." He pushed me on my back again. "You can tell me all about it later, and I'll give you a scalpel for your tool bag. The thing to do now is *rest*."

I drifted off again, gratefully.

A few hours later, recompressed, decompressed, showered and shaved and in a clean suit of white, I was abroad again. I begged leave to be admitted to my cabin and Walters opened the door to me.

"All right?" I asked. "Didn't bring up the wardroom clock by mistake?"

"Perfectly all right," the boffin beamed back. "Their Lordships will be very happy with this. I've had it to bits; but what puzzles me is how you managed to short-circuit the demolition charge without touching it off. The contacts were closed, but—"

"The demolition charge!" I said. "Christ! I forgot all about it!"

*

An Idea for Diving Flippers

When I was a boy, I made two oval palettes, each about ten inches long and six broad, with a hole for the thumb, in order to retain it fast in the palm of my hand. They much resembled a painter's palette. In swimming, I pushed the edges of these forward, and I struck the water with their flat surfaces as I drew them back. I remember I swam faster by means of these palettes, but they fatigued my wrists. I also fitted to the soles of my feet a kind of sandals; but I was not satisfied with them, because I observed that the stroke is partly given by the inside of the feet and the ankles, and not entirely by the soles. . . .

Benjamin Franklin, 1773

Dr. Anton F. Bruun of the Zoologiske Museum, Copenhagen, is a big, hearty seagoing scientist, who likes to fish six miles down. His first oceanographic cruise was on the Dana in 1924: he is now working at the Scripps Institution of Oceanography in California. The very little knowledge we have of life in the ocean abysses is spectacular in itself—that living creatures do exist in pressures of more than fifteen thousand pounds per square inch, as proved by dredgings accomplished by the Soviet research ship, Vitiaz, and Bruun's Danish Galathea Expedition. The following scene opens at dawn, July 22, 1951. The Galathea is at Oceanographic Station 418 above the Philippine Trench, hauling the deepest dredge yet lowered. . . .

Animal Life of the Deep Sea Bottom

BY A. F. BRUUN

*T*here, deep down in the clear water, was the faint outline of the large triangular bag of the sledge-trawl. It was pitch-black night, but the quarterdeck lay bathed in the beams of our spotlights. Standing by the trawl gallows, watching the trawl breaking surface, was the fishmaster, his arm waving in a slow circle.

At the winch all eyes were intently following the motions of his arm, as they slowed down and then came to a stop, the hand raised as a signal to stop hauling in. It all went with the fine rhythm of experienced teamwork, but the occasion was a special one: it was the first time that the indicator had stood at zero after reaching 40,130 feet, the full length of our wire.

During the work of taking in the trawl and the two small dredges that had been fixed to the trawl frame (it took a few minutes but felt like an eternity), we prepared for the disappointment of seeing a bag without any bottom animals in it; for a failure, in short. We comforted ourselves with the thought that it was the first attempt with the full length of our new wire, that everything had gone like clockwork all night, that the wire was safely home and we should be able to try again, even in the Philippine Trench. Then the facts came out in rapid succession. "There's clay on the frame!" somebody cried. "It's been on the bottom!" And then: "There are stones in the bag!" Everybody on board who could leave his job gathered around while nervous fingers unloosed the cords so that the contents could be carefully removed.

We hardly noticed the red prawns, luminescent euphausids, or black fishes; we all knew these to be pelagic animals, caught on the way up through the free water masses. But there, on a rather large stone, were some small whitish growths—sea anemones! Even if no more animals had been found, this would still be the outstanding haul of the expedition. It was proof that higher animals can live deeper than 33,000 feet. Is it surprising that all were overjoyed? And that pleasure became excitement when out of the grayish clay with gravel and stones we picked altogether twenty-five sea anemones, about seventy-five sea cucumbers, five bivalves, one amphipod, and one bristle worm. It was an unexpectedly rich variety of bottom-dwelling animals.

That the haul had been made on the bottom was obvious, and fortunately we had all the proofs that it was at 33,600 feet. We had carefully navigated according to the configuration of the bottom laboriously pieced together from our echo-sounding on many days before; on the bridge they had calculated the driftage due to current with such accuracy that our depth throughout had never been less than 33,600 feet; wind and sea had been very slight from the north, almost head on, as favorable as they could possibly be. Forgotten was the long night vigil; our success had to be followed up, everything repeated if possible.

And repeated it was, except that the second time we trawled for only 90 minutes, compared with 110 minutes the first time. We had to break off the trawl, which was made at a slightly lesser depth, because the ship drifted over the eastern slope and we preferred a rather shorter trawl at the desired greatest depths to the risk of an admixture from other depths, to say nothing of the danger of a torn trawl on the steep valley sides. This trawl produced twelve sea anemones, four sea cucumbers, and a bristle worm, besides the remains of five greenish little echiuroid worms and some decaying vegetation washed out from the shore. The bottom substance here consisted of a number of rather firm lumps of clay.

The third trawl appeared to have been successful, but when we came to hauling in we found that the end two thousand feet had got itself wrapped round the trawl, which had consequently failed to fish. Nor did the fourth trawl produce any bottom animals, as the trawl did not reach the bed, despite our usual careful calculations

according to Dr. Kullenberg's formula. At the fifth attempt some
of the wire again got entangled in the trawl, though this time we
obtained some sea anemones, a sea cucumber, and a bivalve of the
species previously caught, as well as four small crustaceans (isopods).
We made a sixth and last attempt, but were so troubled by bottom
conditions, current, wind, and weather that we dared not send the
trawl to the bottom. For nineteen hours we struggled in vain to keep
a level bottom long enough to have enabled us to fish the approximately five kilometers astern of us. It was a bitter disappointment to
leave the Philippine Trench in this way, but such is the fisherman's lot
and it could not eclipse our pleasure at the successful hauls.

We had found a whole little animal community. All the large groups
of invertebrates were represented—polyps, worms, echinoderms, mollusks, and crustaceans. The known depth limit of life had been pushed
some two miles lower down; and, whereas it might have been doubted
whether we should find anything in the Philippine Trench, there is
now no reasonable ground for supposing that life cannot also
penetrate the few hundred meters further down to the latest record
depth of 36,173 feet in the Mariana Trench, provided that there,
too, there is sufficient oxygen in the water. Our finds of a great variety
of bottom deposits of clay, gravel, and stones in the Philippine Trench
may provide a basis from which to explain why the water masses
from the downflowing depth at about 11,550 feet and beyond can
be so uniform and consequently so stable as they are. The general rule
is that it takes wind or differences of density to create water-inter-
changing currents, and here there do not seem to be sufficient differences of density in the water masses.

But in recent years it has gradually been realized that "turbidity
currents" must play an important part under certain conditions.
Undersea turbidity currents occur if rough weather whisks up clay
in the sea water near the shores. It is obvious that muddy liquid
will have a greater specific density than clear sea water, and consequently will tend to settle in depressions of the continental shelf,
in earthquake fissures or old river beds where the sea bed has been
higher, or the mud current will form a cascade falling down over the
continental slope. The current will now have become so much faster
that, like a swiftly flowing river, it will carry with it sand and perhaps
even larger constituents. This is the sequence which it is imagined was
the chief and perhaps decisive factor in the formation of the vast
steep-sided valleys which cut their way from old and large water
courses like the Congo and Hudson rivers into the continental shelf,

and which can be traced right down into the deep sea just outside.

If we apply this theory to the Philippine Trench there is good ground for supposing that a turbidity current starting in the narrow shelf region (and here there are typhoons, earthquakes, and submarine volcanoes to give it impetus) will flow right down to the bottom. In a stretch of less than seventy-five miles the depth falls six miles, from time to time in abrupt drops, as shown in our echosoundings. Immense phenomena must take place here, and I think that this is a possible explanation of why we found jagged stones and other rough bottom material in the clay from the otherwise flat valley bottom. Apart from this, the significant factor as far as animals are concerned, is that turbidity currents could drag fresh masses of water containing oxygen into the deep, providing their vital requirements of air to breathe.

We now looked forward with a certain amount of confidence to the approaching oceanic trenches. The next was the Sunda Trench, which extends in an immense curve south of Java and westward toward Sumatra. The greatest depths of a little over 23,000 feet lie south of Java, and we made straight for them, as time was short and weather none too good—the southeasterly wind and sea were strong at times and there was also some current. We did not spend much time on sounding, as we found that the configuration corresponded roughly to that of the Philippine Trench, with steep valley sides and a narrow strip of level bed. Here we experienced setbacks from the start, two sledge-trawls failing to reach the bottom and a third coming up with a torn bag. Only the two attached small dredges brought much bottom material, though it was good. There were five starfishes, seven sea cucumbers, some black corals, a bristle worm, five echiuroid worms, an amphipod, a tusk shell, and ten bivalves. We then risked our large otter-trawl at 23,500 feet, keeping it on the bottom for two hours and dragging it at a speed of a good two miles an hour. We should have liked to drag it a little faster, but that would have meant more wire to pay out and haul in, taking more time and involving risk, so we confined ourselves to paying out 35,000 feet. The result was the greatest haul that has ever been made from this depth. First of all there were about three thousand small sea cucumbers (*Elpidia glacialis*) of the same species we had caught in the sledge-trawl, plus about 114 of a rather larger species (*Periamma naresi*). It was an astonishing catch in the Southern Hemisphere. There were also five amphipods and four other crustaceans (*Cumacea*), and about forty sea anemones which we recognized by their pale color, though it is for the specialists to determine their ultimate relationship with those of the Philippine Trench. Two bristle worms in this trawl certainly belonged to species closely related to the one found in the Philippine Trench. Last but not least there was a *Bassogigas*, a fish of the brotulid family about six inches long. This was the deepest live fish caught on the expedition, and it was 3,600 feet deeper than any previously found fish. We took the same species again when we passed through the Bali Strait, at 12,600 feet in the sledge-trawl along with two other bottom-dwelling fishes, which shows that this fish can live under very varying depths.

All in all, the Sunda Trench gave a very rich yield, and sledge-trawls at 12,600 and 10,000 feet nearby produced valuable material for the study of the variation of fauna with the depths, a factor which, though we had considered it, we had not dared to devote any time to in the Philippine Trench, where we were over the greatest depth we should meet with during the expedition.

In the next trench, the Banda Deep, we also concentrated on trawling at the greatest depths, about 23,000 and 24,750 feet. Here we had to consider our reserves of fuel oil, as there was no possibility of stocking up before Port Moresby in New Guinea, but the weather was good and it was fairly easy to find a suitably level bottom for fishing. The first attempt with the sledge-trawl failed to reach the bottom, but the next one, as well as two casts with the otter-trawl, gave quite a number of bottom animals. In the deepest trawl, at 23,925 feet, we obtained nineteen sea cucumbers (at least three species), a sea urchin (*Echinothuria*) and parts of the shells of several others, some polyps (*Stephanoscyphus*), a bristle worm (same species as in the Sunda Trench), six echiuroid worms, some piddocks in a screw-pine fruit which had sunk to the bottom, and a rather large amphipod. In the second trawl at 21,780 feet, there was only a sea spider (the deepest ever caught), some piddocks in a sunken piece of wood, and a number of bristle worms.

We could rely on being able to explore only one more trench; namely, the great Kermadec-Tonga Trench, which extends right from New Zealand and up beyond the Tonga Islands, a distance of 1,250 miles. It is not to be wondered at that we strained every nerve to surpass ourselves. We had to round off our work by comparing the fauna at the bottom of a great trench with that higher up, stage by stage in the immediate vicinity.

The Kermadec Trench gave us more than twice as many species as the four other trenches put together. This means that we now have

a real basis for studying the dependence of the species on the depths
—or pressure, because in this rather limited region we can disregard
the other influencing factors, in the first place food supply and in the
second oxygen supply, temperature, and the minor factor of salinity.

The time set aside for biological work in the Kermadec Trench
ran out. It had justified our boldest hopes, but perhaps that was the
very reason why we felt so tantalized as we steamed north from
Auckland toward Samoa, with the fascinating deep beneath us all
the way. The worst moment of all was when the curve of our
echo-sounder swung down to 34,110 feet; for, with a correction of
plus 970, we were thus only twenty feet short of having found the
first trench in the Southern Hemisphere with a depth of 10,000
meters. It was at 31° 53′ S., 177° 05′ W., and there was a fine
bed for trawling, should anyone wish to try his hand.

When we got home to Denmark, we were able to study more
closely some specimens from the trenches that could not be identified
from our limited library on board. The malacologist, Dr. Henning
Lemche, took thirteen tiny mollusks from the same deep haul, which
we had simply logged as "limpet-like." He cut them into very thin
slices and was examining only the second specimen, when a flash
of recognition came. It was the first living specimen of a class of
mollusks known only in rock fossils of the Cambro-Devonian Age,
some three hundred million years ago!

He named it *Neopilina galatheae*. We were happier about these
amazing survivors than we would have been about landing the great
sea serpent, which after all may be only a giant eel. Neopilina is a
most beautiful connecting link in that long chain of evolutionary
types in the zoological system going back to the dawn of life on earth.

The English writer David Masters has written several popular books on salvage and undersea warfare. This extract is from his Wonders of Salvage.

Raising the Leonardo da Vinci

BY DAVID MASTERS

*B*ritish salvage experts have performed extraordinary feats; the American Navy has produced divers fully equal to our own; but it was left to the Italians to accomplish the seemingly impossible. As a sheer feat of salvage, the raising of the *Leonardo da Vinci* was historic.

The night of August 2, 1916, will long be remembered in Taranto, for just before midnight the whole town was awakened by a tremendous explosion. The people leaped from their beds and rushed toward the harbor, to find searchlights sweeping the bay and the finest battleship in the Italian Navy belching forth flames and smoke. The *Leonardo da Vinci* was doomed. In a moment 250 officers and men were wiped out of existence, and although the survivors fought most valiantly to quell the fire that enveloped the ship their efforts were vain.

Suddenly the decks of the battleship canted beneath them, shooting them like flies into the bay, and she swung right over and sank upside down in thirty-six feet of water. The searchlights from the surrounding battleships lit up the darkness. Round and round they flashed, seeking the enemy who had dealt this mortal blow; but there was no sign of a periscope, nothing but the heads of the Italian sailors fighting for their lives in the sea.

A time bomb, secretly introduced into one of the magazines, had robbed the Italians of one of their most powerful battleships. This loss of a first-class ship of 24,000 tons, equipped with an armament of thirteen twelve-inch guns, was a grave one to the Italian Navy, and the question of salving her at once arose. Famous experts came on the scene, gazed on the visible portion of the keel of the ship which had cost four million pounds and shook their heads dubiously.

"Impossible!" they said. "The only thing to do is blow her to pieces."

The sinking of the *Leonardo da Vinci* was, indeed, a great blow to the pride of the Italian Navy, and there was a general desire on the part of the nation to wipe out the stain and turn defeat into a triumph by refloating the ship. The more difficult the task, the greater the triumph; the more impossible it seemed to foreign experts, the more determined were the Italians to achieve it.

Throwing themselves heart and soul into the matter, the officers of the Italian Naval Engineering Corps studied the problem most carefully and formulated several schemes, among them a plan to build around the ship a floating dock which, when completely pumped out, would automatically lift the wreck. Shortage of steel and other materials at the time made this plan impracticable. Then General Ferrati, the chief of the Italian naval constructors, evolved a plan to raise the ship by means of compressed air and carry her upside down to the dry dock at Taranto, where she could be prepared for righting.

It must never be forgotten that the battleship was upside down, and that not only had she to be raised, but she also had to be righted. Rivet by rivet and plate by plate she had in the course of years been built up by hundreds of men into one of the strongest structures known. All the rivets and plates had been welded into a compact mass of 24,000 tons which now lay at the bottom of the sea. Afloat, she obeyed the hand and brain of man, would go anywhere he desired; at his behest she turned to right or left, sped furiously through the sea or stopped. Now she was immovable as the mountains; to smash her to pieces would have been a gigantic task, costing months of time, tons of much-wanted explosives, and well over a hundred thousand pounds in money. The queer thing is that Ferrati proposed to harness air to lift the sunken monster, just as though she were an airship instead of a battleship.

So brilliantly conceived were Ferrati's plans that orders were at once given to put them into execution. Divers went down to make a survey of the wreck, which was so rent by the explosion that vast hole had been blown right through her from keel to top deck. A further survey indicated that the huge ship was literally digging her own grave. The weight of the upside-down battleship was resting on the funnels and gun turrets, and these, owing to the enormous pressure from above, were piercing a way slowly but surely through the mud. Day by day the ship sank lower and lower, until the whole of her upper deck was completely buried and the greater part of her hull at the stern had disappeared. In six months the funnels cut down through a bed of mud over thirty feet thick before they encountered a bed of clay which arrested the sinking of the ship.

No wonder the experts gave up hope. It really seemed that nothing but a miracle could bring the great vessel to the surface again. There she was, upside down, buried deep in the clinging mud, an enormous, unwieldy mass that the biggest cranes ever invented were powerless to lift. It is a comparatively easy task to raise a weight of ten tons from the sea bed, but it is quite a different proposition to lift a mountain of metal weighing upward of twenty thousand tons.

In no ways discouraged by the difficulties of the problem, General Ferrati and his associate, Major Gianelli, ordered large-sized models of the ship to be built. These were accurately constructed down to the smallest detail, with miniature engines, propellers and guns; and every compartment was loaded to represent the things on board the battleship when she foundered.

A stranger might have laughed at the childishness of the Italian officers who were apparently playing with toy battleships. But things are not always what they seem. Actually these same officers were puzzling out the most abstruse problems, carrying out remarkable experiments which enabled them to determine how the ship should behave in certain circumstances. As a result were evolved some intricate calculations upon which depended the whole operation of raising the ship.

The small part of the keel still showing above the surface was used as a platform on which to build huts for the salvage workers. Other huts were erected, in due course, on platforms built up from the submerged keel. The assembling of the plant for the work was completed by the spring of 1917, when the people of Taranto began to observe the figures of divers about the wreck.

Those divers had no enviable time. They quickly discovered that the explosion had liberated a quantity of thick oil which clung to everything within the ship, and as they went down it obscured the glass of their helmets and rendered the men practically blind. As if the oil were not sufficient handicap, there were thick clouds of rust which fogged the water and added to the discomfort of the divers. Yet the oil, despite its drawbacks, proved something of a blessing, for it adhered to hundreds of shells and protected them so efficiently from the action of the sea that the Italians were able to use them after salving them!

The recovery of the ammunition was the first step to lightening the ship. Day after day shells were hoisted out of the wreck and loaded into lighters. It was dangerous work, but it became rather monotonous to those engaged in it. Monotony, as is well known, is apt to lead to carelessness, and carelessness in handling shells may lead to terrible results. It is a fine tribute to the carefulness of the men engaged on the work to know that they salved nearly a thousand twelve-inch shells, three thousand 4.7-inch shells, some torpedoes, thousands of explosive charges and hundreds of tons of other ammunition without a single mishap.

Meanwhile, a cable was laid from the power station at Taranto right out to the wreck, a distance of a mile and a half; and with the power thus furnished the divers began drilling holes to take the rivets that were to hold the patches over the great rents in the hull. Slow and arduous work it was, and not without danger, for it cost one man his life. The patches were lowered into place, a layer of rubber was fitted betwixt the hull and the edges of the patches to make them watertight, then the patches were successfully bolted home.

More cables were carried out from the power station to work the air compressors, and, as soon as the divers had made a number of compartments watertight, the salvors began to pump air into the sunken vessel. The air which was pumped in naturally rose. It tried to get away to the surface, but the keel of the battleship which had been most carefully repaired and made airtight, prevented it from escaping.

The air was thus caught, as it were, in a trap. There was no way out for it. It was not strong enough to break through the bottom of the ship, but it was strong enough to press down the water within. As the volume of air increased, the belt which it formed grew in depth until it had forced the water down for a distance of twenty-six feet below the level of the sea outside, and men were able to enter the bottom of the vessel through an air-lock, work in security in this belt of compressed air, and lighten the vessel by taking out her stores and coals.

By the beginning of November, 1917, the salvors occasionally felt the battleship stir slightly beneath their feet. Despite the fact that she was buried deeply in the mud, her bow was showing the slightest of inclinations to rise. The engineer in charge noted this with delight. Barely perceptible as was the movement, it was more than sufficient to encourage him to persevere.

Once more the thick oil cropped up to hamper operations and increase the many difficulties. As the water was forced down inside the vessel by the compressed air, the oil was deposited on everything.

In most cases this did not matter much, but it was of far-reaching importance when it came to searching for leaks in the hull. The oil so obscured these places that it was extremely difficult to locate them, yet everything depended on their being discovered, for had they been left unstopped they might have let out the air and made it impossible to refloat the ship, or alternatively, let in the water at a critical time and led to her sinking in such a position that she could never be floated again. Fortunately, the Italian salvage men were able to detect all the leaks and stop them effectively, as the sequel amply proved.

Critics of the operations pointed out that should the salvors succeed in floating the battleship upside down, there was not sufficient depth of water to allow her to be taken across that mile and a half of sea to dry dock. Even if they managed to get her to dry dock, all their work would be wasted, for the battleship floating upside down would draw at least fifty feet of water, and the dry dock at Taranto was only forty feet deep.

These difficulties were fully considered and plans made for overcoming them. As it was an impossibility to increase the depth of the dry dock, the only way to solve this problem was to decrease the depth of water that the battleship would draw. The engineer accordingly proposed to detach the funnels, gun turrets and other top hamper from the deck of the vessel.

So firmly embedded were these things in the mud, that the feat of cutting them off appeared to be more than mortal man could accomplish. It was, too, pointed out that if divers tried to clear the mud away from round the funnels, to enable them to work at their task, the sea would quickly fill up the cavities again. Yet another aspect of the problem was that the mud pressing upward against the deck of the battleship was preventing her from sinking deeper, and if the mud were removed the whole weight of the *Leonardo da Vinci* would once more rest on her funnels and turrets and drive them deeper still into the clay.

But the engineer, with a stroke of genius, made no attempt to clear away the mud at all. Instead, he tackled the job from inside the ship. Certain compartments were pumped out and used as air-locks and in one turret the salvors succeeded, by the use of compressed air, in lowering the water to a level of fifty-six feet below the surface of the sea.

The men who performed the mighty task of detaching the turrets from the ship actually worked twenty feet below the level of the mud.

All around them outside was twenty feet of thick black ooze, and above that the illimitable ocean; yet the air we breathe, properly compressed, held back the deadly waters and enabled the men to work in safety.

Throughout 1918 some 150 men labored about the ship to free her from her top hamper and masts. Despite all difficulties, the gun turrets, funnels and other deck projections were detached from the ship and specially prepared so that when the vessel was raised they, too, could be brought to the surface. The open spaces in the deck left by funnels and turrets were covered in and made quite watertight, scores of tons of cork being packed into the *Leonardo da Vinci* to give her buoyancy.

Early in 1919 one or two tests showed that they could raise the monster when the time was ripe. But Major Gianelli, the engineer in charge, was taking no chances. To make quite sure of lifting her, he caused eight large pontoons to be fixed to her, each capable of sustaining a load of 350 tons, so in all he obtained from them the power to lift 2,800 tons. These pontoons, or camels as they are sometimes called in salvage circles, are strong metal cylinders something like big boilers or tanks. They are of the utmost importance in salvage operations and figure in most wreck-raising work. All were filled with water and sunk into position exactly where their lifting power was most wanted. The divers lashed them with strong steel cables securely to the sides of the battleship, and by the month of June the work was all but complete.

Remained the problem of making it possible to tow her to dry dock. Notwithstanding that all projections had been cut away from her deck, she drew so great a depth of water that it was obvious she would foul the bottom before going any distance. To obviate this danger, the Italians set dredgers to work to cut a channel all the way from the wreck to the gates of the dry dock. The making of this channel, which was a mile and a half long, entailed the removal of thousands of tons of mud, but the salvors regarded this task as trivial compared with the work they had accomplished on the overturned ship.

Then the dock itself required to be specially prepared, for like all dry docks it was planned to take a vessel upright and not upside down. The chocks down the center of the dock, which normally support the keel of a docked vessel, were quite useless so far as the *Leonardo da Vinci* was concerned. So a forest of timber began to spring up in the dry dock. Mighty balks of wood, fifteen inches and more square, were built up from the bottom of the dock. These followed the outline of the ship so that the deck could be brought exactly over them and allowed to sink into place upon them. Other gigantic piles of timber were constructed to support particular parts of the deck.

By September 17, 1919, all these preparations were completed. The air compressors forced the water out of the pontoons and out of the hull. Certain compartments of the ship were filled with water in order to balance her evenly—and then the keel, with the great pontoons straining upward, slowly arose out of the sea. For a time a stern battle went on between the mud which was gripping her and seeking to hold her down and the air which was striving to lift her to the surface. Then the air won. The battleship slipped from the grip of the mud, leaving her guns and turrets still embedded, and floated to the surface once more.

A rapid survey was made to see that she was fit for her journey, then the tugs took up their task and began to tow her slowly along the channel between the lines of buoys marking the passage. A stranger spectacle than the towing of this upside-down battleship was never before seen on the seas. The tugs managed to keep the capsized leviathan right in the center of the channel, and by nightfall the vessel was at the entrance to the dry dock, and was skillfully maneuvered inside on the following day.

For two days she floated, held up by the compressed air within her hull, and during this time certain adjustments were made in the timber frame that was to support her. The water was now drawn off from the dock and the *Leonardo da Vinci* settled down comfortably on her timber framework.

Her settling down placed a huge strain on the timbers, some having to bear the very great pressure of 225 tons to the square inch. The calculations, however, were so cleverly made, and the vast weight was so evenly distributed, that the framework supported her in perfect security. In itself this was a remarkable achievement. The slightest miscalculation, or one weak timber, might have brought about the collapse of the whole structure, and the battleship would have fallen, an absolute wreck, on the bed of the dry dock.

For months men swarmed about the upturned battleship, doing the final repairs that were necessary before she could be righted. The conclusive test of the Italians was nigh. Could they succeed in turning the great mass of metal the right way up again? No power known to man would suffice to right the vessel on land. Before the task could be attempted it was essential to place her once more in her element, the sea. On land she was immovable, on the sea she floated and could be more or less controlled by man, but whether man could perform the miracle of turning her right way up again, nobody knew.

The bottom of a ship, of course, has to be strongly built to withstand the pressures to which it is subjected. The deck, not having to stand the strain that the bottom is called upon to bear, need not be built so strongly. In this case the deck and the bottom had changed places, and it was therefore of the utmost importance that the deck should be strengthened to withstand the increased pressures that would arise in righting the ship.

Out in the bay the dredgers scooped a deep basin to enable her to turn over without fouling the sea bed, and toward the end of January, 1921, the *Leonardo da Vinci* was towed to the place where it was proposed to right her. Four hundred tons of solid ballast had been loaded into her, and the engineers made preparations for pumping 7,500 tons of water into certain compartments on her starboard side. Being above the center of gravity, this weight would make her so top-heavy that she was bound to overbalance and thus turn right side up again.

There in the bay lay the still stricken leviathan. The valves were opened to allow the sea to enter her compartments, and the salvage men scrambled from the upturned keel and pulled away from her in their boats. The water began to flow in, and by the time some eight hundred tons had entered she began to turn ever so slowly. Soon, as the weight of water increased, she swung over with a rush, raising a big wave as the deck swept clear of the water. For a moment it looked as though she would swing right over and finish upside down again. But the engineers had worked out their calculations to such a nicety that the battleship finally came to rest with a slight list, just as they had foreseen.

Across her deck, in big letters, was seen the motto of the famous *Leonardo da Vinci:* "Everything wrong rights itself," painted while the vessel was still upside down in dry dock. It was a happy thought, and a pandemonium of cheering broke out as the legend came into view.

The salving of the ship and her final righting took four and a half years. It was a Herculean task, and from first to last cost the Italian government £135,000. Unhappily, General Ferrati, who conceived the brilliant plan, did not live to see it completed. He was succeeded as director of operations by General Faruffini, who in turn

was succeeded by General Carpi, but during the whole time Major
Gianelli was in charge of the work and to him is due the credit for
carrying out from beginning to end, and bringing to a triumphant
conclusion, the most wonderful salvage feat ever performed up to
that time.

*

"Lycidas," A lament for a friend drowned in his
passage from Chester on the Irish Seas, 1637

Ay me! Whilst thee the shores, and sounding seas
Wash far away, where ere thy bones are hurled,
Whether beyond the stormy Hebrides,
Where thou perhaps under the whelming tide
Visit'st the bottom of the monstrous world;
Or whether thou, to our moist vows deny'd,
Sleep'st by the fable of Bellerus old,
Where the great Vision of the guarded Mount
Looks toward Namancos and Bayona's hold;
Look homeward, Angel, now, and melt with ruth:
And, O ye Dolphins, waft the haples youth.

John Milton

Italy was the only belligerent that entered World War II with frog-men and underwater chariots already developed. Britain, Japan, the United States and Germany later adopted these new weapons. Prince Valerio Borghese was a bold submarine commander and later chief of the Tenth Light Flotilla, which attacked Gibraltar, Malta and Alexandria.

The Consular Agent

BY J. VALERIO BORGHESE

One of the most brilliant enterprises carried out by the Tenth Light Flotilla during World War II was Sub-Lieutenant Ferraro's secret mission, which may now be related in full.

It was apprehended from intelligence received that the Turkish ports of Alexandretta and Mersina were much frequented by enemy shipping; chromium, a metal essential for war production, was being loaded there. In collaboration with our Naval secret intelligence service an expedition was organized with the object of interfering with this traffic, thus carrying our offensive into a zone which had hitherto remained undisturbed.

In view of the hydrographic characteristics of the harbor at Alexandretta, an open roadstead where steamers are anchored about two miles from the coast (and are there reached by lighters loaded with the mineral to be taken aboard), the type of weapon selected was the "explosive limpet," carried by a swimmer.

One of the finest of our swimmers, Sub-Lieutenant Luigi Ferraro, was appointed to execute the operation. He was an athletic Italian from Tripoli, a former pupil of the Physical Culture Academy and later an officer in the coastal militia, who combined traits of determination and seriousness with exceptional physical and moral advantages. With the help of specialists he was disguised as a consular employee of the Ministry of Foreign Affairs and appointed to join the Italian Vice-Consulate at Alexandretta. For this purpose it was necessary to arrange for him to cross the frontiers of Central Europe without arousing suspicion, especially among the extremely wary Turks, very reasonably anxious to maintain their neutrality; also to furnish him with documents justifying his presence in the office of the Vice-Consul of Italy at Alexandretta who, in view of his official functions could not be compromised in the affair; the mission was therefore to take place under his protection but unknown to himself.

In order to obtain the necessary documents, a service passport, letters of credit for the Consul, diplomatic immunity from customs examination and so on, it would have been necessary to apply officially to the Minister for Foreign Affairs; but there were many excellent reasons for going another way about it. In the first place, so as to preserve the military secret involved, which it was always risky to let out of our own restricted circle, and secondly, owing to a feeling of distrust, which was steadily on the increase, of the official bodies in Rome, where the atmosphere was one of masked defeatism which accorded ill with our plans. Lastly, the Ministry of Foreign Affairs, on which we had often previously relied for the solution of such problems, was becoming more and more reluctant to collaborate with us in this way, on the unexceptionable ground that the multiplication of bogus diplomats brought discredit on the institution, so that in the end even those who had a legitimate right to protection under diplomatic immunity would become involved in the distrust which the abuse of privilege would entail.

But there is always a way out: one of our petty officers was acquainted, on somewhat intimate terms, with a good-natured and quick-witted girl, a typist at the Ministry of Foreign Affairs; it did not prove difficult for him, in view of the highly patriotic reason for his request, to persuade her to work in with us. In this way we obtained the passport, some sheets of officially stamped notepaper and lastly the Ministry's rubber stamp itself (which was returned immediately after use).

On one of the first days of June, 1943, the consular employee Luigi Ferraro, an elegant and nonchalant-looking young man of handsome and promising appearance, reported to the Italian Vice-Consul at Alexandretta, the Marquis Ignazio di Sanfelice, armed with every possible credential. He handed the Consul, who was not expecting him, as his arrival had not been previously announced, a letter signed by the Minister for Foreign Affairs appointing him to the office staff to carry out special duties on behalf of the Ministry. The Consul was formally requested to give him every possible assistance.

Ferraro had four suitcases with him, all rather heavy, and bearing diplomatic seals. He soon established amicable relations with the clerk at the consulate, Giovanni Roccardi, really a lieutenant in the naval secret service. It had in fact been Roccardi who, having been at Alexandretta for some time and hence well acquainted with the place and the people, had called the Ministry's attention to the possibility of acting against enemy traffic in the port; he was the originator of the idea of the mission and Ferraro's indispensable collaborator on the organizational and shore side of his activities. Roccardi gave us the following description of the local conditions:

"Ferraro's arrival certainly made the operation possible from the technical point of view but by no means simplified the organization problem, which was that of introducing into our small world, by its very nature extremely prone to gossip, a new subject of curiosity, without excessive shock. The atmosphere in which we had to work was that of a small frontier city, enlivened by the intrigues of six consulates, the American, the British, the French, the Greek, the German and the Italian. The population of twelve thousand, mostly Arabs, was not hostile, it was even potentially friendly to us, but it was kept in subjection by the suspicious attitude of the Turkish police and much influenced by enemy propaganda.

"However, I managed to get everything arranged satisfactorily and our work was carried through right under the noses of two agents of the British intelligence service, whose special duty it was to watch Italian citizens in general and presumably, in spite of our innocent aspects, ourselves in particular. My task was much facilitated by Ferraro's genial and expansive character which was certainly the last that might have been expected to be meditating dark projects concerned with dynamite."

A few days after Ferraro's arrival he was introduced, under the wing of the expert Roccardi, into local consular and fashionable society; he was to be found on the beach every morning (and it was soon discovered by everybody that he could *not* swim) and every night at the café on the front, where he danced, drank and generally had a gay time of it, behaving exactly like any other young diplomat playing the usual diplomatic game.

He preferred sport to anything else; he was an adept at handball and bowls. Every evening a large box was carried down to the beach from the Italian Consul's bathing cabin and the games gear taken out of it in front of everyone; as soon as it began to get dark the games came to an end and the box was taken back to the cabin.

On the evening of the thirtieth of June, by which time the curiosity aroused by the newcomer to the small consular circle had died down, and the vigilance of the British agents had relaxed, for though they were extremely active they were not very intelligent, Ferraro and Roccardi lingered on the beach beyond the usual time; an exceptionally keen games of bowls had made them forget the lateness of the hour. As soon as they were alone, Ferraro darted like a squirrel into the Consul's cabin, rummaged in the games box and shortly afterward came out enveloped in a sheath of black rubber, fins on his feet, a mask on his face (the breathing gear) and two strange objects, oblong in shape and rather heavy, dangling from his waist, while his head was tied up with seaweed. It was an odd sort of beach get-up for a diplomat!

The black figure advanced circumspectly to the edge of the sea and entered the water; a moment later, soundlessly and without leaving visible trace of his progress, he had disappeared into the darkness of the night. He swam 2,300 meters, until he reached a steamer. His first victim was the Greek vessel *Orion*, seven thousand tons, with a cargo of chromium. Ferraro carried out the operation he had so often performed as a training exercise (he was one of our best swimmers and acted as instructor of the younger recruits); under the beams of the searchlights aboard and the alert eyes of the sentries he slipped very slowly along the side of the vessel (it was a tricky job, executed entirely with legs and fins, while the head remained motionless at the level of the water; he kept to the shadows cast by the lighters); on making contact with the steamer he switched on his breathing gear and dived, without a sound or a ripple. He moved, groping, along the hull, under the keel till he found the bilge-keel ledge, then detached those oblong "objects" from his waist, fixed them to the ledge with the clamps, in the right position, so that nothing stuck out; at last they were properly adjusted; he released the safety catches and came to the surface again; the whole job had only taken him a few minutes. In the same cautious manner in which he had arrived he departed; by 4 A.M. he was back in the consulate.

A week later the *Orion* finished taking her cargo in and weighed anchor, but she did not get far. While she was still in Syrian waters an explosion took place under her hull. She was so heavily laden that she sank in a few minutes. The survivors of the wreck were taken to a hospital in Alexandretta; they said the ship had been torpedoed.

Intelligence was received from the neighboring port of Mersina, on the eighth of July, that the steamer *Kaituna*, ten thousand tons, was lying at anchor there. She was a modern vessel, well equipped and well armed. Roccardi and Ferraro left for that city on the ninth, taking with them a small suitcase bearing diplomatic seals. That evening they went bathing. Next day they returned to Alexandretta, where their absence had not been noticed. The *Kaituna* did not leave until the nineteenth; only one of the two "limpets" which had been attached exploded. To avoid sinking, she was obliged to run ashore on the coast of Cyprus; the British found the device, which had not exploded; but it was too late! Ferraro, by that time, had already mined two more ships and disappeared without leaving the slightest trace of his activities.

On the thirtieth of July Ferraro and Roccardi were again at Mersina:

"I took note of the position of the target and at 2200 hours put on practically the whole of my kit in the consulate and wrapped myself in a dressing gown. Roccardi and I went down to the beach for our evening bath. He helped me to carry the 'limpets' and to put on the rest of my gear. I went into action at 2245 hours.

"After swimming about five hundred meters I thought I could hear something. I stopped, listened and became aware, in the darkness, of the heavy breathing of some large animal very close to me. Then I saw, against the light, two big creatures leaping, puffing and blowing, a couple of meters away. More than once they came straight at me and I could feel under me the rush of water caused by the thrashing of their tails. I tried several times to frighten them off and strike them with my knife, but it was no use. They seemed, with astonishing devotion, to consider it their duty to accompany me practically the whole way. I reached my target, some four thousand meters from my starting point at 2 A.M." (From Lieutenant Ferraro's report.)

After carrying out the attack with his usual coolness, Ferraro came ashore at 4 A.M. A few hours later he was in Alexandretta. But the *Sicilian Prince*, of five thousand tons, escaped her fate, for her departure was so long delayed that she was able to benefit by the inspection systematically carried out upon all British ships in Turkish waters after discovery of the unexploded "limpet" under the *Kaituna*.

The Norwegian motorship *Fernplant*, seven thousand tons, in the service of the British with a cargo of chromium, lying at Alexandretta, was not quite so fortunate. On the second of August Ferraro attacked her in the same way as he had attacked the *Orion*. The motorship weighed anchor on the fourth; but a few hours later she was back in harbor.

"The apprehension and anxiety with which we awaited the sequel can be imagined. We resigned ourselves to expecting the explosion about midnight. The time came, and we stared, in suspense, at the target. But, to our incredulous amazement, the minutes passed and nothing happened. We came to the conclusion that it had only been a long time after weighing anchor that the vessel had attained sufficient speed to set the miniature propellers of the explosive devices in motion, so we discontinued observation. Next morning, as soon as it was light, I dashed to the window, sure that I should see the ship, stranded on her side, somewhere along the coast. Instead of that I saw her lying in perfectly good order at her anchorage. Something I had not dared to hope for had occurred: the vessel, at her departure, had not attained the necessary speed. It was a great relief when, at 1800 hours on the fifth, we saw her leave harbor. For some hours we went on keeping a look out, in case she came back a second time." (From the report of Lieutenant Ferraro.)

The *Fernplant* never returned to Alexandretta; a few hours later she reached her last destination at the bottom of the sea.

Three days later Ferraro, having used up all his charges, went down unexpectedly with a dose of malaria! He was at once repatriated; no trace of his past activity remained at Alexandretta. In a single month Roccardi and Ferraro, working in perfect unison, had caused the sinkings of two ships with cargoes of chromium and damage to a third, with a total bag of 24,000 tons.

*

The Encantadas

The winged life crowding Rodondo had its full counterpart in the finny hosts which peopled the waters at its base. Below the waterline the rock seemed one honeycomb of grottoes, affording labyrinthine lurking places for swarms of fairy fish. . . . Here hues were seen as yet unpainted and figures which are unengraved.

Herman Melville

Shark

BY ALEXANDRE DUMAS

*F*or people who like shark, or would like to try it, we recommend the recipe below, given us by M. Duglerez, chief kitchen steward of the House of Rothschild, to whom we owe a number of recipes of this type. But we warn the diner in advance that we have no personal opinion on this dish. We have never eaten it. We have never had any desire to do so.

Shark flesh is tough, leathery, dry, gluey, and hard to digest. This does not prevent the Norwegians and Icelanders from drying it, later actually to cook and eat it. We recommend this recipe to them also.

Young Shark Stomachs. Soak 15 young shark stomachs for 24 hours. Drain. Parboil 20 minutes in lightly salted water. Drain. Freshen with cold water. Dry with a cloth.

Line a pot with strips of bacon and add the shark stomachs. Add 1 bay leaf, 2 cloves, 3 peeled and pitted slices of lemon, 1 ladleful of good poultry consommé, 3 ounces of butter. Simmer until well done.

Just before serving, make a sauce with 1 ladleful of *sauce suprême*, 1 tablespoonful of soubise sauce, 2 good pinches of Indian curry. This sauce should be reduced, but not pasty.

DICTIONARY OF CUISINE

Among the goodly school of all-around underseamen developed in Southern California is young Ramsey Parks, by trade a lifeguard and by avocation a free diver ready for anything. He has helped recover crashed planes from the bottom, assisted scientific studies at the Scripps Institution of Oceanography, and carried out submarine geological surveys.

Exploration of the
Sunken Liner Andrea Doria

BY RAMSEY PARKS

*O*n the evening of August 2, 1956, I was awakened by the ringing of the phone. I had gone to bed early, after rowing a surf dory a couple of miles with my partner, Platzi Miller, in preparation for the annual Southern California Lifeguard Relays. Slightly blurry-eyed, I answered the phone. On the other end of the line was Earl Murray, a geologist and diver from Scripps Institute of Oceanography in La Jolla. I had the good fortune to spend a great deal of time diving with Earl in the year that I worked at Scripps. He said, "How would you like to go to New York?" Thinking he was kidding, I replied, "Sure." Then Earl informed me that *Life* magazine had phoned Scripps in an effort to acquire divers to take color pictures of the sunken *Andrea Doria*. Bob Dill, a geologist and diver from the Naval Electronics Laboratory in San Diego, had secured the deal.

We were to leave within a week. Within that week, many things had to be done. First, I had to get time off from my job as Lifeguard for the County of Los Angeles. Personal gear would have to be put in top shape. Regulators were overhauled and double-checked. Underwater lights, consisting of a seal-beam and a twelve-volt battery, filled with mineral oil to prevent implosion, were constructed. Dive 'N Surf made all of us heavy-duty Thermocline wet suits (which kept us very comfortable in the forty-six-degree water).

Then, the flight to New York, where we met Ken MacLeish of the magazine, Lieutenant Commander James E. Stark, and Peter Gimbel. Gimbel had made the first dive on the *Doria* two weeks before. That night we flew to Nantucket Island, which was to be our base of operations. A fifty-foot, twin-screw diesel cruiser with a portable decompression chamber on board had been chartered. Stark, a diving specialist on leave from the U.S. Navy, was retained to see that we were kept in the best possible physical condition. He also would be irreplaceable if any diving accident might occur which would require recompression or other medical care. We were to be at the dock at 6:00 A.M. the following morning. The skipper had figured it would take about six hours to reach the *Andrea Doria*.

In the next three days, we were to suffer much frustration and disappointment. Each day we went out to the area, we were forced back by time and the weather. The long fifty-mile trip out and back was exhausting. On the fourth day, Dill and Ken MacLeish searched the area from an airplane. On returning, their news was heartening. They had sighted the oil slick, and were able to see the globulets popping up and spreading out on the surface. The buoy that was supposed to be over the ship was not there.

Upon leaving early the next morning, all hands were in good spirits in anticipation of reaching our goal. Even the long, seven-hour trip out did not dull our enthusiasm. We began to see patches of oil. As we headed into the direction from which the current was coming, the slicks became larger. Finally, someone yelled, "There it is!" Looking over the side, we could see the oil droplets rising to the surface, surrounded by a fine curtain of air bubbles. This sight gave one the feeling that the once proud ship was still slowly dying.

A few passes over her with the fathometer, and we dropped the descending line. The skipper backed down a little and the anchor was thrown over. Double seventy-cubic-foot compressed air bottles were hooked up with our lung regulators. Every diver wore an exposure suit, fins, weight belt, mask, a depth gauge, underwater watch, and a double tank lung. Two divers were to carry the underwater lights, while each of the other two carried Rolleimarin cameras. The lights were a necessity in order for the cameraman to see to focus through the ground-glass viewfinder of the camera. They were also necessary in order to see our way once we were inside the ship.

We were at last ready to dive. Gimbel was to accompany Dill and I was to be Murray's partner. We jumped into the water, which was pleasant to our overheated bodies. The crew handed us the lights and cameras. The O.K. signal was given by Doctor Stark; and Murray and I started down the descending line. I found it actually hard to conceive that I was about to see the *Doria*. The week previous to this dive, I had spent a great deal of time imagining what she would look like. At 160 feet I looked at my depth gauge, but the *Doria* was not yet in sight. It was still not reality that I was diving on the ship.

I turned on the seal-beam light. The beam of the light appeared pink. As my eyes became accustomed to the twilight, I could see the white water line on the hull.

Another twenty feet and we were on the side of the *Andrea Doria*. She lay on her wounded starboard side at nearly a right angle. We swam up the side of the boat toward the bridge. On the way, we passed several portholes of which only one was open. I glanced through an open port, from which a curtain was waving slightly in the one- to two-knot current. The cabin inside was in complete disarray. We continued on to the Lido Deck, and the entrance to the Prima Lounge. There were two sets of double doors. The two forward doors were open, while the after two were shut tight, due to the swelling of the wood. Murray slipped down sideways and feet first. I followed, holding the light. Without the light, the passageway was nearly pitch black. We swam down to the elevator shaft and the entrance to the lounge.

Since first landing on the ship, Murray had been continually taking pictures. After shooting each picture, the flash bulb would implode, sounding like a .22 rifle. The underwater world this deep is a multitude of sounds never heard in the world above, or in shallower water. The bubbles leaving your regulator sound like small Chinese bells, and the air leaving the valve of the tank whines and moans.

Down inside the passageway, nearly two hundred feet below the surface, we were literally shaken by the booming sound that caused the whole ship to shudder. My first thought was that the doors had fallen shut, locking us inside. We swam back down the passage and up to the doors. To our relief, there were the faces of Dill and Gimbel peering through the still open doorway. The hindering effect of nitrogen narcosis, plus the situation we were in, had caused us to jump to an irrational conclusion. The noise happened twice again during the dive, but these times we were on the deck of the ship. We could tell then, that it was due to the buckling of one of the huge, steel plates in the side of the ship either by the loss of air, or the ship's settling. When the plate popped back, it caused this sound, and the whole boat would shudder.

I looked at my watch and realized we had less than a minute of bottom time left. We got a couple more pictures and started our ascent. As I watched the *Andrea Doria* disappear beneath me, I felt a sense of frustration at having to leave so soon. The short fourteen minutes we had on the bottom gave us such a little time to see much of the ship that looked more like a city underwater. We continued on up to ten feet and the long dreary waiting to decompress.

During the next five days, only one more dive was made due to the weather. A siege of ptomaine poisoning from a bunch of over-ripe clams kept me from making this dive.

The final dive was made on August 18, as we had to get back to our regular jobs. Also, the weather outlook for the next few weeks was beginning to look rather poor. On this dive, we set the descending line on the stern of the ship. The descent to the *Doria* was relatively uneventful. We made it to the side of the ship, which was 185 feet, in about forty-five seconds.

As my eyes became accustomed to the diffused twilight, I could see forty to forty-five feet horizontally. We took a few pictures at the spot where we landed, then swam down across the windows of the after lounge and bar, looking for an entrance. I saw the first- and second-class swimming pools. Tipped at nearly a right angle and submerged over two hundred feet down, they looked like a crazy dream.

The light was getting dimmer, and the effects of nitrogen narcosis were growing stronger, which, contrary to popular belief, is not immediate; taking thirty seconds to a full minute to feel the maximum effect. These factors told us we were working below two hundred feet. I looked at my depth gauge, which read 225 feet. There seemed to be no entrance to the after lounge here. We took a few more pictures and started back up to the port passageways. We went through the open doors on to the glassed-in Promenade Deck. As we swam along the deck, we saw many shoes and pieces of luggage. These were the first personal things we had seen. They made the *Andrea Doria* seem more closely related to the world above from where she had come. I felt as close to the people that had left these articles, as if I had known them and been on the *Doria* when she was struck.

We continued to swim along the deck, entering and taking pictures in the passageways that ran thwartships. I looked at my depth gauge. It read exactly two hundred feet. My watch said we had about four minutes left. We had swum at least 150 feet down the passageway. A problem presented itself. Would it be best to swim back the way we had come, or continue on and hope for an exit? We had enough air to spend ten or more minutes on the bottom, but this would have us decompressing for a tremendously long time. As we already had forty-one minutes to do with the short time we had been down, we were just about to turn back, when I looked up ahead. There was either a picture window or an opening in the glassed-in passageway. I swam up slowly, not wanting to run into it if it were a window. As I got nearer, I could see there was no organic silt, as on the other windows. Here was an opening! What a relief, if we hadn't found this exit, we would have had to go all the way back. Murray, the smallest of us, had tried to see if he could fit through a window a ways back that had its pane broken out, and could not make it.

We started for the twenty-feet decompression stop. As we left the boat, I experienced a momentary dizziness that is characteristic of the beginning of an ascent from depths below 150 feet. Little is known about its cause and most divers do not experience it every time. Murray prefers to call it the "uglies."

As the *Andrea Doria* faded out of sight, I knew it would be the last time I would have the unforgettable experience of diving on her. I felt slightly nostalgic. Like leaving a helpless old friend.

*

The Diver

Nor will this earth serve him: he sinks the deep
Where harmless fish monastic silence keep.

John Donne, ELEGY ON MISTRESS BOULSTRED

In 1648, more than two hundred years before Jules Verne, John Wilkins anticipated the themes of Twenty Thousand Leagues Under the Sea *in* Mathematical Magick. *He was the Bishop of Chester and Oliver Cromwell's brother-in-law.*

Advantages of a Submarine Vessell

BY JOHN WILKINS

1. 'Tis *private;* a man may thus go to any coast of the world invisibly, without being discovered or prevented in his journey.
2. 'Tis *safe;* from the uncertainty of *Tides,* and the violence of *Tempests,* which doe never move the sea about five or six paces deep; From *Pirates* and *Robbers* which do so infest other voyages; From ice and great frosts which doe so much endanger the passages towards the Poles.
3. It may be of very great advantage against a Navy of enemies, who by this means may be undermined in the water and blown up.
4. It may be of a special use for the relief of any place that is besieged by water, to convey unto them invisible supplies; and so likewise for the surprisal of any place that is acessible by water.
5. It may be of unspeakable benefit for submarine experiments and discoveries: as,

The deep caverns and subterraneous passages where the sea-water in the course of its circulation doth vent itself into other places and the like. The nature and kinds of fishes, the severall arts of catching them, by alluring them with lights, by placing nets around the sides of this Vessell, shooting the greater sort of them with guns, which may be put out of the ship by the help of such bags as were mentioned before, with like artifices and treacheries, which may be more successively practised by such who live so familiarly together. These fish may serve not only for food, but for fewell likwise, in respect of that oyl which may be extracted from them.

The many fresh springs that may probably be met with in the bottom of the sea, will serve for the supply of drink and other occasions.

But above all, the discovery of submarine treasures is more especially considerable, not only in regard of what hath been drowned by wrecks, but the several precious things that grow there, as Pearl, Coral Mines, with innumerable other things of great value, which may be much more easily found out, and fetcht up by the help of this, than by any other usual way of the Divers.

To which purpose, this great Vessell may have some lesser Cabins tyed about it, at various distances, wherein several persons, as Scouts, may be lodged for the taking of observations, according as the Admiral shall direct them. Some of them being frequently sent up to the surface of the water, as there shall be occasion.

All kinds of arts and manufactures may be exercised in this Vessell. The observations made by it, may be both written, and (if need were) printed here likewise. Severall Colonies may thus inhabit, having their children born and bred up without the knowledg of land, who could not chuse but be amazed with strange conceits upon the discovery of this upper world.

The underwater world is beginning to claim visitors from outer space. Arthur Clarke, a founder of the British Interplanetary Society, and author of The Exploration of Space, The Sands of Mars, Islands in the Sky *and* Expedition to Earth, *went underwater in 1951, and space was finished for him. Born in Minehead, England, in 1917, he was a technician with the Royal Air Force in World War II, took honors in mathematics at London University, and edited* Science Abstracts. *He has dived in the Atlantic and Indian oceans with his cameraman-partner, Michael Wilson, a Canadian free-lance. They now work out of Colombo, Ceylon.*

Beneath a Jungle Stream

BY ARTHUR C. CLARKE

Soon after we had arrived in Ceylon, Rodney Jonklass, the splendid free diver, finding the life of government servant incompatible with wealth, liberty and the pursuit of happiness, threw up his job in the Department of Fisheries and went into a business peculiarly suited to his talents. He became head of the tropical fish department of one of the largest commercial organizations in the East, and thus found himself exchanging the spear gun for the hand net.

The capturing and transporting by air of tropical fish to all quarters of the globe is a fascinating and somewhat exotic business of which I knew nothing until I saw Rodney at work. Although the most beautiful fish are undoubtedly the marine ones, the problem of obtaining genuine or acceptably synthetic sea water makes it hard to keep them in captivity, and the most popular aquarium fish are the fresh-water varieties. So when Rodney invited me to accompany him on a trip inland to collect specimens, I was glad to do so—even though it seemed a little odd to pack face masks and then turn our backs on the sea. We drove south of Colombo in the company's van, its interior crowded with the tools of Rodney's new trade—aluminum milk cans, glass jars, nets, and pumps to ensure a good air supply to the captured fish. With us traveled Rodney's assistant Simon, a tough little man whom we had hired for one of our own trips, and who has overcome the usual Singhalese objection to the sea to such good effect that he now goes skindiving for crayfish by night.

Thirty miles south of Colombo we swung inland away from the busy main highway and soon lost ourselves on winding dirt roads which, though bumpy in places, gave the van no trouble. We passed tiny villages set in the lush green of paddy fields, and finally came to a halt beside a bridge over a small, crystal stream. Looming above us was a group of steep hills, completely smothered in the forest which had submerged them like a great wave.

Carrying nets, cans, and collecting bottles we began to walk along the low earth dikes which divided the paddy fields into squares which could be flooded or left dry at will. Zigzagging along the grid of embankments, and occasionally squelching through mud, we finally came to the river again at a point where it disappeared into a wide, leafy tunnel. I was about to step into the water when I noticed what appeared to be a small piece of licorice attached to my ankle. It did not remain there, but started to walk up my leg like an inchworm or looper caterpillar. I had heard about Ceylon leeches, but this was the first one with which I had come into contact, and I wasted no time at all in knocking it off before it could go into the blood-transfusion business. Though only about an inch long, it was such a revolting object that I had no desire to meet one of its really big relatives, the three-inch variety which infest certain jungle areas. The favorite story told about these creatures concerns a hunter who broke his leg in the forest and tried to crawl to safety. He would have made it if the leeches had not reached him first; when his friends found him, he was a drained husk.

Trying to forget this cheerful tale, I stepped into the refreshingly cold water of the river and followed Rodney upstream. He was wearing face mask and swimming trunks, and carried a large butterfly net. Simon, similarly equipped, followed a few yards behind, and a couple of volunteer helpers brought up the rear with the small metal churns in which the captured fish would be carried. The stream was nowhere more than three feet deep, so even though I was carrying a couple of cameras I had no difficulty in wading after the intrepid hunters.

From time to time Rodney would plunge his head into the water, and holding the net in his left hand use his right one to scare fish into it. The technique never failed; fresh-water fish, it seems, are much more stupid than marine ones. Sometimes when Rodney pulled the net out of the water, it would be full of scores or even hundreds of tiny red and silver shapes, few of them as much as an inch long, destined to travel thousands of miles to grace aquaria in distant lands. There were times when a single dip of a net would bring up a hundred rupees'—say twenty dollars'—worth of fish, and I began to wonder if I was in the right business. The little river meandered along under the trees which formed an almost complete archway overhead, shading us from the sun and incidentally making it practically impossible to photograph the operations. It was as fresh and mild as on a fine day in the late English spring; there was none of the oppressive heat or humidity one might have expected. The metal cans became more and more full of fish, mostly ruby barbs and golden rasboras. One of them contained at least a thousand of the tiny creatures, forming a compact, milling ball like a whirling swarm of bees.

The largest fish which Rodney caught were three fresh-water gars—slim, grass-green needles about six inches long. When they concealed themselves among the weeds placed in the tank, they matched the long fronds so perfectly that they were almost invisible. The use of the face mask, Rodney explained to me, had revolutionized the catching of small fresh-water fish. No longer was it necessary to make blind jabs with a net at shapes seen blurrily through the wrinkled surface. By putting his head underwater, the hunter could now see everything that was happening in the river as he waded along it, and could scare the fish straight into his gaping net. The world of rivers and lakes, though less glamorous and less colorful than that of the sea, is almost as crowded with life and is a good deal safer to explore. At its best, visibility is unlimited—you can see as far as there is anything to be seen. I have taken underwater photographs in Florida rivers that looked faked because there was no way of telling that they had not been made in the open air. Visibility in the little stream up which Rodney was working his profitable way was about forty feet, which was as good as infinity for all practical purposes. He had chosen the time with care; had there been any heavy rains, the water would have been too polluted with mud for him to have seen more than a few inches.

There is always a possibility that, sooner or later, Rodney will come across a crocodile as he wades upstream, but he does not let the prospect disturb him. The Ceylon crocodiles eat a couple of careless villagers every year, but if one of them encounters Rodney, even though he may be armed only with a butterfly net, I am quite sure who will come off second best.

After half an hour's wading, over little waterfalls and through quiet pools, Rodney decided we had gone far enough upriver and we started to retrace our steps down the stream, which we had now rather thoroughly muddied, not to mention depleted. (Though of course any inroads which could be made by a couple of men with nets would be fully restored in a few weeks.)

When we had made our way back through the paddy fields to the van (and I had detached another leech which had managed to have a good meal at my expense) Rodney sorted the fish out into their different tanks so that, as soon as they had recovered from their shock, they would not start eating each other with gusto. He was particularly careful to isolate the fierce gars; they could have cut down the profits of the trip by quite a few rupees. To keep the little tanks aerated until the specimens could be placed in proper aquaria rubber tubes were connected to a small pump driven from the van's batteries, and soon streams of air were bubbling briskly through the water.

A few hours later, the hundreds of little fish were getting accustomed to the strange environment of rows and rows of glass tanks neatly laid out in a large shed. After a bucolic existence for untold generations, they had become apartment-house dwellers. But this was nothing to what would happen to them when, in a few days' time, they took to the air.

The key to the air transportation of tropical fish, I was surprised to discover, is the ubiquitous polyethylene film which is now used to wrap everything from sandwiches to stratosphere balloons. Fish which are to be sent by air are placed in a plastic bag containing a gallon or so of water, and the bag is then packed in a suitably padded cardboard box. In this way, the use of heavy or easily broken containers is eliminated; to make quite sure that there will be no leakage, one plastic bag is enclosed in another to give double-walled protection.

However, fish need oxygen to breathe just as badly as we do, and most of them would soon suffocate even in a tank which was open to the air. Accordingly, the plastic bags are blown up with pure oxygen before they are sealed, so that they form tight little balloons half full of oxygen and half full of water. As long as the fish reach their destination inside two days (some consignments have survived for longer) there is no danger of their suffocating.

As Rodney was at pains to point out to me, there is much more to the tropical-fish business than this. Some fish are very hardy and will put up with all kinds of rough treatment; others will die if one as much as touches them with one's fingers. Some will live in any tap water; others will be killed by the slightest impurity. As I realized the equipment and know-how that existed behind the scenes to ensure that all these strange and beautiful little creatures arrived safely in far corners of the world, I decided that it was not, after all, an easy or simple way of making money. It may be just the job for Rodney—but, personally, I haven't the patience to sit up all night nursing a sick scorpion fish.

*

The Vertical Voyage

He goes a great voyage that goes to the bottom of the sea.

Thomas Fuller, GNOMOLOGIA, 1732

Twice during World War II, British midget submarines carried out successful attacks on enemy cruisers. One was the mission deep into Norwegian fiords to mine the Tirpitz *and the other was Ian Fraser's attack on the* Takao, *which won him and diver J. J. Magennis the Victoria Cross, Britain's highest award for valor.*

Midget Attack on a Japanese Cruiser

*E*xcitement was betrayed in my voice. "There she is," I cried. The *Takao* was a crusier of the Atago Class, of 9,850 tons displacement, 630 feet long, with a beam of 62½ feet; and she carried a crew of 630 officers and men. Her armament was formidable—two eight-inch guns in each of three turrets for'ard and two similar guns in each of two turrets aft. She was well armed against air attack, and she could boast eight twenty-one-inch torpedo tubes. She carried four aircraft. She had a triple hull and extra armor plating as a defense against submarine attack. In my small viewfinder, she looked even bigger than that.

At this time she was anchored close into the Singapore side of the strait, with her stern fifty to one hundred yards off the island and her bow pointing directly across to Johore. She hadn't been to sea for some time, according to the reconnaissance photographs taken, and it was thought that her present role was that of a shore battery.

Already British and Allied troops had reached Rangoon, and an ambitious invasion of Malaya was planned. It might only be a matter of weeks before they would be in Singapore, and this cruiser, together with the *Myoko*, formed two very formidable forts, from which eight-inch and four-inch shells could be fired into our advancing men. At the same time they reinforced the antiaircraft strength of the dockyard.

The position of the ship had caused me a certain amount of anxiety when going through the Intelligence reports before leaving for the attack, and I had expressed my feeling of apprehension in no mean terms to Captain Fell and to others on board *Bonaventure*. I had told them that, in my opinion, it would be impossible to get underneath the cruiser in order to place the limpet charges, and that it might be necessary to drop my cargoes alongside. To my annoyance, no one in the depot ship staff appeared to share my doubts.

At that part of the strait where the *Takao* lay the water is shallow, with depths shown on Admiralty charts of from eleven to seventeen feet; but there is a depression in the sea bed, which amounts to a hole, five hundred feet across, fifteen hundred feet long, and some five feet deeper than the water around. The *Takao* lay across this depression so that the first hundred feet of her length, beginning at her bow, lay in water which dropped to less than three feet at low tide; and the same conditions occurred at her stern. It was proposed that I should pass over this shallow patch and down into the hole where I was expected to maneuver my boat under the ship. As I have already said, I had made it clear that I thought this feat impossible.

"Stand by for a bearing, ship's ahead, now." I ordered. Then I translated the bearing into a true bearing and laid it on the chart. The attack had started.

From that moment, until I was back on board our mother submarine, the *Stygian*, all fear left me. I felt only that nervous tautness that comes so often in moments of stress. I let each of the others have a quick look at the *Takao* through the periscope, and then we were ready.

Leading Seaman J. J. Magennis, our diver, finished dressing, and made final adjustments to his equipment. Then he slipped quietly on deck by the steering wheel and operated the periscope, the slide rule and the stop watch to my order. Owing to the ever-changing density of the water, Kiwi Smith, my New Zealand Sub-Lieutenant, had been having some difficulty with the trim, but by the time we started the attack everything was under control, and he had a perfect trim, requiring only a slight movement of the 'planes to keep his depth. Engine Room Artificer Reid, silent and preoccupied as usual, now centered all his thoughts on keeping *XE-3* dead on course. He could quite easily spoil the whole attack by being only one degree out of course. One degree in one thousand yards, the usual final ruling on distance, could make a difference of fifty yards in the final position: fifty yards either side of the planned point of contact, so that one could quite easily miss the ship altogether.

Each of the crew must have been by now feeling the strain of nineteen hours without real sleep, and nine hours' breathing in the confines of a midget submarine. But now had come the supreme moment, which could have been their last. They knew they must concentrate harder than ever before if we were to make a success of our allotted task. And concentrate they did.

It was eight minutes to two when I finally decided that the position of *XE-3* was right enough for us to start the actual run in. By this time the sun was high in the heavens, the sea was as placid as a Scottish loch early on a summer's day, and visibility, both above and under the water, was excellent. Looking through the attack periscope, I could see distinctly the tall outlines of cranes in the dockyard lying behind the *Takao*, and the barrack buildings and numerous small boats making their way back and forth from the vessels anchored in mid-stream. I could see a small destroyer escort, and, tied up between the buoys, a ship of seven or eight thousand tons, which, for a moment, I thought might be worth while attacking, should we get away from the *Takao* quickly. I also saw the mooring buoys of battleships lying in the channel, and always looming up I could see the *Takao* as she came closer and closer. Her three for'ard turrets stood out distinctly like Olympic winners on a rostrum, the center one above the other two, and all three close together. The guns in "C" turret pointed aft, unlike any other cruiser constructed at that time. Her massive bridgework was easily discernible, with the thick black-topped funnel raking astern of it. I could see the second funnel, smaller, and somewhat insignificant, stuck vertically upward between the two tripod trelliswork masts, and on "B" and "X" turrets a sort of tripod framework. From her vertical bow with the acutely curved top, stretched two anchor cables, gently rising and falling in the slowly ebbing tide. I could see the gangway on her starboard side, and, just above, a derrick used for hoisting in aircraft. I saw no aircraft.

When, during a spell on the run in, I glanced through the night periscope, I was disturbed to find that I could see both ends of *XE-3* quite distinctly, showing that the underwater visibility was ten feet or more. I reconciled myself to this disadvantage by thinking that I would at least be able to keep an eye on Magennis as he attached the limpet mines.

Later on, at eight minutes past two, the range was two thousand yards, one mile away, about thirty degrees on our port bow.

"Four hundred and fifty revolutions, steer 218 degrees, stand by to start the attack."

"Course 218 degrees. All ready to start the attack," came the reply.

"Start the attack," I ordered.

Magennis started the stop watch, and we prepared ourselves.
"Up periscope."

Magennis pressed the switch, the motor whirred.

"Whoa!"

The motor stopped.

"Bearing right ahead, range two degrees on her funnel—down periscope."

Magennis changed the degrees into yards by means of the slide rule.

"Length sixteen hundred yards, sir," he called.

I did not answer; there was no need to. Each of us was sweating profusely, and energy and air had to be reserved. In any case, we were only doing now the thing that we had practiced time and time again when stationed in the Scottish lochs and when lying off the coast of Australia.

The only sounds in the boat were the whir of the main motor, the hiss of escaping oxygen from the cylinder in the engine room, and an occasional scraping sound of steel on steel in the well-greased bearings when the hydroplane wheel was turned. Ten feet, forty feet. "Up periscope," range, "Down periscope." So it went on until the range had narrowed to four hundred yards.

"Up periscope, stand by for a last look round."

Click! Down went the handles; I fixed my eye to the eyepiece for the hundredth time, slowly swinging to port.

"Ah, there she is, range eight degrees."

Slowly I swung the periscope round to starboard.

"Flood 'Q,' down periscope, quick, thirty feet. Bloody hell! There's a boat full of Japs going ashore; she's only about forty or fifty feet away on the starboard bow. God, I hope they didn't see us."

So close had they been that I could make out their faces quite distinctly, and even had time to notice that one of them was trailing his hand in the water. The boat, painted white, stood out clearly against the camouflaged background of the cruiser. Similar to the cutters used in the Royal Navy for taking liberty men ashore, she was packed with sailors. The helmsman stood aft, his sailor's collar and ribbon gently lifting in the breeze caused by the boat's headway. She was so close that it seemed that her bow wave almost broke over our periscope. I could see the lips of men moving as they chatted away on the journey ashore. They should have seen us. I do not know why they did not.

"Thirty feet, sir."

My mind refocused.

"All right, Magennis, the range is two hundred yards, we should touch bottom in a moment."

To Smith: "Keep her as slow as you can."

Followed anxious silence, then a jar and the noise of gravel scraping along the keel as we touched bottom. Reid had to fight hard to keep her on course as we scraped and dragged our way across the bank at depths of only fifteen feet, which meant our upper deck was only ten feet below the surface.

Watching through the night periscope, I could see the surface of the water like a wrinkled windowpane above our heads, until it gradually darkened as we came into the shadow of the great ship. Something scraped down our starboard side, and then, with a reverberating crash, we hit the *Takao* a glancing blow which stopped us. I thought we had made enough noise to awaken the dead, and I was worried in case someone above might have felt the jar.

"Stop the motor! I wonder where the hell we are?" I said. I could see nothing through the periscope to give me a clear indication of our position in relation to the enemy ship, only her dark shadow on our starboard side. Obviously I was not underneath it, as the depth on the gauge was only thirteen feet.

I began to fear that we might be much too far forward, that the ominous-sounding scraping along our side had been made by an anchor cable at the target's bows.

"We seem to be too far for'ard," I reported. "We'll alter course to 190 degrees and try to run down her side. Port 30, half ahead group down."

The motor hummed into life again, but we did not budge. "Group up half ahead," I called and we tried many other movements. The motor hummed even faster, the propeller threshed, but still no sign of movement. We were jammed, and looking back on this afterward, I am inclined to think that as the *Takao* veered in the tideway, the slacking cable came to rest on us. Then it lifted as she veered away again, or else we were jammed for the same reason under the curve of her hull at this point. It was only after some really powerful motor movements in both directions, and ten minutes of severe strain, that we finally broke loose and dragged our way out across the shingly bottom to the deeper channel. I had attacked from too fine an angle on the bow, and after running out again, I altered course and steered for a position more on the *Takao*'s beam, which would mean a longer run over the shallow bank, but I decided the risk was worth it, if I were to hit the ship amidships.

At three minutes past three we were ready again, a thousand yards away. Once more we started the run-in for the attack. This time we were more successful. We slid easily across the bank with the gauge at one time registering only thirteen feet, and then, blackness, as we slid into the hole and under the keel of the *Takao*. It was just as I had practiced it so many times before, and I was surprised how easy it was.

The depth gauge began to indicate deeper water, fifteen feet, eighteen feet, twenty feet, and then a graying of the night periscope and upper viewing window.

"Stop the motor."

Then blackness in the night periscope and upper viewing window.

"Full astern."

The bottom of the *Takao* showed dimly, and then suddenly it was distinct, encrusted with thick heavy layers of weed as it fell sharply to her keel.

"Stop the motor!"

The hull stopped sliding overhead. We were under her. We were resting on the bottom with the hull of the *Takao* only a foot above our heads. I wondered if we would be able to go straight through. "Come and have a look at this," I called to the crew, and they left their positions to come and see the encrusted bottom of our prize. "What a dirty bastard," said one of them; and I couldn't have agreed more. It would have been nice to have gone out and written my name on the years and years of growth on the keel, but time was passing and the need for haste cut short our conversations. We were anxious to be away. The *Takao* held no interest for us, other than the need to blow her up.

"Raise the antennae," I called.

Smith operated the lever and the two antennae came up hydraulically from their stowage positions on either side of the bow. "It doesn't matter about the after one," I told Smith, "there's no point in trying to raise it." The after antenna, unlike the two for'ard ones, was raised by hand, and sometimes it was an awful struggle, particularly after several days at sea, to get it up, and in any case, it would not have been effective owing to the sharp slope of the ship down to her keel.

Magennis was ready: he must been stewing in his rubber suit, and I thought, momentarily forgetting the dangers, how pleasant it would be for him to get out into the cool water. He strapped on his breathing apparatus. The only instruction I could give him was to place all six limpets in the container as quickly as possible and not to make a noise. I fitted in the Perspex window, patted him on the shoulder, and into the escape compartment he went. Reid closed the door on him; the valves were opened and shut, and the pumps started. Looking through the observation window into the wet-and-dry compartment, I could see Magennis breathing steadily into the bag as the water rose around him, and then I moved over to the night periscope again, with its larger field of vision and higher magnification. I could see along the keel of the *Takao* for some fifteen yards in either direction, and it was like looking into a dark cave with *XE-3* lying across the center of the sunlit entrance. I swung around the periscope so that the keel of the enemy lay against our upper deck, just for'ard of the periscope bracket, and as the bottom rose away sloping from the keel at a fairly sharp angle, the antennae stuck up from the bow like an ant's feelers. They were not resting on the *Takao*'s bottom. Huge lumps and clusters of seaweed hung down like festoons and Christmas decorations, and the faint sunlight danced between them.

Inside the boat we waited patiently. Suddenly, almost as though we hadn't expected it, the pumps stopped and the wheels controlling the valves began to move, as if controlled by a hidden power, as indeed in a sense they were. Reid again moved across from his seat by the wheel to help Magennis to shut them off, and looking through my only means of communication with the diver now that he was outside, I saw the lever which operated the clip on the hatch swing round in an arc of 120 degrees. A few bubbles of free air escaped and gyrated to the surface, wobbling and stretching as they floated through the tangled weed. I saw that there was not enough room between us and the *Takao*'s bottom for the hatch to rise fully but, fortunately, it opened enough for Magennis to squeeze through as his hands gripped the sides of the hatch: and he was safely out. He looked all right, safe and confident, and he gave me the "thumbs up" sign. I noticed a slight leak from the joint between his oxygen cylinder and the reducing valve on his breathing set. It wasn't really big enough to cause concern, but I imagine that to Magennis it must have seemed like a full-scale submarine venting its air. He shut the lid and disappeared over the side, and we settled down nervously to await his return.

We counted the limpets as he bumped them out of the containers and moved them one by one along the starboard side, and occasionally I caught a glimpse of him as he worked away under that hull above. Six limpets he took—three toward the for'ard end and three toward the after end. In all, the total time taken was somewhere round about thirty minutes. To me it seemed like thirty days. I cursed every little sound he made, for every little sound was magnified a thousand times by my nerves. It was a long wait. I couldn't remember if we talked or kept silent through it. I think and hope we were pretty calm superficially. The inside of the boat was like a boiler, but we had to keep quiet. I dared not start the fan or motor. We had simply to set still and drink tin after tin of orange juice from the Freon container.

The tide was still falling. Although the rise and fall in the Johore Strait is only eight feet, this was more than sufficient to allow the cruiser to sit on us in the shallow hole beneath her hull. High water had been at 1200 zero hour for the attack, and it was now nearly four hours later. I was very anxious to get away. Magennis still seemed to be an age, and just when I could hardly contain myself a moment longer, he appeared on the hatch. He gave the "thumbs up" sign again and in he jumped. I saw the lid shut and the clip go home. He was back, and now at last we could go.

Quickly, we started to release the side explosive cargoes. The fuses on the port charge, four tons of Amytol, had, like the two-hundred-pound limpets, already been set to detonate in six hours' time, so that it was only necessary for us to unscrew the small wheel which started the mechanism, and then to unscrew the larger wheel which released the charge. The first ten turns of this wheel opened a kingston in the charge to allow water to enter the compartment, previously filled by air, and rendered the charge negatively buoyant. The last turn released the charge itself, which should have fallen away and rested on the bottom. In order to relish the full pleasure of placing four tons of high explosive under a Japanese ship, the three of us took it in turns to operate the wheels as Magennis was draining down his compartment. The port charge fell away—we heard it bump down our side, but we hung on for Magennis to re-enter the craft before finally letting the starboard limpet-carrier go. As a result of this delay, it became too heavy and would not release or slide away. Such an emergency had already been thought of by the designers of XE-craft, and an additional wheel had been provided. This operated a pusher to push the side cargo off, and between us we wound the wheel out to its limit, but with no effect. The bottom of the cargo swung out from the ship's side, but the top was still held fast. By now I felt sure that the pins at the top were holding, but I thought to myself that the movement of the craft might shake it loose. We certainly couldn't make headway very far with two tons of dead weight fast to our side.

In the meantime Magennis reported that he had found it very difficult getting the limpets into position; the work of attaching them successfully had exhausted him. I could well imagine his feelings, as, out on the lonely water with only the sound of his own breathing to accompany him, he struggled and fought, first of all to clear an area of the bottom so that the magnetic hold-fasts could be fitted against the bare plate of the ship's hull. With his diving knife he had to cut away the thick weed waving like the feelers of an octopus above his head, too tough to pull away, and all the time a slow leak from his breathing set. After clearing away the weed he had to tackle the encrustation of barnacles and other shellfish attached to the bottom. These had to be chipped off as silently as possible. The limpets themselves, clumsily designed (they were big awkward jobs to drag through the water, all angles and projections, and they caught and tangled in the weeds), had to be attached. Unfortunately, owing to the positive buoyancy of the charge itself and the angular bottom of the *Takao*, there was a tendency for the charges to break loose from the magnetic hold-fasts, which for reasons unknown, had become very feeble, and to run up toward the surface, with Magennis chasing after them to bring them back into position in two groups of three charges. In each group he had secured the limpets some forty-five to sixty feet apart—three away along the cavern to our starboard side, and three along the cavern on either side of the keel, so that they could not dislodge and slide off onto the bottom. He had set the firing mechanism working, but in his exhausted state had become unable to remove three of the countermining pins, which ensure that should one limpet blow up the rest will follow immediately even if the clocks have been wound for the set delay. The countermining device, which was lethal after twenty minutes, also ensured that any diver sent down by the Japanese to render the mines safe, or to remove them, would blow himself to eternity should he give the charges the sightest blow.

Looking back on the limpet-placing part of the operation, I see how wonderfully well Magennis did his work. He was the first frogman to work against an enemy from a midget submarine in the manner designed: he was the first and only frogman during the whole X-craft operations ever to leave a boat under an enemy ship and to attach limpet mines: in fact, he was the only frogman to operate from an X-craft in harbor against enemy shipping.

Perhaps I had, in some undetectable way, made him aware of my own nervousness. The limpets should not have been less than sixty feet apart for successful working, but although we should, perhaps, have moved them away a bit further, it was too late now; a final effort had now to be made to get clear of the harbor.

"Group up, half ahead—let's get to hell out of this hole!"

I gave the order with a feeling of relief.

"Main motor, half ahead, sir," from Smith. "May I start the fan, sir?"

"Yes, start the fan."

Magennis began to take off his breathing set and hood.

"What is the course, sir?" asked good, calm, cheerful Reid.

"Two hundred degrees," I answered. "Let me know if you have any trouble keeping her on."

I moved over to the sounding machine and switched it on, and then back to the night periscope to watch as we moved out under the vast hull which was slowly settling down upon us with the fall of the tide, and through which we hoped our charges would blow a hole big enough to sink her for good.

But although the motor had been running for several seconds, there was no sign of movement.

"Full ahead," I ordered.

Still no movement!

"Stop, full astern, group up."

Glancing at Smith, I sincerely hoped I was not becoming hysterical. I felt certain that the *Takao* must have settled down on us, thus preventing any movement whatsoever. We couldn't go astern as the *Takao*'s keel was lower than the rear periscope standard. We must go ahead if we could go anywhere at all.

"Stop, full ahead, group up, lift the red, stop."

This gave us maximum power, the motors whirred and we could hear the propeller thrusting hard against the water, but it was useless. We seemed to be well and truly stuck, and for a moment I thought of hanging on until half an hour before the charge was due to go off and then abandoning the ship. After all, I consoled myself, it was only two hundred yards or so from the shore, and we might be able to hide in the swamps and forests until Singapore fell into British hands again. Our flags and emblems were going to come in useful after all!

We tried pumping the water aft and then for'ard, out and then in, and finally, we even partially blew No. 2 main ballast tank to try to shake loose from what looked like being *XE-3*'s watery grave.

I was in despair. Sweat poured into my eyes. But still that black menacing shape stood overhead. Then suddenly, with a final effort, she began to move.

"Ship's head swinging to starboard, can't control her."

Once again Reid's quiet voice calmed my turmoil. We began to move slowly ahead, the flooded charge dragging like a broken wing on our starboard side. The black roof slid astern, and fresh pure welcome sunlight streamed through the water into my upturned eyes.

We had a bow angle of some five degrees, and slowly the needle of my depth gauge moved in an anticlockwise direction until it steadied at seventeen feet. The weight on our right swung the ship's head round until we were parallel to the side of the *Takao*, and I reckoned some thirty feet away on her port side.

"Stop the motor, we'll have to try to release the cargo. It'll have to be very carefully done as we're only a few yards away," I explained.

Magennis was still sweating away in his suit, and I felt he had done enough to make the operation a success. As Reid had little or no experience of underwater swimming in the frogman gear, and Smith wasn't particularly good at this either, I considered that it was justifiable for me to take the risk of leaving the boat for a few moments, even if I was the commanding officer. Should anything happen, I had enough confidence in Smith to know that he could get her out to rejoin the *Stygian*.

"Come out of the way, Magennis, I'll go out and release it myself. Get me the spare set from the battery compartment."

"I'll be all right in a minute, sir," said Magennis, "just let me get my wind."

What a wonderful lad he was! He said this with a most hurt expression on his face, quite obviously meaning that since he was the diver it was up to him to do the diving. And so we sat quietly for five minutes, and when he was ready I replaced his hood and Perspex face. "Thanks," he said, and into the wet-and-dry compartment he went for the second time.

The wheels spun, the pumps started and the water began to rise. Reid had equipped Magennis with an elephant-size spanner, and as the lid of the hatch opened, I saw this come through the opening immediately behind a mass of air bubbles, followed by Magennis. Once again I wondered what he was thinking about only thirty feet away from a Japanese cruiser in seventeen feet of clear water, his only weapon being a spanner. The bubbles released from opening the hatch were quite enough to cause me a great deal of worry. Had anybody been looking over the side of the *Takao*—perhaps a seaman gazing idly into the water with his thoughts away home in Yokohama, Nagasaki, or somewhere like that—he must have seen us. The water was as clear as glass, and Magennis in his green diving suit was sending out a steady stream of bubbles from the reducing valve of his set.

Inside the boat it was as quiet as death: none of us spoke. I could hear the ship's chronometer ticking away, the anxious seconds interrupted by an occasional clank as Magennis used his spanner. It took some five minutes to release the cargo; five of the most anxious minutes of my life. Watching through the periscope, I could see the position of both securing pins at which he should have been working, but for some reason or other he was out of sight. I bit my fingers, swore and cursed at him, swore and cursed at the captain and all the staff on board *Bonaventure* who had planned this operation, at the British Admiralty, and finally, at myself for ever having been so stupid as to volunteer for this life, and having volunteered, for being so stupid as to work hard enough to get myself this particular operation. I wished myself anywhere except lying on the bottom of Singapore Harbor.

I don't know what Reid or Smith thought of this little display, but as far as I know they never mentioned my temporary lapse.

I had told Magennis to make no noise, but his hammering and bashing, in what I thought to be really the wrong place, was loud enough to alarm the whole Japanese Navy.

"What the bloody hell is that bloody fool doing?" I asked no one in particular. "Why the hell doesn't he come on top of the charge. Why didn't I go out myself?" Then I saw Magennis for a moment, and at the same time the cargo came away and we were free. He gave me the "thumbs up" sign for the third and last time and slid feet first into the wet-and-dry compartment and closed the lid. Wheels turned, pumps started and down came the water.

Right, I thought. Then:

"Starboard twenty steer 090 degrees half ahead group up," I ordered all in one breath.

"Aye, aye, sir."

"Twelve hundred revolutions."

"Aye, aye, sir."

"O.K.," I said. "Home, James, and don't spare the horses."

I think we all managed a smile at that moment.

Nowadays, digging underwater vehicular tunnels is an art somewhat developed and most tubes are blasted through rock. The world's first river tunnel was a different matter: it was dug through soft clay, sand and muck on the Thames bottom, well over a century ago. The chief engineer, Sir Marc Brunel, devised a compartmented tunneling shield after studying how the shipworm, Teredo navalis, drills into wooden hulls. He and his brilliant son, Isambard, completed the twelve-hundred-foot Thames Tunnel after sixteen years of heroism by the laborers and appalling disaster. The shaft was flooded five times, once after a schooner anchored above and turned the current downward to scour a slight depression in the river bottom. In August, 1828, the worst irruption occurred when the tunnel had reached a point 550 feet under the river. . . .

Breakthrough in the Thames Tunnel

BY ISAMBARD KINGDOM BRUNEL

I had been in the frames with the workmen throughout the whole night and no symptoms of insecurity appeared. At six o'clock this morning a fresh set of men came on. We began to work the ground at the west top corner of the shield. The tide had just begun to flow; and, finding the ground tolerably quiet, we began at the top, and had worked about a foot downward, when on exposing the next six inches, the ground swelled suddenly and burst through the opening. This was followed instantly by a large body of water. The rush was so violent as to force the man on the spot out of the frame onto the timber stage behind the shield. I was in the frame with the man: but upon the rush of water, I went into the next box, in order to command a better view of the irruption. Seeing there was no possibility of their opposing the water, I ordered all the men to retire. I did not leave the stage until the last three men were down the ladder. We proceeded about twenty feet along the west arch of the Tunnel. At this moment the agitation of the air by the rush of the water was such as to extinguish all the lights, and the water gained the height of our waists. I was giving directions to the men on how they ought to proceed in the dark, when we were knocked down and covered by part of the timber stage. I struggled under water for some time and at length extricated myself. By swimming and being forced by the water, I gained the eastern arch, where I got a better footing, and was enabled, by laying hold of the railway rope, to pause a little, in the hope of encouraging the men. I called to them (without reply).

Before I reached the (vertical) shaft (on the riverbank) the water had risen so rapidly that I was out of my depth, and therefore swam to the visitors' stairs—the workmen's stairs being occupied by those who had so far escaped. My knee was so injured by the timber stage that I could scarcely swim or get up the stairs, *but the rush of water carried me up the shaft.* The three men who had been knocked down with me were unable to extricate themselves, and I am grieved to say they are lost: and, I believe also, two old men and one young man in other parts of the work. The water, still rising, flooded over even the visitors' lodge.

The dean of depth explorers, Charles William Beebe, was born in Brooklyn in 1877. His bucket helmet dives in the 1920's and his famous descents in the thirties in "a steel ball on a string"—Otis Barton's bathysphere have inspired undersea explorers ever since. Dr. Beebe's scientific career began in ornithology in 1899, and he campaigned for a quarter of a century as the prince of bird watchers in the jungles of Mexico, South America, Borneo and the Himalayan foothills. In 1926, he published a lavish monograph on pheasants that presaged the wizardry of description, the command of patronage, and the arts of publicity, that Beebe was to wield in his historic undersea explorations. His books on the sea and the jungle are so fetchingly written that they serve both as scholarly results and adventure stories for youth. Beebe takes you down with him and painlessly slips over the twelve-syllable Latin name for an odd fish you see over his shoulder. He knows how to excite, hold and fulfill public interest in a purely scientific endeavor: during the bathysphere dives he broadcast direct from the depths over radio networks in the United States and Britain. Will Beebe has never retired. In his eighty-third year he was nesting with notebook and glasses, in a treetop in Venezuela, spying on jungle birds.

The bathysphere was built and financed by Otis Barton, the noted explorer, who accompanied Beebe's deep dives.

A Descent into Perpetual Night

BY WILLIAM BEEBE

During 1933 the bathysphere had lived quietly in the Hall of Science of the Century of Progress Exposition at Chicago. Half a million people thrust their heads within the narrow doorway and shivered. Then half a million people exclaimed, "Thank heaven, we don't have to go under water in this!"

A summons came at the end of her year, when her paint was still undimmed, her quartz eyes steadily watching; it came to me in a letter from Dr. Gilbert Grosvenor, saying that the National Geographic Society would be glad to sponsor a new dive. Four years ago, in 1930, Mr. Otis Barton and I had reached and returned from a depth

331

of a quarter of a mile, and later we made a still deeper dive. Knowing that my interest in the work lay only in scientific observations, Dr. Grosvenor made no stipulation as to a deeper, record dive. Friendly arrangements were speedily made between the National Geographic and the New York Zoological Societies, and early in March, 1934, the new expedition was well under way.

The bathysphere arrived in Bermuda on July 5 and I visited her while she was deep down in the lowest hold of the *Monarch*, half hidden by cargo. Later in the same day she was hoisted into the blazing sunlight and lowered gently on to her old mother ship, the *Ready*, from whose deck she would again sink deep into the ocean. An entire month was consumed in assembling, refitting and testing all the intricate machinery, from the great seven-ton winch which was as perfect as when I first used it on the *Arcturus* almost ten years ago, to the delicate Friez temperature and humidity recorder.

Day after day as we passed the tourist-laden tender en route to the great Furness Line vessels, we watched the shining black bodies of the colored divers shoot down into the green water in pursuit of far-flung shillings. Here were the Alpha and Omega of human penetration of the water—naked diver and bathysphere.

Again I threw my dice against unsettled weather and again I won, and on Saturday, August 11, at half-past nine in the morning I looked about from the deck of the *Ready* and saw the long, low swell of a calm day. We were well within the magic circle, six and a half miles southeast of Nonsuch Island, and at once slowed down, headed upswell and prepared to dive.

More than three and a half years ago I dived to a depth of fourteen hundred and twenty-six feet, and here I was on the self-same ancient barge with the identical bathysphere, and within a mile and a half of the very spot where I made the former descent.

All the sights which came to my eyes are as vivid now as then, yet on the eve of this new venture I felt as if the former dives had been nothing but amazing dreams, that my ignorance of the world of life beneath our feet was almost complete.

If any of these thoughts went through my mind at the time it must have been as a mere flash, for my chief concern at the present moment was to wriggle over the unpleasant bolts with as little damage as possible, coil myself up in the window sector of the bathysphere, clamp on my telephone outfit and arrange all my instruments and small but necessary possessions.

Adequate presentation of what I saw on this dive is one of the most difficult things I ever attempted. It corresponds precisely to putting the question, "What do you think of America?" to a foreigner who has spent a few hours in New York City. Only the five of us who have gone down even to one thousand feet in the bathysphere know how hard it is to find words to translate this alien world.

At 9:41 in the morning Otis Barton and I splashed beneath the surface, and often as I have experienced it, the sudden shift from a golden yellow world to a green one was unexpected. After the foam and bubbles passed from the glass, we were bathed in green; our faces, the tanks, the trays, even the blackened walls were tinged. Yet seen from the deck, we apparently descended into sheer, deep ultramarine. The only hint of this change of color vouchsafed those above was the increasing turquoise of the bathysphere as it approached the vanishing point, about one hundred feet.

We were dropped several fathoms and dangled there a while, until all the apparatus on deck was readapted to the vertical cable close to the ship's side. I made the most of my last glimpse of the upper world. By peering up I could see the watery ceiling crinkling, and slowly lifting and settling, while here and there, pinned to this ceiling, were tufts of sargassum weed. I could see small dots moving just below the weed, and for the first time I tried, and successfully, to focus low-power binoculars through the water. I had no trouble in recognizing a small ocean turbot and a flying fish, trailing its half-spread wings as it swam. The bathysphere then revolved slightly and the hull of the *Ready* came into view. It was even more like a coral reef than it had appeared four years ago, great streamers of plant and animal life floating out from it. There is something wholly unreal and at the same time rather amusing about an upward view of the slow rolling bottom of an unanchored boat, whose deck, a few minutes before, had seemed so solid and staunch.

The sun was blazing over the ocean, the surface was unusually quiet; conditions were perfect for whatever the eyes could carry to the brain. A question came over the phone, an answer went, and down we slipped through the water. As I have said, the first plunge erases, to the eye, all the comforting, warm rays of the spectrum. The red and the orange are as if they had never been, and the yellow is swallowed up in the green. We cherish all these on the surface of the earth and when they are winnowed out at one hundred feet or more, although they are only one-sixth of the visible spectrum, yet, in our mind, all the rest belongs to chill and night and death.

The green faded imperceptibly as we went down, and at two

hundred feet it was impossible to say whether the water was greenish-blue or bluish-green. At this depth I made my eyes focus in midwater and saw small creatures clearly, copepods and others of the innumerable swarms which haunt the upper layers.

At 320 feet a lovely colony of siphonophores drifted past. At this level they appeared like spun glass. Others which I saw at far greater and blacker depths were illumined, but whether by their own or by reflected light I cannot say. These are colonial creatures like submerged Portuguese men-o'-war, and similar to those beautiful beings are composed of a colony of individuals, which perform separate functions, such as flotation, swimming, stinging, feeding, and breeding, all joined by the common bond of a food canal. Here in their own haunts they swept slowly along like an inverted spray of lilies-of-the-valley, alive and in constant motion. In our nets we find only the half-broken swimming bells, like cracked, crystal chalices, with all the wonderful loops and tendrils and animal flowers completely lost or contracted into a mass of tangled threads. Twenty feet lower a pilot fish looked in upon me—the companion of sharks and turtles, which we usually think of as a surface fish, but with only our pitiful, two-dimensional, human observation for proof.

When scores of bathyspheres are in use we shall know much more about the vertical distribution of fish than we do now. For example, my next visitors were good-sized yellowtails and two blue-banded jacks which examined me closely at 400 and 490 feet respectively. Here were so-called surface fish happy at eighty fathoms. Several silvery squid balanced for a moment, then shot past, and at five hundred feet a pair of lantern fish with no lights showing looked at the bathysphere unafraid.

At six hundred feet the color appeared to be a dark, luminous blue, and this contradiction of terms shows the difficulty of description. As in former dives, it seemed bright, but was so lacking in actual power that it was useless for reading and writing.

There are certain nodes of emotion in a descent such as this, the first of which is the initial flash. This came at 670 feet, and it seemed to close a door upon the upper world. Green, the world-wide color of plants, had long since disappeared from our new cosmos, just as the last plants of the sea themselves had been left behind far overhead.

At seven hundred feet the light beam from our bulb was still rather dim; the sun had not given up and was doing his best to assert his power. At eight hundred feet we passed through a swarm of small beings, copepods, sagitta or arrowworms and every now and then a worm which was not a worm but a fish, one of the innumerable round-mouths or *Cyclothones*. Eighty feet farther and a school of about thirty lantern fish passed, wheeled and returned; I could guess *Myctophum laternatum*, but I cannot be certain. The beam of light drove them away.

At one thousand feet we took stock of our surroundings. The stuffing box and the door were dry, and the noise of the blower did not interfere with the telephone conversation, the humidity was so well taken care of that I did not need a handkerchief over nose and mouth when talking close to the glass. The steel was becoming very cold. I tried to name the water; blackish-blue, dark gray-blue. It is strange that as the blue goes, it is not replaced by violet—the end of the visible spectrum. That has apparently already been absorbed. The last hint of blue tapers into a nameless gray, and this finally into black, but from the present level down, the eye falters, and the mind refuses any articulate color distinction. The sun is defeated and color has gone forever, until a human at last penetrates and flashes a yellow electric ray into what has been jet black for two billion years.

I kept the light on for a while and at 1,050 feet through a school of little flying snails there suddenly passed a "large dark body, over four feet long" (so I telephoned it). I shut off the light, but looked into empty gray space without a trace of lumination—the fish had dissolved. Later, with the light on again, ten feet lower, a pilot fish appeared, showing how easily his kind can adapt itself to a shift of more than 30 atmospheres and from 15 pounds an inch at the surface to 480 at this level.

Lights now brightened and increased, and at 1,100 feet I saw more fish and other organisms than my prebathysphere experience had led me to hope to see on the entire dive. With the light on, several chunky little hatchetfish approached and passed through; then a silver-eyed larval fish two inches long; a jelly; suddenly a vision to which I can give no name, although I saw others subsequently. It was a network of luminosity, delicate, with large meshes, all aglow and in motion, waving slowly as it drifted. Next a dim, very deeply built fish appeared and vanished; then a four-inch larval eel swimming obliquely upward; and so on. This ceaseless telephoning left me breathless and I was glad of a hundred feet of only blue-blackness and active sparks.

At 1,200 feet an explosion occurred, not at the window but a few feet away, so baffling that I decided to watch intently for repetitions. The large fish came again, and a loose, open school of pteropods and small shrimps bobbed about. The snails were shield-shaped as I well knew from having handled thousands in the deep-sea nets. Their empty shells form most of the sea bottom hereabouts.

Suddenly in the distance a strong glow shot forth, covering a space of perhaps eight inches. Not even the wildest guess would help with such an occurrence. Then the law of compensation sent, close to the window, a clear-cut, three-inch, black angler fish with a pale, lemon-colored light on a slender tentacle. All else my eye missed, so I can never give it a name.

One great source of trouble in this bathysphere work is the lag of mind behind instantaneous observation. For example, at 1,300 feet a medium-sized wide-mouthed angler came into sight, then vanished, and I was automatically describing an eight-inch larval eel looking like a transparent willow leaf, when my mind shot back to the angler and demanded how I had seen it. I had recorded no individual lights on body or tentacle, and now I realized that the teeth had glowed dully, the two rows of fangs were luminous. It is most baffling to gaze into outer darkness, suddenly see a vision, record the bare facies—the generality of the thing itself—and then, in the face of complete distraction by another spark of organism, to have to hark back and recall what special characters escaped the mind but were momentarily etched upon the retina. On this point I had thoroughly coached Gloria Hollister at the other end of the telephone, so I constantly received a fire of questions, which served to focus my attention and flick my memory. Again and again when such a question came, I willfully shut my eyes or turned them to the bathy-sphere to avoid whatever bewilderment might come while I was searching my memory for details of what had barely faded from my eye. At a few stops on the descent, as I have said, I permitted myself a minute or two of emotional debauch, of reciting to myself the where and the what of locality, surroundings, time of day, pressure, tem-perature, and so on. But all the rest of the time I allowed myself no rest from direct observation and reporting. The unproductive Oh's! and Ah's! of my first few dives were all too vivid in my mind.

Just above 1,400 feet two black eels, about eighteen inches in length, went through the beam—distinctly *Serrivomer*. At 1,400 feet my recent studies came to mind, and told me that I saw a male golden-tailed sea-dragon with a big cheek light (*Idiacanthus*), but before it vanished I saw it was black and considerably larger even than the giant female of the species. So it was wholly unknown.

At 1,500 feet I swung for two and a half minutes, and here occurred the second memorable moment in these dives—opportunity for the deliberate, accurate record of a fish wholly new to science, seen by one or both of us, the proof of whose existence, other than our word, must await the luck of capture in nets far more effective than those we now use in our oceanographic work. First, a quartet of slender, elongate fish passed through the electric light literally like arrows, about twenty inches long, whether eels or not I shall never know; then a jelly, so close that it almost brushed the glass. Finally, without my seeing how it got there, a large fish swung suspended, half in, half out of the beam. It was poised with only a slow waving of fins. I saw it was something wholly unknown, and I did two things at once; I reached behind for Mr. Barton, to drag him away from his camera preparations to the window to see and corroborate, and I disregarded Miss Hollister's insistent questions in my ears. I had to grunt or say something in reply to her, for I had already exceeded the five seconds which was our danger duration of silence throughout all the dives. But all this time I sat absorbing the fish from head to tail through the wordless, short-circuiting of sight, later to be materialized into spoken and written words, and finally into a painting dictated by what I had seen through the clear quartz.

The strange fish was at least two feet in length, wholly without lights or luminosity, with a small eye and good-sized mouth. Later, when it shifted a little backward I saw a long, rather wide, but evidently filamentous pectoral fin. The two most unusual things were first, the color, which, in the light, was an unpleasant pale, olive drab, the hue of water-soaked flesh, an unhealthy buff. It was a color worthy of these black depths, like the sickly sprouts of plants in a cellar. Another strange thing was its almost tailless condition, the caudal fin being reduced to a tiny knob or button, while the vertical fins, taking its place, rose high above and stretched far beneath the body, these fins also being colorless. I missed its pelvic fins and its teeth, if it had any, while such things as nostrils and ray counts were, of course, out of the question.

There is a small family of deep-sea fish known as *Cetomimidae*, and somewhere in or close to this the strange apparition belongs. Only three species are known, and only twenty-four individuals have so far been captured, sixteen of which have been in our own deep nets drawn through these very waters. I have called the fish we saw the Pallid Sailfin, and am naming it *Bathyembryx istiophasma*, which is a Grecian way of saying that it comes from deep in the abyss and swims with ghostly sails.

Although I had already seen many deep-sea forms on this dive, yet here was one larger than any we had ever taken in nets. The Sailfin was alive, quiet, watching our strange machine, apparently oblivious that the hinder half of its body was bathed in a strange luminosity. Pre-eminently, however, it typified the justification of the money, time, trouble, and worry devoted to bringing the bathysphere to its present efficiency. Amid nameless sparks, unexplained luminous explosions, abortive glimpses of strange organisms, there came, now and then, adequate opportunity to add a definite new fish or other creature to our knowledge of the life of the deep sea. At the possible risk of cumbering taxonomy with a *nomen nudum*, I have chosen to give definite names to a very few of these clearly seen fish, the physical type of which must, for a time, be represented by a drawing, made under my direction, with only the characters of which I am certain. With no visible increase of fin vibration, my Pallid Sailfin moved into outer darkness, and when I had finished telephoning the last details I ordered a further descent. This entire volume would not contain the detailed recital of even a fraction of all the impressive sights and forms I saw, and nothing at these depths can be spoken of without superlatives.

At 1,630 feet a light grew to twice its diameter before our eyes, until it was fully the diameter of a penny, appearing to enamate from some creature which bore irregular patches of dull luminosity on its body. The outline was too indistinct to tell whether it was with or without a backbone.

At 1,900 feet, to my surprise, there was still the faintest hint of dead gray light, two hundred feet deeper than usual, attesting the almost complete calm of the surface and the extreme brilliancy of the day far overhead. At 2,000 feet the world was forever black. And this I count as the third great moment of descent, when the sun, source of all light and heat on earth, has been left behind. It is only a psychological milepost, but it is a very real one. We had no realization of the outside pressure but the blackness itself seemed to close in on us.

At 2,000 feet I made careful count and found that there were never less than ten or more lights—pale yellow and pale bluish—in sight at any one time. Fifty feet below I saw another pyrotechnic network, this time, at a conservative estimate, covering an extent of two by three feet. I could trace mesh after mesh in the darkness, but could not even hazard a guess at the cause. It must be some invertebrate form of life, but so delicate and evanescent that its abyssal form is quite lost if ever we take it in our nets. Another hundred feet and Mr. Barton saw two lights blinking on and off, obviously under control of the fish.

At this level and again on the way up, I saw at the very end of our beam some large form swimming. On earlier dives I had observed this and had hesitated even to mention it, for it savored too much of imagination backed by imperfect observation. But here it was again. The surface did not seem black, and what outline came momentarily to view was wholly problematic. But that it was some large creature or creatures of which we had glimpses five separate times on dives separated by years, we are certain. Whether fish or squid or other organism we cannot say.

At 2,300 some exclamation of mine was interrupted by a request from above to listen to the tug's whistles saluting our new record, and my response was, "Thanks ever so much, but take this: two very large leptocephali have just passed through the light, close together, vibrating swiftly along; note—why should larval eels go in pairs?" And with this the inhabitants of our dimly remembered upper world gave up their kindly efforts to honor us. On down we went through a rich, light-filled 2,400, and to rest at 2,500 feet, for a long half-hour.

A pair of large, coppery-sided scimitar-mouths (*Gonostoma elongatum*) swam past; *Sternoptyx,* the skeleton fish, appeared in a group of four; a fish as flat as a moonfish entered the beam, and, banking steeply, fled in haste. One flying snail, from among the countless billions of his fellows, flapped back and forth across my glass. Three times, at different levels, creatures had struck against the glass and, utterly meaningless as it sounds, exploded there, so abruptly that we instinctively jerked back our heads.

We tried out the full power of the fifteen-hundred-watt light, heating the bathysphere and window considerably, but not too dangerously. At 11:17 o'clock I turned the light on suddenly, and saw a strange quartet of fish to which I have not been able to fit genus or family. Shape, size, color, and one fin I saw clearly, but Abyssal Rainbow Gars is as far as I dare go, and they may be anything but gars. About four inches over all, they were slender and stiff with long, sharply pointed jaws. They were balanced in the center of the electric ray when it was first turned on, and the unheard-of glare affected them not at all. There they stood, for they were almost upright, and I could see only a slight fanning with a dorsal fin. Keeping equal distances apart, and maintaining their upright pose, they swam slowly into the uttermost dark. The amazing thing about them was their unexpected pattern and color. The jaws and head were brilliant scarlet, which, back of the gills, changed abruptly into a light but strong blue and this merged insensibly into clear yellow on the posterior body and tail. Unless in the light of some other fish, or in my electric path, their colors could never have been visible, and were assuredly useless by-products.

I alternated with Mr. Barton's camera at the window and there were hardly any seconds without lights or definite organisms coming into view. In one period of this duration, chosen at random, I counted forty-six lights, ten of which were of unusual size, most of them pale yellow, but a few bluish. The sight I enjoyed most was a momentary glimpse of what I am certain was the same, or another, Pallid Sailfin. In all this vast extent in three dimensions, of black water, the chance of confirming at a wholly different depth a new observation made my satisfaction complete.

The change in the electric beam itself from one thousand feet downward was interesting. At the upper layers it was weak but decidedly yellow, with a turquoise cap at the farther end of the oblique luminous shaft. As we descended, the yellow changed to a luminous gray, and the turquoise crept down, until, at this extreme depth, it reached to the very window. Along each side of the sharply marked beam extended a broad border of rich, velvety, dark blue, and abruptly outside of this came the black pit itself. At two well-separated depths, I focused very carefully on the rain of small creatures passing and repassing through the farthest extreme end of the light. In both cases the focus was the same and I brought the glass to the surface without changing it. On deck, walking back from the bow until it was in perfect focus with the glass I found that the visible end of the beam of electric light was forty-five feet distant from the bathysphere window, five feet farther than I had been estimating.

Over two hours had passed since we left the deck and I knew that the nerves both of my staff and myself were getting ragged with the constant tenseness and strain. My eyes were weary with the flashing of eternal lights, each of which had to be watched so carefully, and my mind was surfeited with visions of the continual succession of fish and other organisms, and alternately encouraged and depressed by the successful or abortive attempts at identification. So I asked for our ascent.

One minute later, at 2,470 feet, all my temporarily relaxed attention was aroused and focused on another splendid piece of luck. A tie rope had to be cut and in this brief interval of suspension, extended by my hurried order, a new angler fish came out of all the ocean and hesitated long enough close to my window for me to make out its dominant characters. I am calling it the Three-starred Anglerfish, *Bathyceratias trilynchnus*. It was close in many respects to the well-known genera *Ceratias* and *Cryptosparas*, but the flattened angle of the mouth and the short, even teeth were quite different. It was six inches long, typically oval in outline, black, and with small eyes. The fin rays were usual except that it had three tall tentacles or illicia, each tipped with a strong, pale yellow light organ. The light was clearly reflected on the upper side of the fish. In front of the dorsal fin were two pear-shaped organs exactly like those of the common *Cryptosparas*. The paired fins escaped me. No pioneer, peering at a Martian landscape, could ever have a greater thrill than did I at such an opportunity.

Once more I rearranged my aching limbs, stretched and twisted to make my muscles cease complaining, and watched the small fry slip downward through the beam, as the winch drew us steadily upward. Everything of interest was still relayed through the phone, but I was slumped down, relaxed. Suddenly I leaned forward, banging my head against the steel but not losing a second of observation. A small school of luminous fish had just passed, when, fortunately at a moment of suspension, came a new and gorgeous creature. I yelled for continuance of the stop, which was at 1,900 feet, and began to absorb what I saw: a fish almost round, with long, moderately high, continuous, vertical fins, a big eye, medium mouth and small pectoral fins. The skin was decidedly brownish. We swung around a few degrees to port, bringing the fish into the dark blue penumbra of the beam, and then I saw its real beauty. Along the sides of the body were five unbelievably beautiful lines of light, one equatorial, with two curved ones above and two below. Each line was composed of a series of large, pale yellow lights, and every one of these was surrounded by a semicircle of very small, but intensely purple photophores.

The fish turned slowly and, head on, showed a narrow profile. If it were at the surface and without lights I should, without question, have called it a butterfly fish (*Chaetodon*) or a surgeonfish (*Acanthurus*). But this glowing creature was assuredly neither, unless a distant relation, adapted for life at three hundred fathoms. My name for it is *Bathysidus pentagrammus*, the Five-lined Constellationfish.

In my memory it will live throughout the rest of my life as one of the loveliest things I have ever seen.

Soon after I returned to the surface I reviewed my telephone notes, especially of the several new fish of which I had been given such excellent sights. I added all the details that came to mind. Then, with my artist Mrs. Bostelmann, I went into an artistic huddle made scrawling attempts myself, and then carefully corrected her trained drawing. Little by little my brain fish materialized, its proportions, size, color, lights, fins interdigitated with those of my memory, and we have a splendid finished painting which represents the vision in front of my window at 11:52 in the morning of August 11, nineteen hundred feet below the surface of the Atlantic Ocean.

In the never-ceasing excitement of abounding life I had completely forgotten the idea of a half-mile record, and when on deck, in exactly another hour, we were reminded that an additional 130 feet would have done the trick, I had no regrets. A man-made unit of measure is of far less importance than my Three-starred Angler, which otherwise we should surely have missed.

Day after day my weather held good and Wednesday, August 15, was no exception. At 6:45 in early morning we were arranging to leave St. George's anchorage, the barge *Ready* with the bathysphere and ourselves, and the tug *Gladisfen* towing. Three hours later Mr. Barton and I were dropped overboard far out at sea. As well as we could determine from sights on the lighthouses we submerged at the identical spot into which we had splashed four days before.

The same spot, but far from the same visible life. Surprises came at every few feet and again the mass of life was totally unexpected, the sum total of creatures seen unbelievable. At 1,000 feet I distinctly saw a shrimp outlined and distinguished several of its pale greenish lights. Although I delayed very little at the hundred foot stops, when the rope guys were attached, yet I dictated page after page of observations. I used the light as little as possible and carefully shielded my eyes, so that very soon they became dark adapted. I was watching for two or three things which I wanted to solve. Large Melanostomiatid dragonfish with their glowing porthole lights showed themselves now and then, by which I mean on three separate occasions; and more than elsewhere, in our electric light, we had frequent glimpses of small opalescent copepods, appropriately called *Sapphirina*, which renewed for us all the spectrum of the sunlight.

I have spoken of the three outstanding moments in the mind of a bathysphere diver, the first flash of animal light, the level of eternal darkness, and the discovery and description of a new species of fish. There is a fourth, lacking definite level or anticipation, a roving moment which might very possibly occur near the surface or at the greatest depth, or even as one lies awake, days after the dive, thinking over and reliving it. It is, to my mind, the most important of all, far more so than the discovery of new species. It is the explanation of some mysterious occurrence, of the display of some inexplicable habit which has taken place before our eyes, but which, like a sublimated trick of some master fakir, evades understanding.

This came to me on this last deep dive at 1,680 feet, and it explained much that had been a complete puzzle. I saw some creature, several inches long, dart toward the window, turn sideways and—explode. This time my eyes were focused and my mind ready, and at the flash, which was so strong that it illumined my face and the inner sill of the window, I saw the great red shrimp and the outpouring fluid of flame. This was a real Fourth Moment, for many "dim gray fish" as I had reported them, now resolved into distant clouds of light, and all the previous "explosions" against the glass became intelligible. At the next occurrence the shrimp showed plainly before and during the phenomenon, illustrating the value in observation of knowing what to look for. The fact that a number of the deep-sea shrimps had this power of defense is well known, and I have had a aquarium aglow with the emanation. It is the abyssal complement of the sepia smoke screen of a squid at the surface.

Before this dive was completed, I had made a still greater refinement in discernment, perceiving that there were two very distinct types of defense clouds emitted, one which instantly diffused into a glowing mist or cloud, and the other which exploded in a burst of individual sparks, for all the world like a diminutive roman candle. Both occurred at the window or near it a number of times, but it was the latter which was the more startling.

At 1,800 I saw a small fish with illumined teeth, lighted from below, with distinct black interspaces; and ten feet below this my favorite sea-dragons, *Lamprotoxus*, appeared, they of the shining green bow. Only sixteen of these fish have ever been taken, seven of which came up in our own nets. The record size is about eight inches, while here before me were four individuals all more than twice that length, and very probably representing a new species. The green side line glowed but the long chin tentacle was quite invisible, certainly giving out no light. At 2,100 feet two large fish, quite three feet over all, lighted up and then became one with the darkness about them, a tantalizing glimpse which made me, more than ever, long for bigger and better nets.

At 2,450 a very large, dim, but not indistinct outline came into view for a fraction of a second, and at 2,500 a delicately illumined ctenophore jelly throbbed past. Without warning, the large fish returned and this time I saw its complete, shadow-like contour as it passed through the farthest end of the beam. Twenty feet is the least possible estimate I can give to its full length, and it was deep in proportion. The *whole* fish was monochrome, and I could not see even an eye or a fin. For the majority of the "size-conscious" human race this MARINE MONSTER would, I suppose, be the supreme sight of the expedition. In shape it was a deep oval, it swam without evident effort, and it did not return. This is all that I can contribute, and while its unusual size so excited me that for several hundred feet I kept keenly on the lookout for hints of the same or other large fish, I soon forgot it in the (very literal) light of smaller, but more distinct and interesting organisms.

What this great creature was I cannot say. A first, and most reasonable guess would be a small whale or blackfish. We know that whales have a special chemical adjustment of the blood which makes it possible for them to dive a mile or more, and come up without getting the "bends." So this paltry depth of 2,450 feet would be nothing for any similarly equipped cetacean. Or, less likely, it may have been a whale shark, which is known to reach a length of forty feet. Whatever it was, it appeared and vanished so unexpectedly and showed so dimly that it was quite unidentifiable except as a large, living creature.

Soon after, when we were both looking out, Mr. Barton saw the first living *Stylophthalmus* ever seen by man, which completely escaped me, although it must have been within a foot of the windows. This is one of the most remarkable deep-sea fish, with the eyes on the ends of long, periscope stalks, almost one-third as long as the entire body. My missing the fish was all the more disappointing because I had recently been thoroughly studying these strange beings, and in fact had abolished their entire family, after proving that they were the larvae of the golden-tailed serpent-dragons, *Idiacanthus*.

The next fish of unusual size was seen at 2,900 feet. It was less than three feet long, rather slender, with many small luminous spots on the body, and a relatively large, pale green, crescent-shaped light under the eye. Near it were five lantern fish, unlike all others I had seen. They swam so slowly that I made certain before they disappeared that they were of the genus *Lampadena*.

At 11:12 A.M. we came to rest gently at 3,000 feet, and I knew that this was my ultimate floor; the cable on the winch was very near its end. A few days ago the water had appeared blacker at 2,500 feet than could be imagined, yet now to this same imagination it seemed to show as blacker than black. It seemed as if all future nights in the upper world must be considered only relative degrees of twilight. I could never again use the word BLACK with any conviction.

I looked out and watched an occasional passing light and for the first time I realized how completely lacking was the so-called phosphorescence with which we are familiar at the surface. There, whenever an ordinary fish passes, it becomes luminous by reflection from the lights of the myriads of the minute animals and plants floating in the water. Here each light is an individual thing, often under direct control of the owner. A gigantic fish could tear past the window, and if unillumined might never be seen.

My eyes became so dark adapted at these depths that there was no possibility of error; the jet blackness of the water was broken only by sparks and flashes and steadily glowing lamps of appreciable diameter, varied in color and of infinite variety as regards size and juxtaposition. But they were never dimmed or seen beyond or through any lesser mist or milky-way of organisms. The occasional, evanescent, defense clouds of shrimps hence stand out all the more strongly as unusual phenomena, and are quite apart from the present theme. If the surface light is emitted chiefly by *Noctiluca* and single-celled plants, the explanation of its abyssal absence is easy, for all surface forms of these groups have died out hundreds of feet overhead.

A second thing which occurred to me as I sat coiled in the bathysphere, *more* than a half a mile down, was the failure of our powerful beam of light to attract organisms of any kind. Some fled at its appearance, others seemed wholly unconcerned, but not a single copepod or worm or fish gathered along its length or collected against the starboard window from which it poured. We sometimes kept the lesser beam on for three minutes at a time, so there was abundance of time for the plankton, which abounded in all parts of the path of light, to feel and react to its influence. The reason for this demands far more study than I had been able to give it. One factor is doubtless not only lack of the rhythm of day and night, but the eternal absence of all except animal light.

Even in this extremity of blackness I sensed the purity of the water, its freedom from sediment and roiling; six miles from shore and a full mile from the bottom insured this. So there was no diffusion of light, no trails, no refraction. When sparks or larger lights moved they were as distinct as when they were motionless. But reflection was noticeable, as upon the eye or skin from a sub-ocular or a lateral photophore, or upon my face when a shrimp exploded close in front.

Now and then I felt a slight vibration and an apparent slacking off of the cable. Word came that a cross swell had arisen, and when the full weight of bathysphere and cable came upon the winch, Captain Sylvester let out a few inches to ease the strain. There were only about a dozen turns of cable left upon the reel, and a full half of the drum showed its naked, wooden core. We were swinging at 3,028 feet, and, would we come up? We would.

Whatever I thought about the relative value of intensive observation as compared with record-breaking, I had to admit that this ultimate depth which we had attained showed a decided increase in the number of large fish—more than a dozen from three to twenty feet having been seen—and a corresponding greater number of lights, though not in actual size of their diameters.

Now and then, when lights were thickest, and the watery space before me seemed teeming with life, my eyes peered into the distance beyond them, and I thought of the lightless creatures forever invisible to me, those with eyes which depended for guidance through life upon the glow from the lamps of other organisms, and, strangest of all the inhabitants of the deeper parts of the ocean, those blind from birth to death, whose sole assistants, to food, to mates and from enemies, were cunning sense organs in the skin, or long, tendril-like rays of their fins.

Before we began to ascend, I had to stop making notes of my own, so numb were my fingers from the cold steel of the window sill, and to change from my cushion to the metal floor, was like shifting to a cake of ice. Of the blackness of the outside water I have already written too much. As to pressure, there seemed no reason why we should not be outside in a diving helmet as well as in. And then through the telephone we learned that at this moment we were under a pressure of 1,360 pounds to each square inch, or well over half a ton. Each window held back over nineteen tons of water, while a total of 7,016 tons were piled up in all directions upon the bathysphere itself. Yes, we had heard clearly, we were ready to be pulled up at once!

At 2,929 feet I heard a metallic twang through the phone, asked what it was, and got some noncommittal answer. I found out later that one of the guy ropes used in spooling the incoming cable on the drum had suddenly given way with a terrific report—a ghastly shock to everyone on deck until they realized it was a rope and not the cable. Truly we in the bathysphere had the best of it at all times.

Whenever I sink below the last rays of light, similes pour in upon me. Throughout all this account I have consciously rejected the scores of "as ifs" which sprang to mind. The stranger the situation the more does it seem imperative to use comparisons. The eternal one, the one most worthy and which will not pass from mind, the only other place comparable to these marvelous nether regions, must surely be naked space itself, out far beyond atmosphere, between the stars, where sunlight has no grip upon the dust and rubbish of planetary air, where the blackness of space, the shining planets, comets, suns, and stars must really be closely akin to the world of life as it appears to the eyes of an awed human being, in the open ocean, one-half mile down.

The author of this piece is one of Italy's free-diving pioneers. Garibaldi started hunting fish underwater in 1938 with motorcycle goggles and an umbrella. (His bow and arrows were made of umbrella ribs.)

The Bufferini Treasure

BY GUIDO GARIBALDI

In 1947 the city of Livorno was an American port of debarkation, and in the confusion following the war, amid the ruins, there appeared in the streets of the city foreign soldiers, adventurers, and fast businessmen. Among these was a certain Marchesi who told the story of how he had been a prisoner of war together with a friend of the ex-Fascist minister Bufferini-Guido, who had been shot by the Germans in Verona. Before his death, the ex-minister confided to his friend the place where he had hidden a strong iron box filled with gold coins and important documents and jewelry. The hidden locality was indicated as the bottom of the sea to the south of Livorno. The authorities believed it, and for months and months they employed a considerable sum of money, divers, motorboats, and other means without ever finding anything.

In the summer of 1948 I was living in that area. One day, while I had been hunting a magnificent *Orata*, I saw half hidden at the foot of a rock and nearly covered with sand, a riveted iron box, covered with algae. I was immediately aroused and, looking about, I judged it lay about two hundred meters from the place where the "Bufferini Treasure" was supposed to be. I concluded that it must be just that, and I tried to move it by grasping the handles, which were barely visible. But it was too heavy. It would be necessary to dig around to free it from the sand. I was certain that it was a strong metal box, and even if it was not the box indicated by Marchesi, it was so heavy and well hidden that it certainly must contain something valuable.

I returned to shore. I wasn't thinking any more about fish, but what to do. To reveal the discovery? But if I was wrong, what kind of a figure would I cut? And, if it really was the box, I certainly would not gain anything because the Marchesi and the authorities would have contested my rights. "What one finds in the sea belongs to him," say the old seawolves, and I decided to apply this law. I could do nothing alone, so I found a friend who was willing to help me recover the treasure. He accepted all my conditions. It was necessary to employ a third man; this was my good friend Cesare, the skipper. And so the great expedition was organized.

The next afternoon, we weighed anchor and started in an opposite direction from our goal in case someone should follow us. After a couple of miles we changed direction toward the treasure. We were all excited, and many were the questions we asked one another. What was really in that metal box? Documents of the Fascist regime? Who would be interested in them? What was their probable value? But what if it was full of gold? Would we have to smuggle it to Switzerland? With these thoughts we became more fascinated by that iron box resting under seventeen feet of water at the bottom of the sea. As soon as we arrived at the spot I dived and saw that the anchor was lowered about a yard from the treasure. Cesare, wanting to assure himself, put on a mask and came down to hold one of the handles of the box, and both of us tried to move it. But it was all in vain. Cesare returned to the surface crying, "You're right, it is truly a treasure, and it must be full."

We lowered a rope and I passed it around one of the handles. But when we tried to lift it the rope slipped off. I turned the rope several times around the handle and tied it securely, and returned to the surface. Finally, after much heaving, we felt the box moving and coming free from the sand. We all cried. "It's coming, it's coming." In my excitement I dived into the water to see it. You can never imagine what depression I felt. That strong box was not a box at all but only the shell of a wheelbarrow used by a road construction gang, which had been thrown in the sea and had landed upside down in the sand. It had a riveted bottom with two side handles which were grasped by the workers when dumping paving material.

It was a real trick of the devil which had placed that wheelbarrow miles from the nearest road. It had fallen in the sand in such a manner that the handles were barely visible. For many years it had been at the bottom of the sea waiting to make a poor fish hunter believe that he had found a treasure.

In the dark of the night and discouraged by our delusion, we swore to each other never to tell this treasure hunting adventure to anyone.

Dr. Eugenie Clark, director of the Cape Haze Marine Laboratory in Florida, was born in New York City of Scottish-Japanese and American parentage. She was trained in marine biology at New York University, the University of Michigan, Scripps Institution of Oceanography, and several other research centers. She is married to a Greek-born physician, Dr. Ilias Konstantinu, and has four children. Dr. Clark has dived for specimens in the Atlantic, Red Sea and Pacific, usually without breathing apparatus, as was the case in these descents in the Palau Islands in the Southwest Pacific.

The Best Spearfisherman in the World

BY EUGENIE CLARK

Siakong was a betel-chewing, wife-beating drunkard. But he was the best spearfisherman in the Palaus—or maybe in the whole world, I sometimes think now. I'm not just biased because he taught me spearfishing and one hundred other things about the underwater world. His stupendous skill was an undisputed fact among all the Palauans.

Siakong was just over fifty when I knew him. What he was like in his youth will be a legend of the Palaus. The stories about him are unbelievable—probably exaggerated by the tellers, including Siakong himself. But I will tell you what facts I know about him— my firsthand experiences with him in the waters around the Palaus.

Siakong worked for the Peter Hills. He was their most valuable general handy man for he could do the work that required the physical strength of three average Palauans. Although Siakong had been recommended to me as the best fisherman I could find, and I had but a few precious weeks to spend in those islands, Peter Hill would not allow me to borrow Siakong during working hours. Fortunately the work day ended at 3 P.M. and so I could hire him to come with me on late afternoon trips and all day Sunday.

A small red loincloth and homemade goggles formed Siakong's diving outfit. The rest of the time he wore an old pair of khaki shorts over his loincloth, a dirty handkerchief tied around his head and a decrepit straw hat over the handkerchief. When he took these off to go into the water he was suddenly metamorphosed from a bum into a Greek god. Siakong knew the best places to get the plectognaths I was after and these seemed to be where there were the most beautiful coral reefs. These reefs were a long way out from the town of Koror. We usually went there via Malakal Harbor where we could look deep down into the clear water and see sunken battleships from the war days. Niraibui's motor conked out every so often and sometimes we found ourselves paddling back so late that the water was inky black, except where our paddles made a trail of phosphorescence given off by the microorganisms we disturbed. Siakong had an exceptionally nice lightweight throw net which he had made himself out of nylon. Even I learned to use this net a little. I had no luck at all with the heavy, bulky cotton throw nets of other fishermen. Siakong's spears, however, were his main equipment. They had metal heads and bamboo handles and were deftly balanced so that you could maneuver them underwater with ease, regardless of their length. Some of them were over twelve feet. And they were just light enough for the bamboo end to float so you could recover them easily. He also had several shorter-handled, four-pronged spears for catching small fish. The prongs on these were small and fine and Siakong could get me a tiny filefish without perceptibly damaging it.

It was great fun to watch Siakong spear fish from above the water. He would stand on the bow of Niraibui's boat as we putt-putted to the outer reefs, a long spear in each hand. I would sometimes stand up searching the water too but I could never spot a fish before Siakong did. A spear was flying through the air as I opened my mouth to call out, "There's a fish!" If the first spear missed, the second one was on its way in a flash and Siakong seemed to predict the direction in which the fish would dodge the first spear. Whether he got the fish or not this was a noisy affair once the spears were thrown, for Siakong would be either cheering or cursing himself at the top of his lungs.

Underwater it was different. He never made a sound but I could see him grinning broadly and his eyes sparkled through his water goggles. Here, there was no suspense about whether or not Siakong would get the fish he was after. It was only a question of how long it would take him and by what trick he would get it.

The first fish I speared was a triggerfish. But it never made a specimen for a museum. It was a beauty about nine inches long of pastel orange and yellow with a large, black spot in the middle of its body.

I'd never seen this species before although I had read about it. I chased it with no more finesse than a child reaching for an ice-cream cone. When I managed to get above it and made ready to lunge with my spear, it turned on its side to give me a last good look and then slipped into a small hole in the reef. But its tail end was still half out. What a cinch, I thought to myself. It was like spearing a stationary object. The first thrust of the spear didn't penetrate the tough skin but the second did. "Got you!" I muttered triumphantly to myself.

Then I tried to pull the fish up by the spear but it was stuck tight in the hole. I pulled and pulled but only succeeded in pulling out my spear and leaving a big gash in my specimen. I speared it again and pulled with the same result. I stuck the spearhead into the hole and then into the front end of the triggerfish. Still no luck. By this time I had done a fine job of tearing my specimen to shreds, but its head was still tightly fixed in the hole. I gave up and joined Siakong, who was spearing fish some distance away.

A large brown triggerfish swam within sight of us. I pointed to it but Siakong was already slowly swimming after it, circling around it to head it off from going into deep water. Finally it went into a hole—but again the rear end was sticking out.

Then Siakong did something I thought was odd. He let his spear float to the surface and he dove after the fish emptyhanded. Siakong went right to the hole, and gripping a piece of heavy coral with his left hand, he slipped his right hand into the hole with the fish. He looked up at me with a triumphant grin as he withdrew the fish with his hand.

Then it dawned on me what he had done. Triggerfish are so named because of an ingenious mechanism in their first dorsal fin. This fin has three spines, the first of which is large and tough. When swimming around, triggerfish usually keep this fin folded flat on their backs. When frightened, however, a triggerfish will often slip into a small opening and then erect its large spine, thus locking itself in its hiding place. No amount of pushing or pulling can lower this spine and it is very hard to break. But the third spine on that same fin, although sometimes so small it shows as nothing more than a tiny button, is actually the *release* for the first spine. A slight pressure on it and the whole fin collapses. Siakong of course knew this trick and had simply pushed the right button to back the fish out of its hole!

It wasn't always quite so simple, however. Sometimes a triggerfish would go deep into a crevice in the coral until it was out of sight and a hand could not reach the release spine on the fin. For this situation Siakong had a chisel and with the help of a stone, he'd break away the coral around the hiding fish. It wasn't easy for a fish to escape Siakong. Once I pointed out a fish to him it was as good as mine. He was a keen observer and his years of underwater experience made him an expert fish psychologist. He knew the ways of every one of the hundreds of varieties of reef fishes. He didn't always go directly after a fish but would watch it a few seconds, calculate its next move, and then head it off into a place where it could easily be caught.

One of Siakong's methods of spearing fish underwater was literally breath-taking, as well as remarkably simple. He would find a reef well populated with fish and then dive calmly to about ten or twenty feet, sometimes weighting himself with a rock so he could sink without swimming. He'd get a firm grip on the reef with his legs or his free arm, poise his spear in readiness and then *wait* for the fish to come to him!

The first time I watched him do this it alarmed me. He dived and lay motionless on the reef, like an animal about to spring on its prey. His brown body and red loincloth blended in with the kaleido-scope of colors on the surrounding reef. The fish began to regard him as part of the corals and came very close. I was watching him from above. Not used to Siakong's extraordinary lung capacity, I began to worry after a long time passed and he didn't move. So I swam down to him and tapped him on the head to make sure he was all right. He turned and looked at me with his usual underwater grin as I reached for a piece of coral to hold myself down. I tried to make a gesture with my face to ask him what he was doing but he was looking at my hand and the grin had dropped from his face. He reached for my arm as I felt the "coral" under my hand suddenly move. I was holding onto the side of a giant "man-eating" clam. The clam had just snapped shut and my fingers were only a fraction of an inch from the opening between the two halves of the shell. These close with a viselike grip that can hold a diver's arm or leg until he drowns.

As we swam up to the surface, Siakong pointed to a wall of coral along which I had carelessly descended. Partly imbedded in the coral were dozens of these clams, all with their shells gaping open. The shells looked like gray dead corals. Inside, the soft flesh had the beautiful colors of the surrounding living corals and the plants and animals that encrust them. Some were iridescent green, others blue, purple, and shades of brown mingled with irregular darker patches. They were well camouflaged but from then on I learned to distinguish them from anything else. Siakong taught me, however, that even the largest of these clams can be handled safely and that they are among the most delicious of raw sea foods. He would dive down to an open clam and wave his hand over it. Often this was enough to stimulate the light-sensitive flesh inside and the clam would close. If not, he tapped the side of the shell. Then he pried the clam loose and brought it up with him. With a rock or his chisel he chipped open a part of the curved meeting edges of the shell—just enough to slip in the blade of his knife. Then a little cut in just the right place and the shell would fall right open and we could reach in and pull out all the "meat."

Almost every part of the giant clam can be eaten raw though actually I think the soft reproductive organs and tough colored parts are better cooked. But the adductor muscle—the large white muscle that connects the two halves of the shell and closes the clam with such force—is truly a gourmet's delight. I have never tasted anything more delicious. It need only be washed off in sea water and it is ready for eating. It has a texture that is like biting into a crisp cucumber. It has a sweet, clean, indescribably pleasant flavor. From the first time I tried it, the raw adductor muscle of the giant clam has been my favorite sea food. It became a regular part of our reef picnics along with raw fish, a tasty pinkish seaweed that grew in spaghetti-like strands, and tiny limpets.

Limpets are distant relatives of snails but with low conical shells that resemble the hats of Chinese coolies. The species we ate clung to the rocks near the water line by the thousands in some places. A twist of a small knife would free the flesh (sometimes no more than the size of a pea) from the shell. The first time we came across them, Niraibui and I sat in the boat eating them by the dozens as fast as grinning Siakong could pick them off the rocks. We never had to bring any lunches with us, for we were always swimming among more good sea food than we could ever eat. Sometimes, if the day was exceptionally cool or rainy, we might head for the nearest island, make a fire, and cook some of our sea food.

Ordinarily rain didn't stop us from spearfishing. The reef water was so clear that it took more than average rain clouds to make vision bad. The first time we started spearfishing in the rain, however, I thought it would prove a waste of time. When I got into the water and looked around it was full of wavy lines and everything was

blurred as if I weren't wearing my face mask. But Siakong and Niraibui were diving without concern. Then I took a dive too and when
my face reached about four feet below the surface, the water became
its usual clear self. Then I realized that the blurring near the surface
was the result of the fresh rain water mixing with salt water, something that always happens when two liquids of unequal densities
are first put together. I've never come across an English word for it
but German chemistry books refer to the phenomenon as *Schlieren*.
So for spearfishing in the rain, one merely has to dive below the
Schlieren layer and reach the homogeneous sea water to see clearly.

It was on such a day that we came across the largest giant clam I
ever saw alive. Siakong and I were swimming across some open
water toward the reef where the boat was anchored. Niraibui was sitting in it chewing betel nut and keeping his head dry under Siakong's
straw hat. We swam along, diving now and then below the *Schlieren*
layer for a look around. Whenever I swim in deep open water, I
keep glancing around through my face mask with a mingled feeling
of fear and hope. I don't want to miss seeing it if a large shark should
be cruising nearby. But on each of these dives I saw only empty water
in all directions. Not the smallest fish was in sight. From above I
could see Niraibui was still over one hundred yards away and I
looked forward to reaching him and seeing the comforting walls
of reef and the mass of familiar fish that would be swimming there.
It is a strange feeling to swim underwater away from any signs of
rock, coral, the bottom, or sea life. It's like swimming in the middle
of the ocean. It was nice to be able to find Siakong in the water
nearby. I was getting a little ahead of him, as he was stopping for
deeper dives, when I heard him call me back, "Nechan, come see
here."

I swam over to him, dove under the *Schlieren*, and looked where he
was pointing down below. I couldn't make out much until I was down
a few more feet. Then I could see a sandy bottom and sitting in the
sand was a clam. It looked like an average-size giant clam. However,
there was nothing around to compare it with and I couldn't estimate
the depth. We swam to the surface and treaded water easily and forced
a long series of deep breaths. We had been swimming for quite a while
and I wasn't prepared for a deep dive. When I felt a little rested
and saturated with fresh air, I nodded to Siakong. He started to dive
toward the clam and I followed, swallowing to adjust my ears to
the increasing pressure.

I've never measured how deep I can dive, but I know that at more than twenty feet under, my face mask cuts into my head and my ears and nose feel uncomfortable. Usually I don't go much deeper for I have always found enough activity in the top twenty-five feet to keep me occupied and satisfied. But this time I followed Siakong until I felt I was well below my usual limit and I knew my breath wouldn't last descending any deeper. Perhaps if I had dived with a weight and not spent so much energy swimming downward, I might have been able to stand another ten feet—but I still wouldn't have been anywhere near bottom. From the depth I did manage to reach, I could see Siakong far below me getting smaller and smaller until he reached the clam. Then I saw it was truly a giant.

Siakong looked like a midget beside the clam which seemed nearly four feet across. I saw him give it a kick to close the huge jaws which could have held all of Siakong with ease. And then I had to shoot for the surface. I was still panting heavily when Siakong finally came up with no sign of strain.

We got Niraibui to come over with the boat. The anchor wouldn't reach the bottom. It hung loose, far above the clam. We couldn't improvise anything long enough to reach bottom and help us haul up the clam. Then the three of us dived toward the clam again but I stopped at a comfortable depth and clung to the dangling anchor while Niraibui continued on with Siakong. I doubted that even the two of them together could lift it an inch. The clam's jaws were open again. Siakong reached it and kicked it shut. Niraibui hovered about Siakong's head for a second and then headed back for the surface, where we met, both well out of breath.

"*O kina ne!*" ("It's a big one isn't it?") Niraibui exclaimed to me. His eyes were bloodshot and I figured he must have been drinking as well as chewing betel nut, for his wind was usually much longer than mine. Siakong still had not come up. Niraibui and I dived under again. As we descended I made out a sight that sickened me with horror. *Siakong was caught in the clam.*

The jaws of the gigantic mollusk were clamped tight and Siakong's arm was in it up to the elbow. Siakong wasn't moving. I expected Niraibui to dive all the way and at least attempt a rescue, but the bleary-eyed fellow swam back to the surface. In the excitement my breath was shorter than ever. I came up gasping and started hollering at Niraibui in panic. My flimsy Japanese came out all mixed up and he looked at me surprised and then blankly. I felt helpless and desperate. Siakong was trapped and would be dead in a few seconds if we couldn't find some way to help him. How could Niraibui tread water there so calmly even if he was drunk!

Short of breath and good for nothing, I nevertheless adjusted my mask to dive again. But just then Siakong popped up beside us—panting but grinning! He lifted his arm out of the water, the one I had seen in the jaws of the clam, and held up the biggest adductor muscle I had ever laid eyes on.

I was doing a mixture of laughing and crying as the three of us climbed back into the boat. Niraibui of course had understood all along that the clam—which must have weighed at least a quarter of a ton—was impossible to lift off the bottom and that Siakong had broken the lip of the huge shell enough to reach into the clam and cut loose the adductor muscle with his knife. The two men got a big kick out of my fright. "She was ready to kill me because I didn't try to save you!" Niraibui told Siakong, who howled with delight. I started to feel a little ridiculous, but when they went on to kid me unmercifully, I got angry. Finally they stopped and the rain which was still falling cooled me back to normal. Soon we all sat contentedly in the boat, munching on a delicious adductor muscle the size of a man's thigh. Niraibui and Siakong stuffed their mouths to keep from laughing any more.

*

A Poor Opinion of Submarines

Underwater weapons, they call 'em. I call them under-handed, unfair, and damned un-English. They'll never be any use in war and I'll tell you why; I'm going to get the First Lord to announce that we intend to treat all submarines as pirate vessels in wartime and that we'll hang all the crews.

Rear Admiral A. K. Wilson, V.C.,
CONTROLLER OF THE ROYAL NAVY, 1902

Professor Kuenen of the University of Groningen, Netherlands, is a widely respected geologist whose interest in the sea started in the 1930's during the global researches of the Snellius, *with which he served as chief geologist. He has published two basic books that are not so technical that they cannot be enjoyed by the inquisitive layman:* Marine Geology *and* Realms of Water. *The latter volume begins with this essay on the nature of water.*

The Cycle of Water

BY P. H. KUENEN

*I*f it were possible to trace the careers of all the water molecules on earth from the earliest times, it would be found that no two were alike. The opportunities for adventure open to such a molecule are circumscribed; but just as writings of limitless variety result from the different grouping of a very small number of letters and symbols, so are the life histories of all water molecules composed of a very restricted range of possible episodes.

Thus one will evaporate from the surface of the sea and rain back into it many times in succession before it is engulfed at the Pole in a submerging stream and drifts through the dark depths of the ocean, year upon year, until it eventually emerges at the Equator or at the opposite Pole. Meanwhile, a neighbor molecule, which has also taken a few turns at rising from and falling back into the sea, has been wafted higher into the atmosphere and, now transformed into the constituent of a snowflake, has landed on a glacier. Years later it may sweep toward a valley in the glacier stream or evaporate from the tongue of ice, only to return to earth again, this time, maybe, flung down in a heavy rain upon a desert, from which it may evaporate at sunrise and return as dew at night again and again.

Elsewhere, water penetrates many hundreds of feet into the earth's crust and follows long, tortuous paths until it spurts upward in a hot spring or unobtrusively makes its appearance in the bed of a river, flowing with the latter toward the ocean. Most water that goes underground, however, eventually evaporates at the surface again, or else is absorbed by vegetation and is thus returned to the atmosphere. Another considerable contingent may have traveled only a little way between sand and particles of clay before oozing into a brook and sweeping rapidly out to sea.

There are, again, prisons, as it were, in which the molecules of water may be trapped. They may be held between grains of sand at the bottom of the sea and smothered there under growing accumulations of deposits. If such be their fate, it will be millions of years before they are released, not until the sea bed has been raised up to mountains and these in turn have been worn down by the teeth of time. Then, carried along by the creeping ground water, a few of those drops of water, which have been imprisoned for whole geological periods, will at last make good their escape. Molecules which are caught up as crystal water in weathering minerals are imprisoned in far smaller but no less escape-proof cells. Their liberation will not come until mountain-forming forces have pushed them deep down into the earth's crust, whence the heat will drive them out once more. Then again there is stagnant water deep down in Norwegian fiords or the Black Sea which, through lack of circulation, becomes foul and saturated with hydrogen sulphide and semidecayed organic remains.

Most of the water absorbed by plants or animals is set free again within twenty-four hours, but those particles which are pressed into service for the building of cells have a much longer period of enforced rest.

In the foregoing summary we have reviewed all the major experiences which fate may have in store for a molecule of water in its life on earth. Though minor incidents and digressions may vary the pattern in many ways, it cannot justly be said that the choice of possibilities for a water molecule's career is extensive! In whatever sequence the events occur and however varied the pattern may be, again and again we come up against the same ineluctable *principle of a cycle*. No matter whether this cycle takes a long or a short time to complete, whether it is a complicated or a simple one, the outcome is always the same: water returns to its point of departure, the ocean.

By far the majority of molecules are congregated in the oceans and it is the exception rather than the rule for some to escape for a comparatively short period full of exciting variety and activity until, having completed their cycle, they return to that same huge reservoir.

Water is the most extraordinary of all compounds known to science and it is precisely these departures from the normal which fit it so eminently for the dominant role it plays in the nature by which we have our being.

Water when purified by distillation is an odorless liquid which, taken neat, has an offensively insipid taste. It is virtually the only inorganic substance in nature which can occur in the liquid state under normal conditions of temperature and pressure; for the same reason it is the only natural product found in three states of aggregation in the open, viz., solid, liquid and gaseous. If we except earthquakes, landslides, and volcanic eruptions—in which, as a matter of fact, water as vapor often plays a conspicuous part—it may be said that there are only two "auto-mobile" substances in inanimate nature, air and water. Thanks to its greater specific gravity and internal friction, water takes the lion's share of all transport on earth. Waves and currents carry not only sand and clay in the sea, but shift great masses of rock on the shore, while a predominant proportion of marine organisms not held fast to the bottom can only be moved from place to place by submitting passively to the action of the water. On the continents the most assiduous vehicles are rivers and glaciers, which move immense quantities of coarse and fine rock fragments and compared with which the wind is a mere lazy dilettante.

No substance has as great a capacity as water for absorbing or transmitting heat. The heat of vaporization, hence the quantity of heat required to convert water or ice into vapor, is greater than that of any other substance, while both the heat of fusion of ice and the specific heat of water are surpassed only by those of ammonia. The value of this enormous thermal capacity can scarcely be overestimated. It is inextricably mixed up with our daily lives. It costs more fuel and time to bring water to a boil than to heat other liquids through just as many degrees. Conversely, hot water cools more slowly and therefore gives off more heat than all other substances, which is why hot-water bottles keep warm for so long; it also obviates the necessity of hastily swallowing our hot toddy or of putting it into the hay box between sips to keep it warm.

This property radically affects the thermal economy everywhere. It moderates temperature fluctuations, not only of the sea and adjacent lands, but of all areas on earth. Even in the desert the formation of dew tempers the nocturnal chill, just as the sublimation of snow, and its melting at a later stage, even out temperature contrasts in the colder regions and on the summits of mountains. The ocean currents carry an enormous mass of heat to the polar regions, thus allaying the rigors of the arctic climate. The tremendous heat of vaporization keeps the evaporation of water within reasonable limits and prevents the drying up of inland seas and lakes in the intervals between the rainy seasons.

The water vapor in the atmosphere collects a substantial percentage of the heat radiated by the earth's surface and reflects it. So it is to water again that we owe part of the hothouse effect of the atmosphere, without which the earth would be too cold to sustain life.

The compressibility of water is very slight. There is a superstition among seamen that a corpse buried at sea sinks only to a moderate depth and there remains drifting unto all eternity. Unconsciously they imagine that the immense pressure in the depths compresses the water into a heavy fluid in which all objects float forever. The facts are that, not only are all submerged objects themselves compressed in equal or greater measure (wood to such a degree, indeed, that it loses its buoyancy and begins to sink), but the compressibility of water is too insignificant to be tangibly manifest. For all that, the slight compression which does exist is responsible for the fact that sea level is one hundred feet lower than it would be if water's compressibility were nil. Were its compressibility suddenly to cease, two million square miles of land would be flooded—more than twenty times the area of Britain.

Ex-Underwater Demolitioneer Jon Lindbergh chose his career in a different element from that of his flying parents. Trained as a marine biologist, Lindbergh is now operating an underwater engineering firm in San Diego, California.

Underwater Duck Hunt

BY JON M. LINDBERGH

A young winter gale blew across the Miura Peninsula on the east coast of Japan. It whistled through the loosely constructed buildings of Camp McGill and sang in the superstructures of a dozen ships offshore in Sagami Wan. D-Day of a big practice landing on Iwo Jima was only days ahead and loading operations were being pushed despite the storm. From a window of the Underwater Demolition Team office we could see landing craft bobbing out over the chop toward the ships, sheets of spray bursting off their flat bow ramps. None of us much envied the people who were loading under such conditions. Small craft beat themselves apart against their parent ships. Amphibious vehicles can swamp in a matter of seconds. Men's lives, too, can go quickly.

The phone rang. Commander Martin Sibitzky, Officer in Charge of the Naval Beach Group, Western Pacific Detachment, wished to see the UDT Diving Officer. In his office I learned that, sure enough, two Marine DUKW's had been lost. The crews, luckily, got clear first. Could UDT begin salvage operations immediately? We weighed the factors involved. First, where were the DUKW's? Radioed position reports indicated they had gone down while attempting to board LST's about two miles offshore. The depth in that area was 80 to 120 feet. One hundred feet of water would help moderate the effects of surge, but it would still be pretty dirty on the bottom. Divers might be able to see three feet. Diving is difficult in rough seas, but not impossible. Actually, the main problem would not be the dive, but holding the diving boat in position over the search area. The Commander checked with the Sea Bee unit and found they had a warping tug with a husky anchor. That should take care of the holding problem.

So far the job looked possible. There was, however, one further question. Were the position reports accurate? Were they taken from the ramp of the "T" when the vehicle foundered? Or from the bridge, or the point the anchor was dropped, or perhaps twenty minutes later after she had swung around on her anchor? Few nondivers have much concept of what is involved in an underwater search problem. What one so often hears in UDT work is, "We lost it just out there. You shouldn't have any trouble." "Just out there" involves quite a bit of ocean bottom when the distance from horizon to horizon is six or eight feet, or even seventy-five to one hundred feet.

A new set of position reports came in over the radio. We compared them with the original set and found several hundred yards of difference. About that time I concluded that to dive without more information would be a waste of time and effort. It would be necessary to talk personally with the officers of the ships involved. Monday would be the first possible time, as the ships were moving out and not returning until then. Commander Sibitzky agreed with us.

Tuesday morning we loaded our equipment onto warping tug "86" and headed out into Sagami Wan. A warping tug is an odd-looking craft constructed of pontoon causeway sections welded together with a boom on the forward end and a shack on the after end. It is propelled by two huge outboard engines. The search group consisted of Harry Tindall, John Stringer, Prince Gallagher, Bert Maas, and myself of UDT 12 and Darrel Hubbard, Johnny Miller, and Robert Inman of UDT 11. We were almost the total diving complement at Camp McGill. Everyone else was reported bound for Iwo Jima.

On the previous day I had talked with the people on the LST's concerned and pinpointed the positions of the sunken DUKW's. They were theoretically located seven hundred yards apart some two miles off the coast. A red buoy had been dropped by one of the ship's crew within a few yards of a DUKW just as it went down. That one shouldn't be too hard to find. I also talked with the Marines. They wanted their "ducks" back, but were much more interested in a 105 mm. howitzer carried in one as cargo. The DUKW with the howitzer was the one marked by the red buoy. So I had high hopes of success Tuesday morning.

We never found the buoy. The sea was flat calm and the sun bright. Anything on the surface could be seen for half a mile. Several objects appeared and were eagerly investigated. They amounted to two or three gulls, some Japanese fish traps, and odd bits of debris. I took a series of sextant fixes and navigated the tug over the plotted position of the buoy. By taking two sextant angles on three known points on shore and plotting the angles on a chart with a three-armed protractor it is possible to locate your position within a few feet. The buoy just wasn't there. Whether it was torn loose by the storm or "borrowed" by a local fisherman I don't know.

The warping tug dropped her anchor on the spot where the buoy should have been. A position check showed we were about twenty-five yards east of the mark. One of the men swam a weight with a buoy attached out that far and dropped it. Might as well start out as accurately as possible. Stringer and Maas got ready for the first dive. Pirelli exposure suit seals were checked for possible leaks. A suit full of fifty degree water can be extremely uncomfortable. The two strapped on their Aqua-Lungs and jumped over the side. Their instructions were to attach a hundred-foot–line to the buoy weight, move out to the end of the line, and swim a complete circle. The line would catch on any large object, such as a vehicle, in the area covered. A "circle search" is not as thorough as some types of search techniques, but it is fast and would give a check on conditions. Later we would set up other systems if they seemed advisable.

From the warping tug we traced the progress of the search by the bubbles of the Aqua-Lungs. They hesitated for a while by the buoy; then moved out and started around. Big disks of air came up in front. They were regularly spaced every eight or ten feet, one for each breath. One could see them twenty or twenty-five feet down, wobbling and shimmering until they burst in a big boil on the surface. Some yards behind hundreds of smaller ones followed in an unceasing stream. The divers stopped close under the tug. Had they found something already? After a moment they moved on. We learned later that they caught the line on our own anchor cable.

Stringer and Maas came in sight below. I looked closely. Coils of line trailed behind them. Nothing. Had they found anything that line would still be on the bottom—a guide from the buoy to the weight to the find. I held a short interrogation when the men had removed their heavy lungs and been given hot coffee. Visibility was exceptional, they said, perhaps fifty or seventy-five feet. The bottom was mostly rocky; low rounded ledges with one or two sandy valleys. Depth in the area covered was from eighty to one hundred feet. The visibility was very encouraging, the depth not so encouraging. Diving time for purposes of decompression is computed from the greatest depth attained, even momentarily. It was UDT policy at that time to avoid decompression except in cases of an emergency nature. In accordance with the Navy Standard Decompression Tables at 110 feet a man has twenty minutes' bottom time over a twenty-four-hour period before a decompression stop becomes necessary. So Stringer and Maas, with fifteen minutes of bottom time, were through for the day.

I took the next dive myself. In view of the unexpected clarity of the water I decided on another search technique. Hubbard, my swim buddy, and I tied ourselves together with a length of light line. We planned to swim a compass course due north for ten minutes, make a long half-circle and return on a parallel course. This would cover an area 300 yards by 150 yards, counting to the limit of visibility on each side of each swimmer.

We spaced ourselves just north of the buoy and started down. Hubbard was plainly visible at the other end of the line fifty feet away. Twenty feet down he suddenly turned and went back to the surface. I followed. His regulator wasn't giving enough air. Someone on the tug attached a new one and we started over again. Pressure began to build up in my ears. I swallowed and it cleared in a series of pops and squeals. At thirty feet the deep blue gray below began to turn brown. A few prominent rocks became distinguishable and then the whole bottom—an irregular expanse of bedrock covered with marine growth. The coolness of the water became evident as my exposure suit tightened around my body. We touched at eighty feet. I rolled over to blow a trace of water out of my face mask. After taking a compass azimuth I motioned to Hubbard and we commenced the search.

The bottom stayed pretty much the same for the first one hundred yards. Occasional valleys dropped off to over one hundred feet. We stayed out to avoid decompression. The water was clear enough for us to see anything which might be in one. Small gorgonians were plentiful on certain ledges. Some were bluish in color and others a drab white. I picked one of the latter to look at more carefully when we surfaced. The rock gave way to flat gray sand. We moved easily along at about ten feet "altitude," looking constantly from side to side. Promising-looking objects appeared several times on the vague limit of visibility. They materialized into boulders, accumulations of seaweed, and a rusty oil drum. I saw one moray eel a few feet to the right. It lay unmoving on the sand, giving me the usual open-mouthed stare. Other fish were surprisingly scarce.

I glanced at my watch. Ten minutes were gone; time for the return leg. I jerked the line as a signal to Hubbard to stop and began to make the turn. Halfway around there were two strange marks in the sand. They were parallel, five or six feet apart, and led straight to the southeast. Duck tracks! I was tempted to leave our search pattern to follow them. But the idea of a DUKW rolling along the ocean floor leaving tracks was absurd. I continued to swing into the return leg. More duck tracks appeared. They all ran in the same general direction, south to southeast. I couldn't figure those tracks for a minute. The answer appeared at the end of the swing. A ragged three-foot trench running as far as I could see north and south. Someone's anchor had been dragging. The duck tracks were merely marks where the anchor cable had scraped as the ship heaved and swung. Both of us moved laterally east about fifty feet to avoid duplicating too much of the same area. I was swimming directly down the trench. It looked new; the edges were rough and a few uprooted sea worms still lay in the bottom. Was it from the LST that lost our duck? There was no telling. If it was, then the vehicle was probably several hundred yards north. It is a long way from the grounded stern hook of a "T" to the bow ramp. More likely this trench was from the ship which lost the other DUKW.

Blurs of white appeared ahead. Papers. Then more debris; tin cans, bones, milk cartons, all manner of stuff. Our ship had unloaded her garbage. I dropped down to look at an envelope in the trench. The address was clearly legible. It was postmarked in November in some little town in Ohio. We paralleled the trench all the way to the end of the leg. Small wonder those ships had moved out Friday evening.

I was glad to come up. My exposure suit was beginning to pinch. At any depth over seventy-five feet a dry suit tends to become annoyingly tight: a condition known as squeeze. As the cushion of air between the suit and the diver is compressed, skin is forced into creases in the rubber and the wool underwear. All of us were covered with thin red welts at the end of the day. My attention was caught by something bright orange in my right hand. The "dull white" gorgonian! I learned afterward that red light waves don't penetrate very far through water.

The third pair of divers covered an area to the south of the buoy and found nothing. The fourth a parallel area to the east. They found the drag marks of another ship, but little else. Wednesday and Thursday we enlarged on the same area with the same results. I double-checked on the original position fix again by taking several more sextant cuts on different shore points. The plots were identical.

Our fixes and the chart were unquestionably correct. On Friday we had to use our own LCPR (small landing craft). The warping tug had commitments elsewhere. When we found something, they said, they would come out and pull it up. By Friday afternoon I was getting discouraged. Had we by some chance missed a small area on our earlier searches? I didn't think so. Search overlaps seemed adequate. If we did we were out of luck. There would not be time to repeat the week's work.

John Stringer came up with a suggestion. There was an old planing board in the warehouse. He could construct another if necessary. With planing boards men could be towed behind the LCPR and cover considerably more area than by swimming. The idea was certainly worth trying. I told him to go ahead with another board and to lay out two three hundred-foot lengths of nine-thread line for towing purposes.

On Monday afternoon the planing boards were ready. We dropped a buoy 150 yards west of the original search point. The plan was to make six hundred-yard north-south sweeps past the buoy. The divers would be within visual distance of each other side by side on the boards. One would keep watch on each side.

Stringer and Maas made the first run. We gave them the boards, payed out the towing lines and made them fast to cleats. The LCPR was moving about 3½ knots. The two men planed along the surface for a few seconds and then dropped from sight. We watched the lines angle slowly down into the wake. Three and a half sweeps later the towlines suddenly went slack and the divers surfaced. Stringer reported that the boards worked O.K.; he and Maas had little difficulty cruising at about eighty feet. The visibility, though, was getting bad.

Inman and I made the second dive. I dipped the nose of the board into the wash and glided effortlessly down ten or fifteen feet. That board was little more than a piece of half-inch plywood twenty inches wide and three feet long with a rounded nose and two handles. A towing bridle was attached to eyes halfway aft on the sides. It would climb, dive, or go in any direction you pointed the nose. Little white blobs of plankton which had begun to appear the previous week were really thick. They streamed past my faceplate like windblown snowflakes. We were within fifteen feet of the bottom before we could see it.

Rocks loomed up out of nowhere. I had to climb sharply to avoid a collision. We skimmed along close to the bottom for a while before the rock dropped away just as rapidly. One found it necessary to kick a little to get below eighty-five feet to see into deep holes. More rock appeared. We passed a couple of encrusted five hundred-pound bombs, relics of World War II. Then some big sea anemones and a couple of strange-looking animals resembling two-foot-high heads of cauliflower. Lots of things to see, but no DUKW's.

I unconsciously let go of one of the planing board handles to clear my face mask. The board instantly slewed sideways and began spiraling rapidly upward. There were several seconds of frantic clawing before I got that handle back. The rocks gave way to sand as we turned into another leg. Once or twice I felt an inclination to turn around and see what might be coming up behind. There was a vaguely disturbing feeling of being bait trolled along on the end of someone's giant fishline. After twenty-five minutes Inman and I let go of the boards and swam slowly to the surface.

Tuesday morning we set up our search pattern to cover an area north of the position plot for the first DUKW and including the plotted position of the second. Maybe we would run into one while looking for the other. Stringer and Gallagher were about thirty minutes down when the towlines went slack. We were nearing the second DUKW area at the time. Visibility was down to ten feet and I wasn't expecting to find much. We swung the LCPR around to pick the pair up. Stringer waved his arm and pointed down.

"Found it!" he yelled. He had no line going down so we dropped a buoy as quickly as possible. Back in the boat Stringer related he had been running out of air when he saw an ammunition case. He held on another ten seconds and ran into the duck. It was upright; looked ready to drive away. Ammunition cases were strewn about the interior and on the sand below. Stringer at that point was so low on air that he and his buddy were unable to attach a line and had to surface.

Tindall and Miller went down with a line. They made a circle and came up. No duck. I roughly gauged the current, dropped another buoy, and sent them down again. Needless to say, I was quite relieved when they surfaced with a report that they had located the vehicle and tied in.

We returned with the warping tug in the afternoon, hoisted our prize and hauled it to shore. The Marines had to be satisfied with one duck and no howitzer. Another week of searching failed to locate the other one. Months later Darrell Hubbard and three other men were making a training dive on a dark August night and they swam right into the other DUKW. Such is the search game.

Dr. Stanley J. Olsen is a paleontologist—a student of fossil animals— with the Florida Geological Survey. He worked previously at the Harvard Museum of Comparative Zoology. He is one of the alert scholars who have realized what free-diving techniques offer to many earth sciences, including speleology (cave exploration), limnology (study of lakes), hydrology (concerned with water in general), archaeology, anthropology, and several branches of geology.

The Wakulla Cave

BY STANLEY J. OLSEN

The immensity of the cosmos that astronomy and its allied sciences present to the general reader, together with the lure of the "unknown" hidden in outer space, has brought a host of new followers to its study. Yet, many unanswered questions still lie locked in the depths of our old familiar planet, Earth. Geology and paleontology, earth-rooted as they are, are two fields that offer a comparable measure of "unknown" time to balance the "unknown" space that serves to attract the inquisitive student.

In this day, moreover, few places on the earth's surface are available to the daring soul who wishes to do original investigation in an area never before visited by man. Yet, the student of the earth sciences need only turn to underwater exploration or to the dry caves of the "spelunker" in order to discover areas that remain as yet unprospected and uncharted.

Much of the earth's strata, and in particular that covered by water, has not been explored, sampled or mapped. Reconnaissance by frog-men, in the open currents of rivers, bays or lakes, or dry "caving" by speleologists, are interesting enough activities in themselves. However, when a combination of underwater and cave exploration is undertaken, the enjoyment and hazards of both are united in a quantity sufficient to satisfy the appetite of any scientific adventurer.

Just such a geological reconnaissance—of a vast underwater cave at Wakulla Spring, Florida—was carried out by six young men of my acquaintance: Garry Salsman, Wally Jenkins, Henry Doll, Andy Harrold, Gordon Whitney and Lamarr Trott. The Florida Geological

Survey co-operated in this project, both by supplying technical information, and by identifying the mineral and fossil specimens that were collected during numerous dives by those of the six who were students of the Florida State University at Tallahassee.

One of Florida's largest, Wakulla Spring discharges 183 million gallons of water a day, forming the source of the Wakulla River. Although many tourists have viewed the springhead through glass-bottomed boats, the casual visitor can little guess what lies hidden in the dark, submarine shadows beneath an overhanging limestone cliff to be glimpsed a hundred feet beneath the keel.

Salsman and his associates, using free-diving apparatus, undertook to probe the unknown. The Wakulla cave proved to have an arched ceiling, with a floor varying in width from seventy to one hundred and fifty feet. Above, the ceiling may be as low as a crowded five feet but rises in places to the proportions of an arena, with a height of over a hundred feet. The cavern at first extends in a southeast direction for a distance of some six hundred feet. There, it angles sharply toward the southwest, blotting out the feeble light that had linked the young divers with the outside world.

For its first two hundred feet the cave floor is sand, interrupted by an occasional limestone boulder from some ceiling breakdown of a forgotten age. From a depth of one hundred feet at the cavern's mouth, the bottom slopes sharply downward, reaching one hundred and eighty feet before it levels off and the sand floor gives way to limestone rubble. Soon, the cave continues to deepen.

Three hundred feet further, the depth reaches two hundred and twenty-five feet. Here, the wall of the cave on one side makes a sharp right angle, while the opposite side opens into a depression, its bottom two hundred and forty feet below surface. Dubbed "Grand Canyon" by the divers because of the layers of clay exposed in bands along its sides, this depression—with chunks of the layered clay in a tumble at its bottom—appears to be a sinkhole in the cave floor.

Beyond "Grand Canyon" lies a glistening white sand bar which rises to a depth of two hundred and fifteen feet only to dip back to the natural cave floor. Eleven hundred feet inside the cavern, at a depth of two hundred and fifty feet, the passage continues to slope down out of sight. Able to spend only scant moments here, the divers pointed their lights ahead into the utter darkness, only to see an ever-deepening, ever-widening cavern that beckoned them onward.

This, however, was the limit of the geographical reconnaissance—

a limit imposed by physiology. At such depths, co-ordination is seriously reduced by nitrogen narcosis.

The geography of the Wakulla cavern was only one part of the young divers' work. Their first paleontological discovery came in November, 1955, when they found a large bone lying amid the limestone rubble at the two-hundred-foot level. It was subsequently identified as the limb bone of a mastodon. This first discovery was followed by others until, at a depth of two hundred and twenty feet, the floor was found to be literally strewn with the bones of mastodon, sloth and deer. A mastodon jaw was discovered, with the teeth still intact, embedded in a clay pocket.

How these remains reached the depths at which they were found is a question not yet answered. Water action will transport such objects a good distance, particularly when helped by a sloping floor, but at Wakulla the flow is in the opposite direction. Some objects can be easily rolled but not, for example, a crescent-shaped tusk weighing hundreds of pounds. Yet, surely Wakulla cavern had never been dry at this depth, and thus had not been visited by these animals at the time when they were alive.

Also among the finds were over six hundred bone spear points, similar in design to those found with Florida's prehistoric inhabitant, the Vero Man. But interpreting underwater finds in Florida is no easy occupation and the excitement of this juxtaposition of man and mastodon is quickly dampened by experience. In the Itchtucknee River, one of Florida's most productive fossil localities, for example, it is possible to find the remains of mastodon and tapir in juxtaposition with pop bottles and beer cans. Until extinct animal bones are found with a spear point actually embedded in the bone—and preferably with *the bone growing around the point*—positive, contemporary association of the two cannot be claimed in the case of a stream deposit.

What, then, is the answer to the Wakulla Spring finds? At present, we can only speculate. Did these bones and artifacts find their way from some ancient surface into the depths of the spring by means of a sinkhole or fissure through the ceiling of the cavern now blocked and filled with rubble?

What is it like to be down in such a cavern, out of touch with the sun and the world of air? Following is the log of a typical fifteen-minute descent to photograph and remove a recently discovered mastodon bone.

Donning their equipment the divers step down a ladder from the diving pier into the air-clear water of the spring, and swim down to a limestone ledge thirty feet below the surface. Here, they pick up heavy weights and step off the ledge, descending effortlessly to the sloping sand bottom of the pool, one hundred feet down. Relinquishing their weights, they continue to swim down, aided by the fins, until they pierce the shadow of the ponderous, overhanging ledge which will intercept their exhaled air bubbles for the duration of the dive.

Gliding down an ever-darkening corridor past the one-hundred-and-fifty-foot level and on to the one-hundred-and-eighty-foot point, they turn on their flashlights and locate the white safety rope leading deeper into the cavern. The rope, running eleven hundred feet into the depths of this submarine river, is the established base line of the exploration.

Six minutes have elapsed before they find themselves nearing the bone embedded in the clay at a depth of two hundred and twenty feet. The photographer moves in first, careful not to stir up the bottom and destroy the visibility. One flash bulb, and then another, bursts the scene into brilliance for a moment: now the other divers can move in to do their work. The distance from the base line is measured, the orientation of the bone is noted and its condition is checked for the best method of removal without breakage. Only a few minutes of deep-dive time remain.

As the fifty-pound bone is freed of its clay matrix, a pillowcase—lined with plastic—is produced. The open end of the sack is tried to the bone, and the sack filled with air from a diver's mouthpiece until the whole becomes neutrally buoyant. Then, it is an easy task for the divers to push the weightless discovery ahead of them as they make their way back out of the cave. Ascending, they find that the buoyed bone rises more rapidly as the air in the sack expands so that, periodically, air must be spilled out to control the specimen's rate of rise.

Now, with the fifteen minutes run out, the team is clear of the cavern mouth. But the ascent is slow, and a thirty-six-minute decompression stop must be made at a depth of ten feet, to eliminate the danger of "bends." Nor can too much emphasis be placed on the need for extreme caution in work of this kind. It is a tribute to the skill, planning and care of these six young divers, that in over a hundred descents to beyond the two-hundred-foot level, there was not one mishap or accident.

Further exploration of greater depths is certain to come, as faster means of propulsion and safer mixtures of breathing gases are developed. For the challenge remains, and all of us want to know what lies at the end of those passages—as at Wakulla cavern—that disappear into the gloom beyond the range of our feeble lights.

*

From "Ode to the West Wind"

         . . . Thou
For whose path the Atlantic's level powers
    Cleave themselves into chasms, while far below
The sea-blooms and the oozy woods which wear
    The sapless foliage of the ocean, know
Thy voice and suddenly grow gray with fear,
And tremble and despoil themselves: O Hear!

Percy Bysshe Shelley

"Diving is not a career in itself. It is not even a trade. It is just a means of transport to one's place of work," says Harry Grossett. This unromantic definition comes from a shipwright-diver who has worked a half-century underwater, from Scapa Flow to Hong Kong, from the North Sea to tropical Africa, with pneumatic drill and hammer, Cox belt gun, crosscut chisel, gelignite and detonator, hacksaw, wrecking bar, oxyhydrogen cutter and oxyarc cutter and welder. He has dived for gold, copper, cotton, and, during World War II, he performed secret underwater jobs that are still classified by the Royal Navy. His autobiography, Down to the Ships in the Sea, *is highly recommended for wisdom, range and wit. Harry Grossett marked his seventieth birthday at the bottom of the Thames, slinging lines under a sunken launch. Here is an African experience he had as a lad of sixty.*

The Accra Pipe-Line

BY HARRY GROSSETT

*T*here were about fifty civilians on the SS *Highland Brigade*, and we traveled first class. There were sixteen ships in our convoy. We were told that an earlier convoy had lost eighteen ships to the U-boats, but our own trip was quiet enough, except at Christmas. Most of the troops on board were R.A.F., and they gave us a gay time, although my own style was a bit cramped as I shared a table with two colonels, three padres, a gold-mining engineer, and another diver who was going with me—a fellow countryman named Glennie, from Aberdeen.

We arrived in Freetown, Sierra Leone, on my sixtieth birthday: January 2, 1943. We went on to Takoradi, on the Gold Coast, where Glennie and I were to build underwater foundations for Admiralty jetties. We put up a few miles inland, at the Finsbury Pavement Hotel, Sekondi. This seemed to be a sort of home of rest for tired gold-mining engineers, and they talked enough shop to pave the streets of Finsbury with gold. We had gold with breakfast, lunch and dinner. Glennie and I did not retaliate, because for some reason divers hardly ever talk shop.

374

We got our orders from the representative of the Consulting Engineers' Department, a man named Kennedy. Gold Coast bauxite, which is the chief commercial source of aluminum, was needed desperately then, and it was decided to build a concrete jetty at Takoradi for ships of deep draft. The site of the proposed jetty was a seawall which, when we arrived, was being used for mooring by Admiralty corvettes. So the first job was to build jetties for the corvettes.

The resident engineer, a Scot named Storer, introduced us to our native attendants. "Get on the right side of the number one boy, and you'll be all right," he said. The number one boy was grinning and cheerful, but I did not quite see how I was going to win him over. Storer advised me to give him a uniform. "Any sort of uniform," he said.

I took Storer at his word—I scrounged a petty officer's peaked cap, and at the hotel I was lucky enough to get hold of a pair of old-fashioned white linen cuffs and a white dicky. I kept a pretty solemn face when I gave them to the number one boy, and he was delighted. All he was wearing was a pair of ragged shorts and a bit of a khaki shirt. When he put on the adornments, with the peaked cap at a rakish angle, he strutted about like an admiral. He was my friend for life—or at least for as long as the job lasted, which was all that mattered. His uniform was useful from my point of view, too, because it made it easy for me to pick him out from the others even at a distance; although this advantage diminished slightly each day, as the cuffs and dicky got grubbier.

We needed the good will of the number one boy, for our attendants knew nothing about diving. Luckily we were working in shallow water—only about two or three fathoms—but I am never very happy going down when my lines are in the hands of someone who does not really know what he is doing. An incompetent or ignorant attendant is more of a danger to the diver than all the sharks in the sea. Of course we did not try to use a telephone. We taught the natives the elementary signals, and just had to hope for the best. My main worry was that they seemed to have very short memories. I thought they would be able to do the job provided there were no mishaps, but I did not fancy our chances in the case of an accident. As it turned out, everything went smoothly. Still, I cannot help think of all the time and money and care spent on perfecting a diver's equipment—and in fifty years my equipment has never let me down—it seems odd that the provision of attendants, who hold the diver's life in their hands, should be treated so casually.

Our attendants were not very good at dressing us. They did not pull the bib up properly, and often we got pretty wet. But the water was warm and clear, and the work was easy enough in these conditions. We lived comfortably, and in our spare time we watched the R.A.F. playing football. They had a big station there, and ran eleven teams.

One evening at the hotel we heard a man with a strong American accent asking for "the two English divers." There were no English divers at Takoradi, only we Scots, but Glennie and I took it he meant us, and introduced ourselves. We did not correct his mistake; for all we knew this Yankee might have come from the Deep South.

"I'm Brown," he said. "Oil. Socony-Vacuum. Have a drink."

We sat down in wicker chairs, and over tall, ice-cold gin slings Brown told us he was in a fix, or perhaps it was a spot, and wanted us "boys" to help him out. I liked the bit about boys, and I took a liking to Brown generally, once I could bring myself to believe he was real. He was one of those fast-talking, high-pressure, top-business executives you see in Hollywood films. He said he had come over from Accra. We knew there was a big U.S. Army Air Force station there and that tankers could not get inshore. All their aviation spirit had to be taken from Takoradi. We did not know that the Americans proposed to lay a pipe-line along the sea bed to make this unnecessary. This was what Brown was telling us.

"The flexible end of the pipe has got to be moored at least fifty feet deep," he said. "Then deep-draft tankers will come and connect up, and pump the oil ashore to our storage tanks."

"How far out is fifty feet depth?" I asked.

"Two miles."

"Some pipe," said Glennie.

"The pipe's all ready for laying," said Brown. "The storage tanks are up. Everything's ready—but we've lost our divers."

"Lost them?"

"They were being flown out. Got shot down. Will you take the job on?"

More gin slings, while Brown waited for us to reply.

"I've got a car waiting," he added.

Glennie and I exchanged glances. Then I explained that although we were civilians, we were not free agents, but had been sent out to do a particular job at Takoradi. For my part, I said, I would like to do the pipe-laying—Glennie nodded to show that he was with me—but we were under contract, and took our orders from the representative, Kennedy—

"Where's Kennedy?" Brown interrupted.

Kennedy was found, and Brown spent a few more seconds repeating what he wanted. "I shan't keep the boys long," he promised. Kennedy shook his head. "Sorry, I can't release them," he said. They argued for a bit, in a friendly way. Brown explained how important the pipe-line was, and Kennedy explained the necessity for the jetties at Takoradi. Kennedy said we were on a priority job. Brown said the pipe-line was top priority. Kennedy said we were under Admiralty contract, and he could not release us if he wanted to. He did not say he wanted to. He was ready to help, though. When we had finished the Admiralty contract, if Brown still needed divers, perhaps—

"Thanks a lot," said Brown. "Be seeing you," he told Glennie and me, and off he went.

We went back to the jetties. Four days later Kennedy called us off, and told us we were to go to Accra to lay the pipe-line. "Orders from London," he said, and did not sound very pleased. The car was waiting for us. "How did you manage it?" I asked Brown, when we had stowed our diving gear into the car. "I had to call Washington." He was quite apologetic. "This pipe-line's very important."

We were driven through 150 miles of African jungle, and suddenly came out in an American village. It was made up of prefabricated bungalows with every modern convenience. We were shown to our quarters, and allotted a car for our personal use any time between 7 A.M. and midnight. Our neighbors were American oilmen, mostly Texans—tall, rangy-looking fellows who might have stepped out of a Western film. They took us into their mess, where we had an American-style meal, which included mountains of ice cream served on soup plates.

The Americans had everything except a proper diving boat. For this we were to use a native surfboat, with six men paddling on each side; and of course, native attendants, who knew no more about diving than our own boys at Takoradi. That was not their fault, but it was our bad luck. The worse luck came when Glennie went down with dysentery, and had to be packed off to a hospital. I was asked if I would carry on by myself. I said I would, but added that I was not happy about the attendants. While there were two of us, one could have stayed in the boat and showed the natives what to do, while the other went down. Now I had to go down by myself and leave everything to them—and not one of them had even seen an air pump before. At this point one of the Americans, a fellow named Howe, volunteered to act as my attendant. He knew nothing about diving, but a bit about pumps, and at least we talked roughly the same language. I jumped at the offer, and we got ready to go.

I had already studied the plans, and understood why the pipe had got to be two miles long. The sea bed at Accra shelves very gradually. My job was to survey the sea bed and clear away any obstructions that might damage the pipe when it was flooded and dropped to the bottom. This looked easy enough, for the sea bed was of good sand and the water was clear; but, of course, for a survey of this kind the boat has got to be kept moving, at the right speed and in the right direction, while the diver walks along the bottom. This was why I was worried about the attendants.

We got the diving boat rigged up, and set off. There is always a heavy swell at Accra, and on that day it was worse than usual. It was not bad enough to prevent diving, however; and at least I knew that the natives were used to the swell of the sea, as pulling boats was their daily job, so I did not expect them to be seasick. But poor Howe was a very bad sailor, and he turned queasy the moment we left the shore. I asked him if he wanted to go back, but he was very game and said he would be all right. So I went down and began my survey, while Howe held my lines and kept an eye on the pump.

All went well for a time. Then I suddenly found myself unable to go any farther forward. Something was holding me back. I stopped and investigated, and found my breast rope slack and my air pipe completely taut. I signaled on my air pipe, and got no reply. It was impossible to signal on the slack breast rope. I did not like the look of it, but at least the air was still coming through all right. I decided to go up. I could not give the usual four pulls on the breast rope, but just closed my outlet valve enough to float up to the surface. I came up ahead of the diving boat and got a shock. No one was paddling. Howe had disappeared. The natives were dancing round excitedly—all except two of them, who were still manning the air pump. God bless them!

Then I saw Howe, or at least his head, bobbing above the water by the side of the diving boat. There were two black heads bobbing about beside his. Then black hands were stretched down from the boat, and Howe was pulled inboard. A few minutes later they pulled me in too. The explanation was simple. A heavy comber had jerked the boat violently to starboard, and Howe had toppled overboard—taking my lines with him. He was a nonswimmer, and had lost hold of the lines in his effort to keep afloat. The breast rope had gone down to the bottom. The air pipe, of course, was still connected to the pump. The crew had stopped paddling at once. They were all good swimmers, and two had jumped overboard to rescue Howe. Meanwhile I had walked on until the air pipe was fully stretched: to have gone any farther then I should have had to tow the boat.

The inboard end of my air pipe was connected to the pump by a small screw. Any sudden jerk or lurch of the boat might have broken that connection, and then the compressed air in my helmet and dress would have rushed to the loose end at the surface, and—well, they would not have got me up alive. It would have been fatal for me also if, in the panic, the pump men had stopped working the pump that gave me my air. When you sit down and look at it calmly, it is obvious that in such an event the pump must be kept going; but when you consider the panic there must have been in the boat, and when you remember that these natives were completely ignorant and inexperienced about diving, then you must admit that the pump men showed great coolness and presence of mind in keeping at their job. But you may say I am prejudiced in their favor.

A British frigate was anchored two miles out, marking the spot where the pipe-line was to go to, and I had to survey and clear the sea bed as far as that. There were no more accidents, and soon after I had finished Glennie came out of the hospital and back on the job. We were now ready to lay the pipe-line. It lay on the ground, stretching far inland, nine inches in diameter and looking like a giant snake. Three vessels were used to tow the line out—a frigate and two boom-defense boats. We took the flexible end inboard, and ten tractors hauled the line down to the shore, over rollers and trolleys, each tractor casting off as it reached the beach. As the line went out, empty forty-gallon petrol drums were lashed to it with strong Manila rope. The pipe-line was made airtight by plugging both ends with steel valves. The petrol drums gave it buoyancy. There were 360 of them, lashed on at intervals of about thirty feet.

At last we reached the two-mile mark. Looking back, we could see the long, straight line of petrol drums. Then the flexible end was moored to a permanent buoy, in such a way that it would be easy for incoming tankers to take it inboard and supply Accra with oil. Finally the signal was given, and the pipe-line was flooded. Down she went, taking the petrol drums with her.

Glennie and I were already dressed ready for going down to make a survey. We did this, checking that the pipe-line was hard on the bottom and that all joints were intact. That left us with one more job: the removal of the petrol drums. We took it in turns, one going down, and the other supervising in the diving boat, which had to be kept moving at the same speed and in the same direction as the diver. I went down first. I knew the drum would go up pretty smartly when I cut the rope, but its actual speed took me by surprise. I should have called it jet-propelled if I had known the word in those days. After that I was very careful to make sure that my lines were well clear before I cut each drum adrift. If either my breast rope or air pipe had been fouled by a released drum I should have been hauled up to the surface at great speed, and then possibly would have fallen down to the bottom again while my lines were still slack. It was easy work, and I must have averaged about one drum a minute. Glennie, in the boat, watched the drums break the surface. Naturally he kept the boat well clear, so that they came up about twenty feet away on the lee side. I counted the drums as I went along. I got as far as seventy when I received four pulls on my air pipe— the emergency signal, meaning "Come up." I obeyed and found that the diving boat was sinking. What had happened was that the seventieth drum, instead of breaking surface, had broken the boat. Whether the drum had taken an unusual course, or whether the boat had veered off its course, we never knew; but the fact was that the drum had struck the bottom of the boat with such force that it started one of the planks, and the boat was filling with water at an alarming rate.

A boat of that sort does not need to take much water to flood the air inlets of the pump, and when I was hauled inboard these inlets were already only a few inches above water. I thanked Glennie for saving my life as he took my facepiece off, and wondered if it had been worth the trouble, for our chances looked pretty thin. Glennie, like me, was in full diving dress and wearing his breastplate and lead-soled boots. You could not swim or even tread water in that costume. You would sink like a plummet. So we were in the same boat—a heavy, already waterlogged, old surfboat which looked due to go down any moment. We knew we had not time to get out of the dress, so our only hope was to try to stop the boat from sinking. The natives were already bailing like mad with buckets and tins, but the water was gaining on them. We tried to plug the fracture using the only material that was handy, which happened to be the shirts on the backs of the crew. While they were busy bailing, we literally tore their shirts off them and stuffed them into the bottom of the boat. This slowed down the rise of the water, but it did not stop it, and we had not saved enough time to undress for a swim. We were a good way out from the shore, and the ships at the other end of the pipe-line were much farther away.

But the Navy had been watching us through a telescope and just as we were giving up hope we saw a launch speeding toward us. I left my weights and helmet on the surfboat, and jumped onto the launch. We all got off safely, and the Navy took our boat in tow. But it sank on the way to shore, and had to be cut adrift.

The next day we borrowed some diving gear and went down and salved our own—helmets, weights, and pump. Then we finished the job. The Americans gave us a great send-off, and we left just before the first oil tanker arrived. We had been there for three weeks, and were paid diving money from the time we left Takoradi—every day, whether we dived or not—so it was quite a profitable job. It was also unusual and, we were told, important.

Shark Close-ups

BY J.-Y. COUSTEAU WITH FRÉDÉRIC DUMAS

On a goggle dive at Djerba Island off Tunisia in 1939 I met sharks underwater for the first time. They were magnificent gun-metal creatures, eight feet long, that swam in pairs behind their servant remoras. I was uneasy with fear, but I calmed somewhat when I saw the reaction of my diving companion, Simone. She was scared. The sharks passed on haughtily.

The Djerba sharks were entered in a shark casebook I kept religiously until we went to the Red Sea in 1951, where sharks appeared in such numbers that my census lost value. From the data, covering over a hundred shark encounters with many varieties, I can offer two conclusions: The better acquainted we become with sharks, the less we know them, and one can never tell what a shark is going to do.

Man is separated from the shark by an abyss of time. The fish still lives in the late Mesozoic, when the rocks were made: it has changed but little in perhaps three hundred million years. Across the gulf of ages, which evolved other marine creatures, the relentless, indestructible shark has come without need of evolution, the oldest killer, armed for the fray of existence in the beginning.

One sunny day in the open sea between the islands of Boavista and Maio, in the Cape Verde group, a long Atlantic swell beat on an exposed reef and sent walls of flume high into the air. Such a sight is the dread of hydrographers, who mark it off sternly to warn the mariner. But the *Élie Monnier* was attracted to such spots. We anchored by the dangerous reef to dive from the steeply rolling deck into the wild sea, where there is abundant life.

Small sharks came when we dropped anchor. The crew broke out tuna hooks and took ten of them in as many minutes. When we went overside for a camera dive, there were only two sharks left in the water. Under the racing swell we watched them strike the hooks and thrash their way through the surface. Down in the reef we found the savage population of the open ocean, including some extremely large nurse sharks, a class that is not supposed to be harmful to man. We saw three sharks sleeping in rocky caverns. The camera demanded lively sharks. Dumas and Tailliez swam into the caves and pulled their tails to wake them. The sharks came out and vanished into the blue, playing their bit parts competently.

We saw a fifteen-foot nurse shark. I summoned Didi and conveyed to him in sign language that he would be permitted to relax our neutrality toward sharks and take a crack at this one with his super-harpoon gun. It had a six-foot spear with an explosive head and three hundred pounds of traction in its elastic bands. Dumas fired straight down at a distance of twelve feet. The four-pound harpoon tip exploded. We were severely shaken. There was some pain involved.

The shark contined to swim away, imperturbably, with the spear sticking from its head like a flagstaff. After a few strokes the harpoon shaft fell to the bottom and the shark moved on. We swam after it as fast as we could to see what would happen. The shark showed every sign of normal movement, accelerated gradually and vanished. The only conclusion we could draw was that the harpoon went clear through the head and exploded externally, because no internal organ could survive a blast that nearly incapacitated us six harpoon lengths away. Even so, taking such a burst a few inches from the head demonstrated the extraordinary vitality of sharks.

One day we were finishing a movie sequence on triggerfish when Dumas and I were galvanized with ice-cold terror. It is a reaction unpleasant enough on land, and very lonely in the water. What we saw made us feel that naked men really do not belong under the sea.

At a distance of forty feet there appeared from the gray haze the lead-white bulk of a twenty-five-foot *Carcharodon carcharias*, the only shark species that all specialists agree is a confirmed man-eater. Dumas, my bodyguard, closed in beside me. The brute was swimming lazily. In that moment I thought that at least he would have a bellyache on our three-cylinder lungs.

Then, the shark saw us. His reaction was the last conceivable one. In pure fright, the monster voided a cloud of excrement and departed at an incredible speed.

Dumas and I looked at each other and burst into nervous laughter. The self-confidence we gained that day led us to a foolish negligence. We abandoned the bodyguard system and all measures of safety.

Further meetings with sharp-nosed sharks, tiger sharks, mackerel sharks, and ground sharks, inflated our sense of shark mastery. They all ran from us. After several weeks in the Cape Verdes, we were ready to state flatly that all sharks were cowards. They were so pusillanimous they wouldn't hold still to be filmed.

One day I was on the bridge, watching the little spark jiggle up and down on the echo-sound tape, sketching the profile of the sea floor nine thousand feet below the open Atlantic off Africa. There was the usual faint signal of the deep scattering layer twelve hundred feet down. The deep scattering layer is an astounding new problem of oceanography, a mystifying physical mezzanine hovering above the bedrock of the sea. It is recorded at two to three hundred fathoms in the daytime and it ascends toward the surface at night.

The phenomenon rises and falls with the cycle of sun and dark, leading some scientists to believe it is a dense blanket of living organisms, so vast as to tilt the imagination. As I watched the enigmatic scrawls, the stylus began to enter three distinct spurs on the tape, three separate scattering layers, one above the other. I was lost in whirling ideas, watching the spark etch the lowest and heaviest layer, when I heard shouts from the deck, "Whales!" A herd of sluggish bottlenosed whales surrounded the *Élie Monnier*.

In the clear water we studied the big dark forms. Their heads were round and glossy with bulbous foreheads, the "bottle" which gives them their name. When a whale broke the surface, it spouted and the rest of the body followed softly, stretching in relaxation. The whale's lips were curved in a fixed smile with tiny eyes close to the tucks of the lips, a roguish visage for such a formidable creature. Dumas skinned down to the harpoon platform under the bow while I stuck a film in the underwater camera. The whales were back from a dive. One emerged twelve feet from Dumas. He threw the harpoon with all his might. The shaft struck near the pectoral fin and blood started. The animal sounded in an easy rhythm and we paid out a hundred yards of harpoon line, tied to a heavy gray buoy. The buoy was swept away in the water—the whale was well hooked. The other whales lay unperturbed around the *Élie Monnier*.

We saw Dumas's harpoon sticking out of the water; then it, the whale and buoy disappeared. Dumas climbed the mast with binoculars. I kept the ship among the whales, thinking they would not abandon a wounded comrade. Time passed.

Libera, the keen-eyed radioman, spotted the buoy and there was the whale, seemingly unhurt, with the harpoon protruding like a tooth-pick. Dumas hit the whale twice with dum-dum bullets. Red water washed on the backs of the faithful herd, as it gathered around the stricken one. We struggled for an hour to pick up the buoy and tie the harpoon line to the *Élie Monnier*.

A relatively small bottlenosed whale, heavily wounded, was tethered to the ship. We were out of sight of land, with fifteen hundred fathoms of water under the keel, and the whale herd diving and spouting around the ship. Tailliez and I entered the water to follow the harpoon line to the agonized animal.

The water was an exceptionally clear turquoise blue. We followed the line a few feet under the surface, and came upon the whale. Thin streams of blood jetted horizontally from the bullet holes. I swam toward three other bottlenoses. As I neared them, they turned up their flukes and sounded. It was the first time I had been under water to actually see them diving and I understood the old whaler's word, "sound." They did not dive obliquely as porpoises often do. They sped straight down, perfectly vertical. I followed them down a hundred feet. A fifteen-foot shark passed way below me, probably attracted by the whale's blood. Beyond sight was the deep scattering layer; down there a herd of leviathans grazed; more sharks roamed. Above in the sun's silvery light were Tailliez and a big whale dying. Reluctantly I returned to the ship.

Back on deck I changed into another lung and strapped a tablet of cupric acetate on an ankle and one on my belt. When this chemical dissolves in water it is supposed to repulse sharks. Dumas was to pass a noose over the whale's tail, while I filmed. Just after we went under he saw a big shark, but it was gone before I answered his shout. We swam under the keel of the ship and located the harpoon line.

A few lengths down the line in a depth of fifteen feet we sighted an eight-foot shark of a species we had never before seen. He was impressively neat, light gray, sleek, a real collector's item. A ten-inch fish with vertical black-and-white stripes accompanied him a few inches above his back, one of the famous pilot fish. We boldly swam toward the shark, confident that he would run as all the others had. He did not retreat. We drew within ten feet of him, and saw all around the shark an escort of tiny striped pilots three or four inches long.

They were not following him; they seemed part of him. A thumb-nail of a pilot fish wriggled just ahead of the shark's snout, miraculously staying in place as the beast advanced. He probably found there a compressibility wave that held him. If he tumbled out of it, he would be hopelessly left behind. It was some time before we realized that the shark and his courtiers were not scared of us.

Sea legends hold that the shark has poor eyesight and pilot fish guide him to the prey, in order to take crumbs from his table. Scientists today tend to pooh-pooh the attribution of the pilot as a seeing-eye dog, although dissection has confirmed the low vision of sharks. Our experiences lead us to believe they probably see as well as we do.

The handsome gray was not apprehensive. I was happy to have such an opportunity to film a shark, although, as the first wonder passed, a sense of danger came to our hearts. Shark and company slowly circled us. I became the film director, making signs to Dumas, who was co-starred with the shark. Dumas obligingly swam in front of the beast and along behind it. He lingered at the tail and reached out his hand. He grasped the tip of the caudal fin, undecided about giving it a good pull. That would break the dreamy rhythm and make a good shot, but it might also bring the teeth snapping back at him. Dumas released the tail and pursued the shark round and round. I was whirling in the center of the game, busy framing Dumas. He was swimming as hard as he could to keep up with the almost motionless animal. The shark made no hostile move nor did he flee, but his hard little eyes were on us.

I tried to identify the species. The tail was quite asymmetrical with an unusually long top, or heterocercal caudal fin. He had huge pectorals, and the large dorsal fin was rounded with a big white patch on it. In outline and marking he resembled no shark we had seen or studied.

The shark had gradually led us down to sixty feet. Dumas pointed down. From the visibility limit of the abyss, two more sharks climbed toward us. They were fifteen-footers, slender, steel-blue animals with a more savage appearance. They leveled off below us. They carried no pilot fish.

Our old friend, the gray shark, was getting closer to us, tightening his slowly revolving cordon. But he still seemed manageable. He turned reliably in his clockwise prowl and the pilots held their stations. The blue pair from the abyss hung back, leaving the affair to the first comer. We revolved inside the ring, watching the gray, and tried to keep the blues located at the same time. We never found them in the same place twice.

Below the blue sharks there appeared great tunas with long fins. Perhaps they had been there since the beginning, but it was the first time we noticed them. Above us flying fish gamboled, adding a discordant touch of gaiety to what was becoming a tragedy for us. Dumas and I ransacked our memories for advices on how to frighten off sharks. "*Gesticulate wildly*," *said a lifeguard.* We flailed our arms. The gray did not falter. "*Give 'em a flood of bubbles*," *said a helmet diver.* Dumas waited until the shark had reached his nearest point and released a heavy exhalation. The shark did not react. "*Shout as loud as you can*," *said Hans Hass.* We hooted until our voices cracked. The shark appeared deaf. "*Cupric acetate tablets fastened to leg and belt will keep sharks away if you go into the drink*," *said an Air Force briefing officer.* Our friend swam through the copper-stained water without a wink. His cold, tranquil eye appraised us. He seemed to know what he wanted, and he was in no hurry.

A small dreadful thing occurred. The tiny pilot fish on the shark's snout tumbled off his station and wriggled to Dumas. It was a long journey for the little fellow, quite long enough for us to speculate on his purpose. The mite butterflied in front of Dumas's mask. Dumas shook his head as if to dodge a mosquito. The little pilot fluttered happily, moving with the mask, inside which Dumas focused in cross-eyed agony.

Instinctively I felt my comrade move close to me, and I saw his hand clutching his belt knife. Beyond the camera and the knife, the gray shark retreated some distance, turned and glided at us head on.

We did not believe in knifing sharks, but the final moment had come, when knife and camera were all we had. I had my hand on the camera button and it was running, without my knowledge that I was filming the oncoming beast. The flat snout grew larger and there was only the head. I was flooded with anger. With all my strength I thrust the camera and banged his muzzle. I felt the wash of a heavy body flashing past and the shark was twelve feet away, circling us as slowly as before, unharmed and expressionless, I thought, *Why in hell doesn't he go to the whale? The nice juicy whale. What did we ever do to him?*

The blue sharks now climbed up and joined us. Dumas and I decided to take a chance on the surface. We swam up and thrust our masks out of the water. The *Élie Monnier* was three hundred yards away, under the wind. We waved wildly and saw no reply from the ship. We believed that floating on the surface with one's head out of the water is the classic method of being eaten away. Hanging there, one's legs could be plucked like bananas. I looked down. The three sharks were rising toward us in a concerted attack.

We dived and faced them. The sharks resumed the circling maneuver. As long as we were a fathom or two down, they hesitated to approach. It would have been an excellent idea for us to navigate toward the ship. However, without landmarks, or a wrist compass, we could not follow course.

Dumas and I took a position with each man's head watching the other man's flippers, in the theory that the sharks preferred to strike at feet. Dumas made quick spurts to the surface to wave his arms for a few seconds. We evolved a system of taking turns for brief appeals on the surface, while the low man pulled his knees up against his chest and watched the sharks. A blue closed in on Dumas's feet while he was above. I yelled. Dumas turned over and resolutely faced the shark. The beast broke off and went back to the circle. When we went up to look we were dizzy and disoriented from spinning around underwater, and had to revolve our heads like a lighthouse beacon to find the *Élie Monnier*. We saw no evidence that our shipmates had spied us.

We were nearing exhaustion, and cold was claiming the outer layers of our bodies. I reckoned we had been down over a half-hour. Any moment we expected the constriction of air in our mouthpieces, a sign that the air supply nears exhaustion. When it came, we would reach behind our backs and turn the emergency supply valve. There was five minutes' worth of air in the emergency ration. When that was gone, we could abandon our mouthpieces and make mask dives, holding our breath. That would quicken the pace, redouble the drain on our strength, and leave us facing tireless, indestructible creatures that never needed breath. The movements of the sharks grew agitated. They ran around us, working all their strong propulsive fins, turned down and disappeaared. We could not believe it. Dumas and I stared at each other. A shadow fell across us. We looked up and saw the hull of the *Élie Monnier's* launch. Our mates had seen our signals and had located our bubbles. The sharks ran when they saw the launch.

We flopped into the boat, weak and shaken. The crew were as distraught as we were. The ship had lost sight of our bubbles and drifted away. We could not believe what they told us; we had been in the water only twenty minutes. The camera was jammed by contact with the shark's nose.

On board the *Élie Monnier*, Dumas grabbed a rifle and jumped into the small boat to visit the whale. He found it faintly alive. We saw a brown body separate from the whale and speed away, a shark. Dumas rowed around to the whale's head and gave the *coup de grâce*, point-blank with a dum-dum bullet. The head sank with the mouth open, streaming bubbles from the blowhole. Sharks twisted in the red water, striking furiously at the whale. Dumas plunged his hands in the red froth and fastened a noose to the tail, which is what he had started out to do when we were diverted by our friend.

We hoisted the whale aboard and were impressed by the moon-shaped shark bites. The inch-thick leather of the whale had been scooped out cleanly, without rips, ten or fifteen pounds of blubber at a bite. The sharks had waited until we were cheated away from them before they struck the easy prey.

The whale became Surgeon Longet's biggest dissection. He swept his scalpel down the belly. Out on deck burst a slimy avalanche of undigested three-pound squids, many of them intact, almost alive. In the recesses of the stomach were thousands of black squid beaks. My mind leaped back to the fathogram of the deep scattering layer. The coincidence of the whale's lunch and the lines drawn on the fathogram may have been entirely fortuitous. It was not strict proof. But I could not dispel an unscientific picture of that dark gloaming of the scattering layer twelve hundred feet down, and whales crashing into a meadow writhing with a million arms of squids.

Standing for Dakar we met a porpoise herd. Dumas harpooned one in the back. It swam like a dog on tether, surrounded by the pack. The mammals demonstrated a decided sense of solidarity. Save that the whale was now a porpoise, Dumas and Tailliez dived into a re-enactment of the previous drama. This time the dinghy carefully followed their air bubbles.

I watched the porpoise swimming on its leash like a bait goat a lion hunter has tied to a stake. The sharks went for the porpoise. It was cruelty to an animal but we were involved with a serious study of sharks, and had to carry it out.

The sharks circled the porpoise as they had circled us. We stood on deck remarking on the cowardice of sharks, beasts as powerful as anything on earth, indifferent to pain, and splendidly equipped as killers. Yet the brutes timidly waited to attack. Attack was too good a word for them. The porpoise had no weapons and he was dying in a circle of bullies.

At nightfall Dumas sent a *coup de grâce* into the porpoise. When it was dead, a shark passed closely by the mammal, and left entrails in the water. The other sharks passed across the porpoise, muddying the sea with blood. There was no striking and biting. The sharks spooned away the solid flesh like warm butter, without interrupting their speed.

Sharks have never attacked us with resolution, unless the overtures of our friend and the two blues may be called pressing an attack. Without being at all certain, we suppose that sharks more boldly strike objects floating on the surface. It is there that the beast finds it usual meals, sick or injured fish and garbage thrown from ships. The sharks we have met took a long time surveying submerged men. A diver is an animal they may sense to be dangerous. Aqua-Lung bubbles may also be a deterrent.

After seeing sharks swim on unshaken with harpoons through the head, deep spear gashes on the body and even after sharp explosions near their brains, we place no reliance in knives as defensive arms. We believe better protection is our "shark billy," a stout wooden staff four feet long, studded with nail tips at the business end. It is employed, somewhat in the manner of the lion tamer's chair, by thrusting the studs into the hide of an approaching shark. The nails keep the billy from sliding off the slippery leather, but do not penetrate far enough to irritate the animal. The diver may thus hold a shark at his proper distance. We carried shark billies on wrist thongs during hundreds of dives in the Red Sea, where sharks were commonplace. We have never had occasion to apply the billy, and it may prove to be merely another theoretical defense against the creature which has eluded man's understanding.

A naval officer who has shown many new applications of free diving, Commander Francis Douglas Fane, USN, has led Underwater Demolitioneers in the Atlantic and Pacific and in combat in the Korean War. Originally a merchant navy officer, Fane accompanied Byrd's Antarctic Expedition, and has conducted valuable experiments on the question of sharks vs. divers. His underwater life was told in a motion picture, in which Fane's own underwater shots were superior to the Hollywood contrivances. He is now stationed in Japan.

Diving in Polar Seas

BY FRANCIS D. FANE

*T*he skillful navigation of the polar ice cap by the submarines *Nautilus* and *Skate* has focused attention on the roof of the world. But despite the domination of frigid regions by nuclear vessels, high-powered icebreakers, and caterpillar snow tractors, there is still a demand for the services of swimmers, men who can enter areas inaccessible to ships or machines. Immersion in polar waters—bone-chilling, spine-freezing waters—what a great challenge to man! When we constructed the Distant Early Warning (DEW) Line across the Arctic coasts of Alaska and Canada, U.S. Navy Underwater Demolition Teams (UDT) played a prominent part. They are now in the Antarctic, in company of the scientists engaged in the studies and exploration of the Geophysical Year. However, when the writer first proposed that UDT swimmers accompany the U.S. Navy Expedition to the Antarctic in 1946–47, he was considered to be quite mad by some and an extremist by the most charitable. But swimmers have proved their ability to operate polar areas, and now serve every task force which enters the ice.

The first purpose in sending swimmers to the polar regions was to blast a way through ice floes and to assist ships in working free from ice jams; secondly, to test the capability of swimmers in the reconnaissance of landing beaches beset by ice. It was obvious after World War II that future warfare would not always be conducted in the tropical areas of the Pacific. The Russian Bear was an Arctic animal, and into his element we would have to go—my underlying reason for sending swimmers to the polar regions. There, under actual operating conditions, the UDT personnel proved that they could endure extreme cold water temperatures (29° F.) for extended periods of time and also perform vital tasks aside from their primary combat missions—such tasks as underwater inspection of hull damage, changing propellers, recovery of equipment lost through the ice, and the location and the recovery of crashed, submerged aircraft.

A great wealth of scientific endeavor is being directed toward adapting man to the polar environment. Studies have even been made of the personal habits and physiology of the Eskimo. Perhaps—dread the thought—a training requirement for prospective polar swimmers will be a diet of seal oil and whale blubber.

UDT swimmers learned much by personal experience in cold weather areas. The experiments conducted were of a practical, empirical nature, to determine the limits of exposure men could withstand, primarily for military purposes. In early experiments within the UDT organization, we quickly found that there was no hope of making polar bears out of humans. It would be necessary to clothe men to withstand immersion in frigid waters and the environment of extreme cold air temperatures. In the Korean War, UDT swimmers were exposed to subzero air temperatures while swimming in relatively warm (39° F.) sea water. As the Eskimo very carefully clothes himself in hides, with the fur turned in to the body, so does the underwater swimmer don successive layers of wool underwear under a watertight, close-fitting, rubber sheath. So clad, with only the lips exposed, swimmers can operate for periods of one to two hours in water temperatures near freezing. It is as simple as that, though there is much that can be done to improve the technique. Thought should be given to chemical heating of the suits. The requirement for pressure suits for high-altitude fliers is similar to the need of suits for divers. In fact, a case of bends was recently treated by placing the deep-sea diver in a high-altitude pressure suit.

The physical condition of swimmers is of primary importance. Experience has proved that it is not necessary for swimmers to be exposed to cold for a period of acclimation before entering the polar zones. In modern warfare it is not desirable to maintain military units for long periods in Arctic areas, for reasons of morale, logistics, and training. A man thoroughly conditioned physically (as are all UDT swimmers, in fact, all expert swimmers) can be transported from tropical training areas into the Arctic and immediately subjected to cold without deleterious physical effects. As an example, the UDT swimmers first employed on the DEW Line were flown from Southern California in June. Two days after arrival in Simpson Strait, located above the Arctic Circle in Canadian Northwest Territories, Lieutenant (jg) Jon Lindbergh blasted holes through seven feet of sea ice and conducted dives to determine the nature of the sea floor, sea water temperature 28° F. GM1 William Gianotti dove to a depth of sixty-five feet in 32° water to place a retrieving cable around the major control panel lost overboard at Cambridge Bay, Northwest Territories. This diver worked on the bottom for forty minutes and, although chilled through because of a torn suit, accomplished a task vital to the establishment of a main DEW Line site. In another instance, UDT swimmers who had been diving for a period of three months in the waters of the Virgin Islands, sea temperature 86° F., were transported to Newfoundland, where they conducted extensive diving operations off Argentia in sea temperature 39°–42° F. The success of these operations was due to excellent physical condition and adequate protective clothing, not to acclimatization.

Men have survived for long periods in frigid seas. This is possible by the generation of heat in the muscles when swimming at a hard rate. As soon as the swim rate is reduced, numbing and loss of body heat will quickly follow and the swim soon terminates. There is a verified instance of an Alaskan fisherman swimming through a night in water off Nome, Alaska. The channel swimmer type can plow through waters in the 45°–55° F. range for hours. Men with the massive physique of Lamor Boren, the famous underwater photographer, and that human walrus, Boatswain's Mate Leonard McLarty of UDT, have much more tolerance for cold seas than the lean wiry type and can stand long periods of immersion in 50° F. waters with no protection. However, there are unfortunately too many records of "man overboard" cases in Arctic waters in the 30°–40° F. temperature range, where the man failed to survive, though still swimming when rescued, and immersed for as short a period as ten minutes. Also, when swimmers have torn their suits, even though the area exposed was limited to a small part of the body or extremities, the swimmer is soon forced to give up. The ability of man to withstand cold should not be judged by the capability of a few, as the range of individual tolerance is great. This is also true in relation to other divers' diseases. Controlled tests of UDT swimmers exposed to oxygen toxicity, nitrogen narcosis, and carbon dioxide poisoning showed surprising variation in tolerance. There seems to be a relationship between the tolerance of the individual to whiskey and to the other toxicities associated with diving. Whether this would hold true to exposure to cold, I do not know.

Extracts from the log of an Underwater Demolition Team operating off Kodiak, Alaska, January, 1948, are of interest:

> The reconnaissance was conducted by twenty-six swimmers. The water temperature was 36° F. Slush and ice was encountered near the beach which probably lowered the temperature three to five degrees.
>
> The average time spent in the water was fifty-five minutes with the maximum one hour fifty minutes and the minimum twenty minutes. The swimmers covered distances of one-half to 1¼ miles.
>
> The average body temperature of swimmers returning to the ship was 93° with an average time of thirty minutes being required for temperatures to return to normal. This was aided by supervised shower baths, starting with cold water increasing to room temperature, about 70° F. All swimmers suffered from chilling of the hands and feet.
>
> During the entire operation in Arctic waters, five members contracted colds, four of these did not participate in the three months of physical and swim training conducted at San Diego, California, prior to departure.

In addition to the above records, many dives have been made in polar waters in depths to sixty feet and water temperatures of 28°–40° F. In all cases experience proved that divers could endure extreme cold temperatures if adequately equipped. In diving operations conducted under adverse conditions, there are apt to be psychological problems. In a group of men with the high morale, competitive urge, and the team spirit of UDT there is no such problem. Well-trained men desire to dive and meet the challenge of a tough assignment. There are hazards in all diving operations, and the onset of diver's disease is heightened by the cold. Some hazards are unique to the Arctic environment. In Cambridge Bay, Canadian Northwest Territories, during the survey of the DEW Line, the ice started to break up in July. Two officers, Lieutenant Charles Aquadro, MC, USNR, and Lieutenant (jg) Alan Jones, USNR, of UDT were apparently struck with spring fever one Sunday and started to swim across the bay toward an Eskimo camp. They were clad in black exposure suits, rubber gloves, and large swim fins. Alternately crawling over ice floes and swimming through the water, they neared shore. The sled dogs started howling. Eskimo hunters, who had never seen a man swimming, came out of their tents and, on seeing the figures, rushed for their high-powered rifles. The UDT men had been mistaken for seals, the favorite food of the Eskimo and husky. Only wild cries and frantic gestures prevented a fusillade.

We have read much concerning the beauties of diving in tropical waters, amid gorgeous-hued corals, friendly fish, the "raptures of the deep," the profound glory of the silent world bathed in beautiful sunlight, and other romantic platitudes. Such joys will not be encountered in polar waters. My acclaim and admiration go to the divers who, in daily pursuit of their hazardous trade, descend into the cold gloom of turbid waters where the light of sun is seldom noticed and the hand cannot be seen in front of the face—where the diver crawls through mud, enters jagged wrecks, wrestles with snaky coils of air and communication lines, and expends his strength in handling cumbersome tools and forcing rusted fittings—where he feels the terror of a sudden cut-off of air supply, or the dread of entrapment. To the military divers of World War II and the Korean War— the British, American, and the gallant Italian and German divers, who swam in mined waters carrying large demolition charges, who suffered long hours in the dark and cold, who felt the concussion of charges detonated with the intent to destroy them, and yet carried on—to these men should go the applause and recognition. The knowledge and experience gained from such divers as these makes the task of entering polar waters a relatively simple one for today's skindivers.

Man is rapidly becoming acclimated to life under the sea, his ancestral home. He is able to plumb its deepest depths while enclosed in submersible and bathyscaph. With artificial lungs and the equivalent of blubber, hair and hide on his body, he can join the seal, the walrus and the polar bear in and under the limitless ice of the polar seas.

The able underwater photographer Folco Quilici accompanied an Italian expedition to the Red Sea in the Formica *in 1953. Professor Francesco Baschieri Salvafori was the head of the scientific party and the diving chief was the formidable naked diver, Raimond Bucher, who has attained an authenticated depth of 128 feet without breathing apparatus. The Giorgio of this story is Giorgio Ravelli, an engineer.*

The Phantoms of the Gubbet

BY FOLCO QUILICI

Around Gubbet Mus Nefit, a seemingly endless bay of the Dahlak Archipelago, extends flat sandy land, almost level with the sea and absolutely deserted. One large and one narrow channel give Gubbet contact with the sea, and through the larger one the *Formica* passed to cast anchor in the bay.

In the Red Sea, the tides are violent and strong, with a considerable rise and fall. The channels act as valves for the loading and unloading of water in the bay. Four times each day great volumes of water pass through the channels, causing a rushing flood. Diving into the channel when the sea was moving, we used to feel ourselves dragged away as if by a strong mountain torrent. We sailed ahead at top speed in the midst of big and little fish, without a stroke of the fins.

Why did I go down in Gubbet Bay? To find a shipwreck—the wreck of a boat sunk about twelve years before. I thought it would be interesting to shoot some photographs of it. Our nakhoda, who knows all about wrecks, gave careful navigational instructions based on sightings of a scrubby acacia and some white cliffs on the distant horizon. With this information Masino located it, and Giorgio and I descended. We poked about on the bottom for a while, not feeling too comfortable. The light was dim, but that was not the real reason. Probably it was the presence of a wreck, the atmosphere of death and destruction.

We slipped along the edge of the boat, seeing nothing but a dark wall. Finally we found the prow and under it the name painted in white letters: *Panaria*. I took a rapid turn around the old propeller blades, while Giorgio took several pictures. But we had no heart for our work and soon surfaced, to talk with our nakhoda about the shipwrecks of Gubbet Mus Nefit. In the bosom of the bay lay several ships, taking us back to a day in April, 1941. Here was the last chapter of the story of the Italian Navy, caught in a trap in the Red Sea at the outbreak of World War II.

One night the silence of the bay had been broken by the roar of bombers. There was a sharp explosion, and the *Mazzini*, loaded with torpedoes, was hit squarely. The *Prometeo*, filled with naphtha, burned like an immense torch, as if in honor of its own name. For two days, the flames burned, illuminating the end of the other sinking ships. The *Urania*, the *Bottego*, the *Sauro*, the *Panaria*—all lay stretched out on the bottom of the bay. Our nakhoda, who had served the Italian Navy command and knew all about these events, pointed out to us the two dramatic masts of the *Sauro* poking up through the waves, and the rusted framework of the *Urania* lying on its side.

The nakhoda's tales of these dead ships of the Red Sea aroused our curiosity, and soon they were an irresistible attraction. The last remnants of the *Sauro* and the *Urania* seemed to beckon to us, inviting us to come below and see all. Finally, when a day came on which the waters of Gubbet had tossed away their fogs of plankton, we went in search of an extraordinary experience.

The prow of the *Urania* poked half out of the water. The rest lay on the bottom, pointing down abruptly toward the deep center of the bay. The ship was on its side and seemed to be cut in two by the sea. A metal rail round the prow rose partly above the water, where was perched a white heron with a long neck, which seemed annoyed at our presence; below, it served as a pole round which little fish danced. The heron flew away with short sharp cries, cries that reverberated in a silence so deep that one could feel it. Round a dead ship, where one is overwhelmed by the enormous mass so devoid of life, the smallest noise—the lapping of a wave against an iron plate, the rustle of the wind in the emergent superstructure—rebounds and swells.

We moored our little boat under the ruin of a helm that remained above the water. The immobile hub of the propeller, the blades of which were hidden, pointed like a cannon toward the white sky of the Dahlak. One after another we put on our auto-respirators and entered the water.

I expected the sunken *Urania* to be covered with soft greenish seaweeds, all one color, mimicking the color of the sea; I expected deep shadows, dark inaccessible recesses, and an air of death. The tropical sea, however, cannot conceive of the word "death." It wants to see life always flourishing with thousands of brilliant colors and in a multitude of forms. And that was what we found as we completed a marvelous voyage around the wreck, at depths of fifteen, thirty, fifty feet. The *Urania* did not remind me of any ship I had seen beneath the water. It was not empty; it did not disappear in the folds of sea-colored seaweed. Thousands of fish populated it, fish of every size, shape and color—from the brilliant parrot fish to the fantastic arbalest, from the silvery, shimmering scad and *liche* to the slender barracuda. Never had the *Urania* entertained so many passengers and such lively ones.

Covered all over by a bright cloak of little corals, sponges, madrepore, sea urchins, oysters, the *Urania* was a formidable polychrome spectacle of yellow, green, red, black, violet, white, orange. The ship sank dramatically, lighted up with a great explosion. Since then, it had been covered with beautiful drapery, from the inside of its long smokestack to its first-class cabins.

Near the keel, huge rusted steel plates, broken at the time of the explosion, waved back and forth, pushed by currents of water and giving the impression of the gills of a giant fish. That was how Giorgio and I slipped inside the *Urania*, calculating the space to the fraction of an inch and timing our movements to dart in when the plate swung widest. It was like passing under a huge guillotine with jagged edges.

Inside, lights and shadows played through the rooms, the corridors, and in the large salon. We crossed mysterious openings, accompanied only by the sound of the air discharged from our apparatus. In the machine room, among the boilers, ladders and pipes, square rays of light from far-off hatchways made topsy-turvy patterns. I came to a black wall, in the center of which a porthole showed the yellowish green water of the sea outside. Suddenly a face appeared in the porthole: Giorgio, exploring the next room. He was a phantom-like vision, a mask from which extended tubes and valves, two eyes dilated to see in the darkness, all framed by a hole studded with yellow sponges and shells of black oysters. We found a passage and followed it together around the labyrinth. Occasionally the flash of a camera lit up the surrealist scene. A mysterious gong kept sounding from somewhere, as if announcing the dinner hour, so we started looking for the dining room. A winding passage carried us almost to the top, and we discovered the cause of the sound: one of the big metal plates that "breathed."

Then we heard a siren. We stopped, bewildered and stared at each other. Its sound, distorted by the mass of water into something that reminded us of a phonograph record running down, still reached our ears clearly despite our disbelief. It really *was* the sound of a siren. But not the siren of the wrecked *Urania*. It was the *Formica*, circling around the wreck to tell us that the sun was setting, that it was time to return. We had no idea that the time had passed so quickly. And suddenly we realized that we had not really paid any attention to our winding route through the wreck, that we did not know how to get back to the entry.

Seeing a gleam of light above us, we headed that way quickly, and emerged into a small, square mirror of water at the top of which was the sky. We were in a transverse alleyway that went straight upward through the ship. We surfaced, gulped some welcome fresh air, and saw that we could not escape that way. The alleyway continued straight up for some distance without anything to hold on to.

"Air?" I asked Giorgio, who in such matters is always more precise than I am.

"Enough for five or six minutes, I think."

Waiting there would do no good, so we dived again. The walls of yellow sponges and little rose-red leaves of madrepore faded quickly as the light disappeared. We were not really frightened, but we were certainly beginning to feel uneasy. Inside the enormous framework, among tons of steel floors and walls, we could not imagine which direction we ought to take. With everything on its side, floor plans did not make much sense. Through a crack we saw a little light, but there was no space for an exit.

We decided to go as deep as possible and look for those waving plates by which we had entered. As we descended, we breathed with great economy, hoarding the little air left us. Finally the plates were in front of us, but then a blood-chilling fact stopped us dead. They were no longer waving. The were not moving at all. The water currents which had moved them had ceased, and our trap doors were shut. The guillotine had fallen.

We could have gone back to the long corridor where there was air to breathe, but then we would have been trapped, and in going there would have used the last remaining air in our respirators. I had to try the impossible. I pushed against the big plate, braced my feet against a projection and pushed harder. Against my expectations, it slowly moved—not much, but it moved. I nodded to Giorgio, who darted through like lightning, streaking along the sand and scraping his back on the lower edge of the plate. I let the door swing shut, hoping that my friend outside would find some way to pull from there. With my heart in my mouth, I watched a line of light on the sand at the bottom to see if it grew wider. Two seconds, three seconds, four seconds. The big plate moved, began to open. Clever Giorgio had found a way to brace himself and was pulling with all his might. I crouched low and at the first possible moment slipped through.

The nightmare was ended. We sped for the surface, gulped in fresh air and signaled to the boat to pick us up.

*

Caribbean Pearl Divers

From this port, Margarita, more than three hundred canoes leave every day, going a league offshore to fish for pearls in ten or twelve fathoms. The fishing is done by Negro slaves of the king of Spain, who take a little basket under their arm, and with it plunge to the bottom of the sea, and fill it with oysters, and climb back into their boats.

Samuel Champlain, WEST INDIAN JOURNAL, 1599

Aside from the visions of poets, the only fiction included in this book is an extract from Twenty Thousand Leagues Under the Sea, *a book almost as misunderstood as* Gulliver's Travels. *The American submarine engineer Simon Lake said, "The fantasy of Jules Verne is the fact of today." The tribute is incorrect. The undersea paraphernalia of Verne's wonderful work is based on scientific results reported and diving equipment in use before he wrote. Born in 1828, Verne's seventy-seven years spanned the technological revolutions of a highly creative century. He closely followed advances in nineteenth-century science with an eye out for pregnant ideas to use in his moral tales, of which the greatest is the undersea novel. Verne did not disguise the actual inventors of undersea apparatus: Rouquayrol and Denayrouze, who are cited in the tale, were the inventors of a semiautomatic compressed-air diving lung which was used commercially several years before Verne wrote. Also mentioned is Professor Henri Milne-Edwards of the Sorbonne, the first naturalist to dive (in 1844), who wrote many papers which Verne drew upon to validate his undersea settings. The septuagenarian novelist wrote Simon Lake in 1898, "My book is entirely a work of the imagination." He had forgotten that at least fifty practical submarine boats had navigated under water before he wrote* Twenty Thousand Leagues.

Why, then, in this day of achievements exceeding Verne's projections—nuclear submarines under the North Pole, men swimming in the depths like fish, and bathyscaphs taking observers two and one-half miles down—does his book remain the evergreen delight it is? We submit the secret is Captain Nemo's protest against social injustice. Generations of children have sublimated rebellion against family and adults their resentment of systems, in the deeds of the Master of the Nautilus.

In his seventy-sixth year, deaf and nearly blind, Verne wrote The Invasion of the Sea, *an attempt to summon up again the magic of the deeps. He died in 1905 at Amiens and on his tomb is written,* "Onward to Immortality and Eternal Youth." *Jules Verne's last goal is secure.*

Twenty Thousand Leagues
Under the Sea

BY JULES VERNE

A moment after, we were seated on a divine in the saloon smoking. The Captain showed me a sketch that gave the plan, section, and elevation of the *Nautilus*. Then he began his description in these words—

"Here, M. Aronnax, are the several dimensions of the boat you are in. It is an elongated cylinder with conical ends. It is very like a cigar in shape, a shape already adopted in London in several constructions of the same sort. The length of this cylinder, from stem to stern, is exactly 232 feet, and its maximum breadth is twenty-six feet. It is not built quite like your long-voyage steamers, but its lines are sufficiently long, and its curves prolonged enough, to allow the water to slide off easily, and oppose no obstacle to its passage. These two dimensions enable you to obtain by a simple calculation the surface and cubic contents of the *Nautilus*. Its area measures 6,032 feet; and its contents about 1,500 cubic yards—that is to say, when completely immersed it displaces 50,000 feet of water, or weighs 1,500 tons."

"Ah, Commander! your *Nautilus* is certainly a marvelous boat."

"Yes, Professor; and I love it as if it were part of myself. If danger threatens one of your vessels on the ocean, the first impression is the feeling of an abyss above and below. On the *Nautilus* men's hearts never fail them. No defects to be afraid of, for the double shell is as firm as iron; no rigging to attend to; no sails for the wind to carry away; no boilers to burst; no fire to fear, for the vessel is made of iron, not of wood; no coal to run short, for electricity is the only mechanical agent; no collision to fear, for it alone swims in deep water; no tempest to brave, for when it dives below the water, it reaches absolute tranquillity. There, sir! that is the perfection of vessels! And if it is true that the engineer has more confidence in the vessel than the builder, and the builder than the captain himself, you understand the trust I repose in my *Nautilus;* for I am at once captain, builder, and engineer."

"But how could you construct this wonderful *Nautilus* in secret?"

"Each separate portion, M. Aronnax, was brought from different parts of the globe. The keel was forged at Creusot, the shaft of the screw at Penn & Co.'s, London, the iron plates of the hull at Laird's of Liverpool, the screw itself at Scott's at Glasgow. The reservoirs were made by Cail & Co. at Paris, the engine by Krupp in Prussia, its beak in Motala's workshop in Sweden, its mathematical instruments by Hart Brothers of New York, etc; and each of these people had my orders under different names."

"But these parts had to be put together and arranged?"

"Professor, I had set up my workshops upon a desert island in the ocean. There my workmen, that is to say, the brave men that I instructed and educated, and myself have put together our *Nautilus*. Then when the work was finished, fire destroyed all trace of our proceedings on this island, that I could have jumped over if I had liked."

"Then the cost of this vessel is great?"

"M. Aronnax, an iron vessel costs £45 per ton. Now the *Nautilus* weighed 1,500. It came therefore to £67,500 and £80,000 more for fitting it up, and about £200,000 with the works of art and the collections it contains."

"One last question, Captain Nemo."

"Ask it, Professor."

"You are rich?"

"Immensely rich, sir; and I could, without missing it, pay the national debt of France."

I stared at the singular person who spoke thus. Was he playing upon my credulity? The future would decide that.

The portion of the terrestrial globe which is covered by water is estimated at upward of eighty millions of acres. This fluid mass comprises two billions two hundred and fifty millions of cubic miles, forming a spherical body of a diameter of sixty leagues, the weight of which would be three quintillions of tons. To comprehend the meaning of these figures, it is necessary to observe that a quintillion is to a billion as a billion is to unity; in other words, there are as many billions in a quintillion as there are units in a billion. This mass of fluid is equal to about the quantity of water which would be discharged by all the rivers of the earth in forty thousand years.

During the geological epochs, the igneous period succeeded to the aqueous. The ocean originally prevailed everywhere. Then by degrees, in the silurian period, the tops of the mountains began to appear, the islands emerged, then disappeared in partial deluges, reappeared, became settled, formed continents, till at length the earth became geographically arranged, as we see in the present day. The solid had wrested from the liquid thirty-seven million six hundred and fifty-seven square miles, equal to twelve billion nine hundred and sixty millions of acres.

The shape of continents allows us to divide the waters into five great portions: the Arctic or Frozen Ocean, the Antarctic or Frozen Ocean, the Indian, the Atlantic, and the Pacific Oceans.

The Pacific Ocean extends from north to south between the two polar circles, and from east to west between Asia and America, over an extent of 145 degrees of longitude. It is the quietest of seas; its currents are broad and slow, it has medium tides, and abundant rain. Such was the ocean that my fate destined me first to travel over under these strange conditions.

"Sir," said Captain Nemo, "we will, if you please, take our bearings and fix the starting point of this voyage. It is a quarter to twelve, I will go up again to the surface."

The Captain pressed an electric clock three times. The pumps began to drive the water from the tanks; the needle of the manometer marked by a different pressure the ascent of the *Nautilus*, then it stopped.

"We have arrived," said the Captain.

I went to the central staircase which opened on to the platform, clambered up the iron steps, and found myself on the upper part of the *Nautilus*.

The platform was only three feet out of the water. The front and back of the *Nautilus* was of that spindle-shape which caused it justly to be compared to a cigar. I noticed that its iron plates, slightly overlaying each other, resembled the shell which clothes the bodies of our large terrestrial reptiles. It explained to me how natural it was, in spite of all glasses, that this boat should have been taken for a marine animal.

Toward the middle of the platform the longboat, half buried in the hull of the vessel, formed a slight excrescence. Fore and aft rose two cages of medium height with inclined sides, and partly closed by thick convex glasses; one destined for the steersman who directed the *Nautilus*, the other containing a brilliant lantern to give light on the road.

The sea was beautiful, the sky pure. Scarcely could the long vehicle feel the broad undulations of the ocean. A light breeze from the east rippled the surface of the waters. The horizon, free from fog, made observation easy. Nothing was in sight. Not a quicksand, not an island. A vast desert.

Captain Nemo, by the help of his sextant, took the altitude of the sun, which ought to give the latitude. He waited for some moments till its disk touched the horizon. Whilst taking observations not a muscle moved, the instrument could not have been more motionless in a hand of marble.

"Twelve o'clock, sir," he said. "When you like—"

I cast a look upon the sea, slightly yellowed by the Japanese coast, and descended to the saloon.

"And now, sir, I leave you to your studies," added the Captain; "our course is N.N.E., our depth is twenty-six fathoms. Here are maps on a large scale by which you may follow it. The saloon is at your disposal, and with your permission I will retire." Captain Nemo bowed, and I remained alone, lost in thoughts all bearing on the commander of the *Nautilus*.

For a whole hour was I deep in these reflections, seeking to pierce this mystery so interesting to me. Then my eyes fell upon the vast planisphere spread upon the table, and I placed my finger on the very spot where the given latitude and longitude crossed.

The sea has its large rivers like the continents. They are special currents known by their temperature and their color. The most remarkable of these is known by the name of the Gulf Stream. Science has decided on the globe the direction of five principal currents: one in the North Atlantic, a second in the South, a third in the North Pacific, a fourth in the South, and a fifth in the Southern Indian Ocean. It is even probable that a sixth current existed at one time or another in the Northern Indian Ocean, when the Caspian and Aral seas formed but one vast sheet of water.

At this point indicated on the planisphere one of these currents was rolling, the Kuro-Sivo of the Japanese, the Black River which, leaving the Gulf of Bengal where it is warmed by the perpendicular rays of a tropical sun, crosses the Straits of Malacca along the coast of Asia, turns into the North Pacific to the Aleutian Islands, carrying with it trunks of camphor trees and other indigenous productions, and edging the waves of the ocean with the pure indigo of its warm water. It was this current that the *Nautilus* was to follow. I followed it with my eye; saw it lose itself in the vastness of the Pacific, and felt myself drawn with it, when Ned Land and Conseil appeared at the door of the saloon.

My two brave companions remained petrified at the sight of the wonders spread before them.

"Where are we, where are we?" exclaimed the Canadian. "In the museum at Quebec?"

"My friends," I answered, making a sign for them to enter, "you are not in Canada, but on board the *Nautilus* fifty yards below the level of the sea."

"But, M. Aronnax," said Ned Land, "can you tell me how many men there are on board? Ten, twenty, fifty, a hundred?"

"I cannot answer you, Mr. Land; it is better to abandon for a time all idea of seizing the *Nautilus* or escaping from it. This ship is a masterpiece of modern industry, and I should be sorry not to have seen it. Many people would accept the situation forced upon us, if only to move amongst such wonders. So be quiet and let us try and see what passes around us."

"See!" exclaimed the harpooner, "but we can see nothing in this iron prison! We are walking—we are sailing—blindly."

Ned Land had scarcely pronounced these words when all was suddenly darkness. The luminous ceiling was gone, and so rapidly that my eyes received a painful impression.

We remained mute, not stirring, and not knowing what surprise awaited us, whether agreeable or disagreeable. A sliding noise was heard: one would have said that panels were working at the sides of the *Nautilus*.

"It is the end of the end!" said Ned Land.

Suddenly light broke at each side of the saloon, through two oblong openings. The liquid mass appeared vividly lit up by the electric gleam. Two crystal plates separated us from the sea. At first I trembled at the thought that this frail partition might break, but strong bands of copper bound them, giving an almost infinite power of resistance.

The sea was distinctly visible for a mile all around the *Nautilus*. What a spectacle! What pen can describe it? Who could paint the effects of the light through those transparent sheets of water, and the softness of the successive graduations from the lower to the superior strata of the ocean?

We know the transparency of the sea, and that its clearness is far beyond that of rock water. The mineral and organic substances which it holds in suspension heightens its transparency. In certain parts of the ocean at the Antilles, under seventy-five fathoms of water, can be seen with surprising clearness a bed of sand. The penetrating power of the solar rays does not seem to cease for a depth of one hundred and fifty fathoms. But in this middle fluid traveled over by the *Nautilus*, the electric brightness was produced even in the bosom of the waves. It was no longer luminous water, but liquid light.

On each side a window opened into this unexplored abyss. The obscurity of the saloon showed to advantage the brightness outside, and we looked out as if this pure crystal had been the glass of an immense aquarium.

"You wished to see, friend Ned; well, you see now."

"Curious! curious!" muttered the Canadian, who, forgetting his ill-temper, seemed to submit to some irresistible attraction; "and one would come farther than this to admire such a sight!"

"Ah!" thought I to myself, "I understand the life of this man; he has made a world apart for himself, in which he treasures all his greatest wonders."

For two whole hours an aquatic army escorted the *Nautilus*. During their games, their bounds, while rivaling each other in beauty, brightness, and velocity, I distinguished the green labre; the banded mullet, marked by a double line of black; the round-tailed goby, of a white color, with violet spots on the back; the Japanese scombrus, a beautiful mackerel of those seas, with a blue body and silvery head; the brilliant azurors, whose name alone defies description; some banded spares, with variegated fins of blue and yellow; some aclo-stones, the woodcocks of the seas, some specimens of which attain a yard in length; Japanese salamanders, spider lampreys, serpents six feet long, with eyes small and lively, and a huge mouth bristling with teeth; with many other species.

Our imagination was kept at its height, interjections followed quickly on each other. Ned named the fish, and Conseil classed them. I was in ecstasies with the vivacity of their movements and the beauty of their forms. Never had it been given to me to surprise these animals, alive and at liberty, in their natural element. I will not mention all the varieties which passed before my dazzled eyes, all the collection of the seas of China and Japan. These fish, more numerous than the birds of the air, came, attracted, no doubt, by the brilliant focus of the electric light.

Suddenly there was daylight in the saloon, the iron panels closed again, and the enchanting vision disappeared. But for a long time I dreamt on till my eyes fell on the instruments hanging on the partition. The compass still showed the course to be N.N.E., the manometer indicated a pressure of five atmospheres, equivalent to a depth of twenty-five fathoms, and the electric log gave a speed of fifteen miles an hour. I expected Captain Nemo, but he did not appear. The clock marked the hour of five.

Ned Land and Conseil returned to their cabin, and I retired to my chamber. My dinner was ready. It was composed of turtle soup made of the most delicate hawk-bills, of a surmullet served with puff paste (the liver of which, prepared by itself, was most delicious), and fillets of the emperor-holocanthus, the savor of which seemed to me superior even to salmon.

I passed the evening reading, writing, and thinking. Then sleep overpowered me, and I stretched myself on my couch of zostera, and slept profoundly, whilst the *Nautilus* was gliding rapidly through the current of the Black River.

Man's deepest penetration in the sea has been by bathyscaph, an underwater dirigible with gasoline instead of gas in its envelope and a pressure-proof steel ball to accommodate its two cramped passengers. There are two bathyscaphs: the one described here, which belongs to the French Navy, and another built by August Piccard, which has been purchased by the U.S. Navy. Commandant Houot has made nearly a hundred descents in FNRS 3 in the Atlantic, Mediterranean and Pacific. Here is the deepest dive as he described it in the National Geographic Magazine.

Two and a Half Miles Down

BY GEORGES S. HOUOT

*O*ld residents of Dakar said, "The best weather for your big dive will be just before the full moon." The almanac showed the February full moon of 1954 was due on the seventeenth. As the day neared, the meteorological forecasts swung into agreement with the local sages, and at dawn on the thirteenth we began to load the bathyscaph with shot ballast. A few hours later the Navy tug *Tenace* took her in tow, and, with sun breaking cheerfully through the overcast, we headed out into the swells of the eastern Atlantic. All night and well into the next day we steamed along at our four-knot towing speed, the submarine following easily and without incident. Some 160 miles southwest of Dakar we neared our diving site. Soundings showed a depth of about 13,300 feet; the echoes were clear, and the bottom appeared smooth and level, favorable for our "landing."

None of us got much sleep the night before the dive. My brain worked over the precautions, the unforeseen elements, the fantastic anticipation itself. I comforted myself with the reflection that at least this operation seemed to be going better than the pilotless 13,450-foot dive on January 27. That affair had been a hard trial indeed of the bathyscaph and the men who handled her. The waves had been twelve feet high. The tow cable had parted, casting the *FNRS 3* adrift, and we had had to scatter the convoy to avoid collisions in the darkness. All night the *Élie Monnier* had kept the submarine in her searchlight beam. In the morning, two parties of seamen and a diver had to struggle for hours on the pitching bathy-scaph before they could pass a new towline. Even so, that pilotless dive had been a success. When a Navy flying boat radioed, "Bathy-scaph on surface, 15:05," we knew we had witnessed a historic day in the annals of undersea exploration. For the dive had proved that the bathyscaph met specifications. Our aim had always been to create a vehicle capable of descending repeatedly to 13,125 feet (4,000 meters), slightly more than the average depth of the oceans. Now all that remained was for Lieutenant Pierre Henri Willm and me to go there ourselves.

Everyone turned out early. In the first light of the winter day, February 15, 1954, our little ships gathered around the tiny sub-marine in the heaving ocean. Willm and I put on heavy pullovers; it would be cold down there. To this costume Willm added a brief case, making him look like a serious young lawyer on his way to the office. The brief case, however, contained sandwiches. At 7:40 he and I went over the side to a dinghy with Midshipman André Michaudon. Not trying to hide the worry on their faces, Lieutenant Commander Georges Ortolan of the *Élie Monnier* and Commander Philippe Tailliez of the Undersea Research Group said good-by.

We crossed the waves to the bathyscaph, and Willm leaped aboard her. Disappearing down the air-lock, he unbolted the entrance hatch to the sphere, closed while under tow. From the conning tower I directed the lowering of the guide chain, while a quartermaster and two divers swam under the "deepboat" and removed the security dogs from the electromagnets. They found, unfortunately, that one of the dogs had been insecurely fastened, jarring loose the electromagnet on a shot silo. We had no way of replacing the magnet without breaking the electric circuit, interrupting the magnetic field that bars the shot from falling and emptying the silo of its pellets. For a moment it looked as if this mishap had canceled our dive. Then Willm reminded me that he had put aboard the *Élie Monnier* an extra ton of shot before leaving Dakar. His lucky inspiration saved the day. We jettisoned the silo's contents into the sea and refilled the tube with twenty bags of shot, paddling them over to the bathy-scaph in two rubber dinghies. It was hard work, but the men were full of ardor and good will. They finished a few minutes before ten. We said good-by to Michaudon, who was to add the final pounds of shot, then hurried down the ladder of the air-lock and bolted our-selves in the steel ball. By telephone we told Michaudon in the conning tower to open the sea cocks of the air tanks, release the towline, and get off on the dinghy.

From now on, no one could help us. We were the masters of our fate.

To start the dive, we turned the valve flooding the air-lock. From the *Élie Monnier* Ortolan's voice came over our loudspeaker: "The bathtub is halfway under. The base of your antenna is covered. So long and good. . ."

We heard no more. The antenna was drowned at 10:08.

Once again we relived the stirring minutes of passing through the photosynthetic zone, sinking into the blue sea—the blue that deepens and grows dark. Softly, softly we were falling into a hostile world where men can live only in a globe of steel. Our dive plan called for a swift passage through the first 6,600 feet. We wanted to spend the time we saved on the virgin depths below. The hands of the pressure gauges turned slowly while we worked feverishly to arm the cameras. Mounted on the outside was a new "three-mile" electronic flash unit built by Dr. Harold E. Edgerton for the National Geographic Society. We called it the three-mile flash because it could withstand the pressure of that depth without crushing. With this margin of safety we need think no longer of an implosion destroying the bathyscaph.

At eleven we attained 3,280 feet, with everything going smoothly, almost noiselessly, when the stuffing box on a pressure gauge gave way slightly, leaking tiny drops of oil onto Willm's neck as he crouched at the porthole. He looked up at once, for we were going to a level where the pressure, four times greater, might cause a gusher of oil to spurt from that gauge. Picking up a huge monkey wrench, Willm tried to tighten the nut. In our clutter of instruments, clothing, snacks, extra gear, and ourselves, it was difficult to swing the wrench, but we got the leak stopped. Our descent continued at greater speed, about one hundred feet per minute. Outside we now observed small jellyfishes among the trailing siphonophores. The "soup" was thick. The comparison with a starlit night, in fact, was never more striking.

At 11:30 our pressure gauges read 6,560 feet: we were passing through the lowest strata we had reached in the Mediterranean dive last August. Willm pressed the button which cut off the electro-magnets on our four silos and held it down for one hundred seconds. A ton of iron pellets fell on the sphere and bounced into the sea, greatly reducing our speed. I tapped out an ultrasound message to the ship far above:

"Everything going well: 6,560 feet."

Now the vertical-speed indicator stood almost at zero. We were inching through the black unknown, with a circus outside the window. In the bright light, magnificent red shrimps with long antennae swam past.

By noon we had reached 9,845 feet, close to the greatest depth hitherto attained—by Professor August Piccard in his *Trieste* bathyscaph on September 30, 1953. Releasing another ton of ballast, we stopped almost dead. Every square inch of the sphere was now being subjected to a load of 4,370 pounds. Carefully we inspected our weakest points—the outlets through which control cables pass outside to the lights, motors, and electromagnets. We had sealed these small holes with conical plastic washers, so designed that the pressure of the water against the sphere should make them tighter than ever. Was the theory sound? Though our ears strained for suspicious noises, we heard only the normal hum of the transformers, the hiss of the oxygen, the regular tick-tock of the clockwork in the pressure recorder. "All control apparatus functions perfectly," I wrote in the ship's log. Releasing some of our buoyant gasoline, we started downward once more. As we encountered increasing pressure, our remaining gasoline slowly contracted, and sea water filled the space in the bottom of the buoyancy "balloon." Heavier now, our ship picked up speed. Willm said, "It's about time we heard the Duralumin frames cracking. In this pressure the sphere should contract about one millimeter (.04 inch) and pull a bit on the support frames." But we heard nothing. The frames proved sufficiently elastic to adjust to the shrinkage of the ball.

At 12:45 our pressure gauges registered 11,800 feet. I started the echo sounder. At once the stylus started drawing pictures of the sea bottom. On the graph the depth profile sloped up toward us. It gave us a rather queer feeling, for on a moving ship, when one sees the graph climbing, it means a hill rising from the floor. Our "hill" was caused by the submarine falling toward a level plain. When we reached 660 feet "altitude," it was time to decelerate. We didn't know whether the bottom was smooth or jagged, and the bathyscaph must land very lightly.

Systematically we shed ballast—first 550 pounds of shot, then 330 pounds, until the *FNRS 3* had a negative buoyancy of only a few pounds. With our craft so nearly in balance, we could rise by dropping only the guide chain. Slowly the curve of the echo graph climbed toward us: 330 feet . . . 260 feet . . . 165 feet . . .

65 feet. The soup outside seemed motionless. Only the echo sounder and the log acknowledged the descent. We were more than 2½ miles down.

I was at the porthole in the profound silence of those last moments. Finally—

"I see the bottom!"

It was thrilling. Our droplights made a theatrical circle about ten feet in diameter on the sea floor. The yellow sand was carved in low ripples. Everywhere extended mounds with animal holes about an inch wide. Though we never saw a creature go in or out of the holes, we felt there must be many living things under this rumpled surface. The guide chain touched bottom, and the *FNRS 3* came to a dead stop, hanging above the floor by a steel tendril. There were no more maneuvers to be made. The water temperature was 41° Fahrenheit, and the inside of the ball was very cold to the touch. I checked the temperature gauge of the gasoline in our "balloon": 50° F. Soon, as the gas cooled, contracted, and became heavier, the sub sank gently to the bottom. A cloud of very fine sand bloomed around the gondola and drifted away in a slight current.

We had landed at 1:30. Above us, thirteen Eiffel Towers could have been stacked on end without reaching daylight. We were alive inside a 3½-inch shell, withstanding a total pressure of 68,000 tons, or 5,900 pounds per square inch.

We took turns at the porthole, staring at the sea floor at a depth no man had ever reached before alive. Beautiful colonies of sea anemones were clinging to the bottom. Tulips of crystal, they swayed lightly in the gentle current.

Willm took over the porthole. In a moment he shouted, "A shark!"

It is a cry that should become frequent among men who go to these depths. It would be odd to parachute aimlessly into mid-Sahara and land beside a lion; yet each time we have visited the bottom wastes in the bathyscaph we have seen at least one shark. Unless our luck has been phenomenal, this must mean there are thousands of them living in the world's dark basement. Willm's fish was about 6½ feet long. Though it must have known nothing but everlasting darkness, it swam without hesitation into the glare of our lights and looked at the porthole with its great protruding eyes. The long body undulated lazily in the droplight.

Our dive plan had provided for three hours on the bottom. In no hurry, we amused ourselves by nudging the bathyscaph here and there with the electric motors, extending our vision. Our only concern was to surface before nightfall, so that the little submarine could be taken under tow in daylight. The air seemed fresh and tonic, and we thought ourselves the kings of the sea.

It was 2:06 when our elated trance was broken. A tremor shook the bathyscaph. Remembering past accidents, we realized at once that one of the magnets above us must have failed and that a 1,300-pound battery was loose. A second quake followed as the remaining magnets cut out, and a dull rumble told us the batteries were skidding off and crashing into the sand. The exterior lights went out.

After only thirty-six minutes in our new realm, we were helplessly soaring to the surface at top speed, about two miles an hour. I took the ultrasound key and tapped out dash-dash. On the *Élie Monnier* they read our disappointment in the single code letter "M," which meant "*Je monte*"—"I ascend." (We didn't have a letter standing for "Blast it all, anyhow!") "M" meant that the escorts and tenders were to scatter to avoid the risk of *FNRS 3* crashing against a keel.

At 15:21, seventy-five minutes after our batteries had fallen, we broke the surface, eleven hundred yards from the *Élie Monnier*. As soon as the antenna was out of the water, I phoned Ortolan:

"We have been half an hour on the bottom at 13,287 feet."

He replied, "We picked up your signals. Congratulations, old man!"

Rear Admiral Jean Georges Gayral, commanding the Navy in French West Africa, buzzed us in his flying boat, sending us his felicitations by radiotelephone.

We blew the water from the air-lock and climbed through the hatch. A blast of cold, wet sea air swept down the lock to greet us. After staggering up the ladder to the conning tower, we stood blinking in the sun, our eyes dazzled after so long below.

The first man aboard was Midshipman Michaudon, grinning broadly. I am afraid he heard no historic utterances. I asked him something practical, which I no longer remember. He turned to Willm. The engineer said: "Oof!" Throughout the French Union, however, from Indochina to the islands of St. Pierre and Miquelon, the victory signal chattered on the keys of the fleet. Aboard the *Calypso* in the Persian Gulf the radioman posted a bulletin headed, "*Gloire à la Marine Nationale!*"

We had set a record; but that was only incidental to our true purpose—to prove that the *FNRS 3* could attain the depth which she was designed to reach and explore. Well, she can and she will. From now on, the bathyscaph belongs to science. In Paris, we knew a committee was already weighing research projects submitted by Belgian and French scientists eager to go below. A worthy use for our little ship, but sad news for Willm: under such a plan he will have to surrender his berth to a succession of savants.

The *FNRS 3* will go no deeper than we have taken her; that is her habitat. But her adventures on the ocean floor have only begun. What mysteries of marine life will she yet probe? What relics of our ancient past—buried wrecks, encrusted marbles, sunken cities —may she not stumble upon? What curious new creatures will she perhaps discover in the vast, unknown continents that lie beneath our salty wastes? We know not. But for ourselves, for Willm and me, the strongest lure the future holds is the building and testing of the abyssal bathyscaph. Prompted by the scientists, we shall continue to modify and improve the present machine, learning to equip her with new tools, new antennae to extend our senses into this dark, watery world. But always we shall be looking beyond to her eventual successor, the ship that we shall someday launch and take down to the 36,173-foot depth, between the Caroline Islands and Guam, the profoundest known deep in all the oceans lapping our globe.